Lura E. Hiatt

TABERNACLE HYMNS
NUMBER THREE

For the
Church and Sunday School

Printed in Round and Shaped Notes

MADE IN U. S. A.

TABERNACLE PUBLISHING COMPANY
Corner Lake St. and Waller Ave.
CHICAGO, ILL.
1937

O could I speak the matchless worth,
O could I sound the glories forth
Which in my Savior shine,
I'd soar, and touch the heav'nly strings,
And vie with Gabriel while he sings
In notes almost divine.

I'd sing the precious blood He spilt,
My ransom from the dreadful guilt
Of sin and wrath divine:
I'd sing His glorious righteousness,
In which all perfect heavn'ly dress
My soul shall ever shine.

I'd sing the characters He bears,
And all the forms of love He wears,
Exalted on His throne:
In loftiest songs of sweetest praise,
I would to everlasting days
Make all His glories known.

"Worthy is the Lamb that was slain to receive power, and riches, and wisdom, and strength, and honour, and glory, and blessing."

Revelation 5:12

TABERNACLE HYMNS
NUMBER THREE

1 His Matchless Worth

SAMUEL MEDLEY — LOWELL MASON

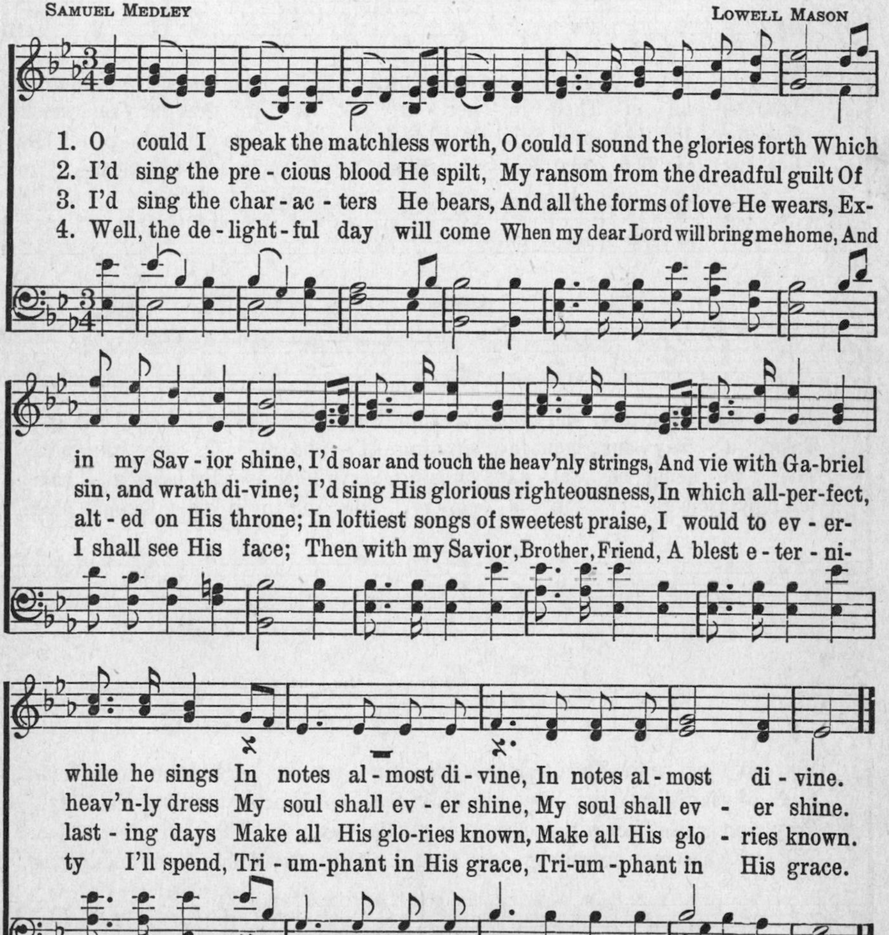

1. O could I speak the matchless worth, O could I sound the glories forth Which
2. I'd sing the pre - cious blood He spilt, My ransom from the dreadful guilt Of
3. I'd sing the char - ac - ters He bears, And all the forms of love He wears, Ex-
4. Well, the de - light - ful day will come When my dear Lord will bring me home, And
in my Sav - ior shine, I'd soar and touch the heav'nly strings, And vie with Ga-briel
sin, and wrath di-vine; I'd sing His glorious righteousness, In which all-per-fect,
alt - ed on His throne; In loftiest songs of sweetest praise, I would to ev - er-
I shall see His face; Then with my Savior, Brother, Friend, A blest e - ter - ni-
while he sings In notes al - most di - vine, In notes al - most di - vine.
heav'n-ly dress My soul shall ev - er shine, My soul shall ev - er shine.
last - ing days Make all His glo-ries known, Make all His glo - ries known.
ty I'll spend, Tri - um-phant in His grace, Tri-um -phant in His grace.

Love Divine

CHARLES WESLEY — JOHN ZUNDEL

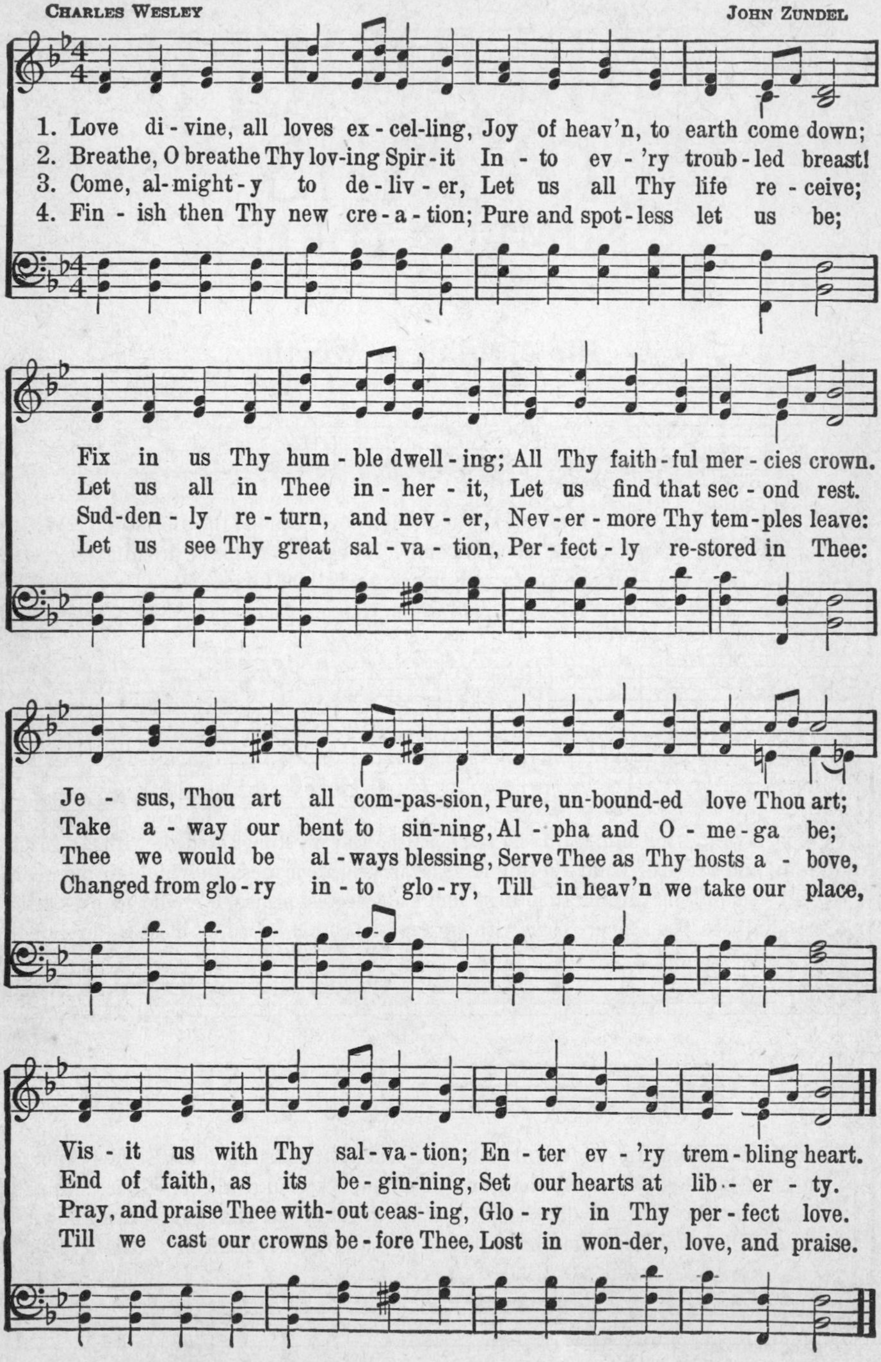

1. Love di - vine, all loves ex - cel-ling, Joy of heav'n, to earth come down;
2. Breathe, O breathe Thy lov-ing Spir - it In - to ev - 'ry troub - led breast!
3. Come, al-might - y to de - liv - er, Let us all Thy life re - ceive;
4. Fin - ish then Thy new cre - a - tion; Pure and spot - less let us be;

Fix in us Thy hum - ble dwell - ing; All Thy faith - ful mer - cies crown.
Let us all in Thee in - her - it, Let us find that sec - ond rest.
Sud-den - ly re - turn, and nev - er, Nev - er - more Thy tem - ples leave:
Let us see Thy great sal - va - tion, Per - fect - ly re-stored in Thee:

Je - sus, Thou art all com-pas-sion, Pure, un-bound-ed love Thou art;
Take a - way our bent to sin-ning, Al - pha and O - me - ga be;
Thee we would be al - ways blessing, Serve Thee as Thy hosts a - bove,
Changed from glo - ry in - to glo - ry, Till in heav'n we take our place,

Vis - it us with Thy sal - va - tion; En - ter ev - 'ry trem - bling heart.
End of faith, as its be - gin-ning, Set our hearts at lib - er - ty.
Pray, and praise Thee with - out ceas - ing, Glo - ry in Thy per - fect love.
Till we cast our crowns be - fore Thee, Lost in won-der, love, and praise.

3 I've Found the Way

P. R. PAUL RADER

1. Oft - en my heart longed to pray; Sin - ner, so what could I say?
2. Righteousness now I have found; Cal - va-ry's cleans-ings a - bound;
3. Wan-der-ing days now are done; Guess-ing days now are all gone;
4. Ask - ing, I now may re - ceive; Seek - ing, I know He'll re - lieve;
Then I was told of the blood-cleansing way O-pened by Je-sus my Lord.
Tak-ing this blood-way I'm on sol-id ground, Ground of Christ's merits alone.
Now a new pathway of prayer is be - gun, O-pened by Je-sus a - lone.
Knocking, I get, for I take and be - lieve Je - sus is pray-ing for me.
REFRAIN
I've found a way thro' the blood past the veil To the Holy of Holies with God.
There by His pow'r o-ver sin I pre-vail, I can walk in the path that He trod.
1 2
There in the presence of Je-sus I stand, Glorified Son at the Father's right hand;
There I can plead, I can claim, I can have All that He purchased for me.

4 "Thou Remainest"

D. W. WHITTLE (El Nathan)
JAMES MCGRANAHAN
Moderato, with expression
1. "Thou re-main-est," blest Re-deem-er, Lord of peace and Lord of strife;
2. Sat - is - fy - ing ev - 'ry long-ing Of my sin - ful soul for grace;
3. One by one my loved may leave me, Voic-es sweet no more be heard;
4. When from earth Thou, Lord, shalt call me, Calm I'll lay my bur - den down;
Je - sus, Sav - ior, Lord for - ev - er, "Thou re-main-est," Christ my life.
From my weak-ness nev-er turn - ing, "Thou re-main-est," Christ my peace.
But of God naught can be-reave me, "Thou re-main-est," Christ my Lord.
For I know, what-e'er be - fall me, "Thou re-main-est," Christ my crown.
CHORUS
"Thou re - main - est," "Thou re - main - est,"
"Thou re-main-est," "Thou re-main-est,"
"Thou re - main - est," Christ my all; (Christ my all;) Peace or
con - flict, joy or sor - row, "Thou re - main - est," Christ my all.

5 Sunlight

J. W. VAN DE VENTER — W. S. WEEDEN

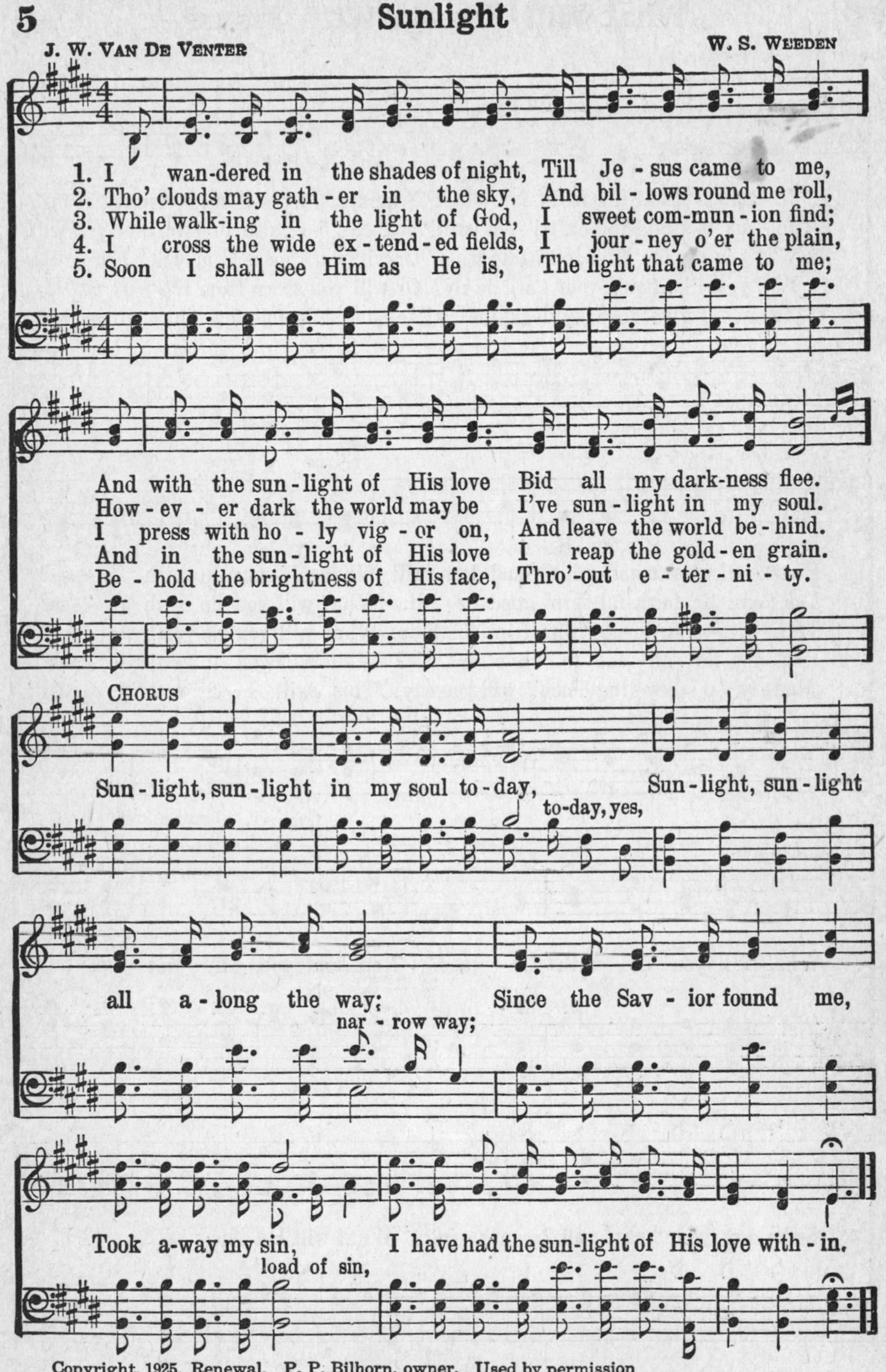
1. I wan-dered in the shades of night, Till Je - sus came to me,
2. Tho' clouds may gath - er in the sky, And bil - lows round me roll,
3. While walk-ing in the light of God, I sweet com-mun - ion find;
4. I cross the wide ex - tend - ed fields, I jour - ney o'er the plain,
5. Soon I shall see Him as He is, The light that came to me;
And with the sun - light of His love Bid all my dark-ness flee.
How - ev - er dark the world may be I've sun - light in my soul.
I press with ho - ly vig - or on, And leave the world be - hind.
And in the sun - light of His love I reap the gold - en grain.
Be - hold the brightness of His face, Thro'-out e - ter - ni - ty.
CHORUS
Sun - light, sun - light in my soul to - day,
to-day, yes,
Sun - light, sun - light all a - long the way;
nar - row way;
Since the Sav - ior found me, Took a-way my sin,
load of sin,
I have had the sun-light of His love with - in.

6 What Will You Do With Jesus?

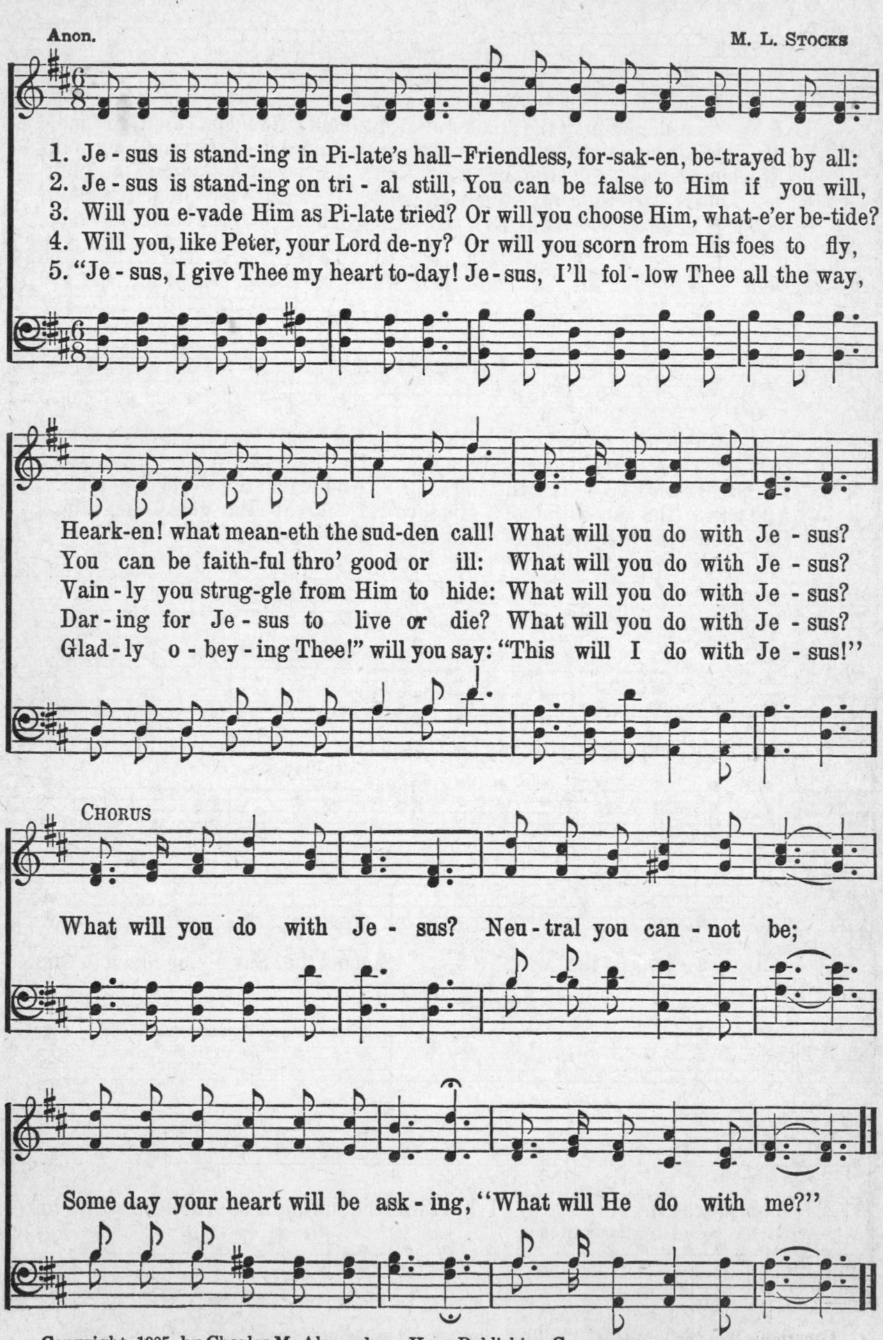

Anon.
M. L. Stocks
1. Je - sus is stand-ing in Pi-late's hall–Friendless, for-sak-en, be-trayed by all:
2. Je - sus is stand-ing on tri - al still, You can be false to Him if you will,
3. Will you e-vade Him as Pi-late tried? Or will you choose Him, what-e'er be-tide?
4. Will you, like Peter, your Lord de-ny? Or will you scorn from His foes to fly,
5. "Je - sus, I give Thee my heart to-day! Je-sus, I'll fol - low Thee all the way,
Heark-en! what mean-eth the sud-den call! What will you do with Je - sus?
You can be faith-ful thro' good or ill: What will you do with Je - sus?
Vain-ly you strug-gle from Him to hide: What will you do with Je - sus?
Dar-ing for Je - sus to live or die? What will you do with Je - sus?
Glad-ly o - bey - ing Thee!" will you say: "This will I do with Je - sus!"
Chorus
What will you do with Je - sus? Neu-tral you can - not be;
Some day your heart will be ask - ing, "What will He do with me?"

7 The Heavenly Vision

H. H. L. HELEN HOWARTH LEMMEL

With expression
1. O soul, are you wea - ry and troub - led? No light in the
2. Thro' death in - to life ev - er - last - ing He passed, and we
3. His word shall not fail you—He prom - ised; Be - lieve Him, and
dark-ness you see? There's light for a look at the Sav - ior,
fol - low Him there; O - ver us sin no more hath do - min - ion—
all will be well: Then go to a world that is dy - ing,
And life more a - bun-dant and free!
For more than con-qu'rors we are!
His per - fect sal - va - tion to tell!
REFRAIN
Turn your eyes up-on Je-sus, Look full in His won-der-ful face; . . . . And the things of
earth will grow strange-ly dim In the light of His glo - ry and grace.
p

8 Make Me a Blessing

IRA B. WILSON — *To the Moody Memorial Church Choir* — GEORGE S. SCHULER

Slowly
1. Out in the high-ways and by-ways of life, Man-y are
2. Tell the sweet sto-ry of Christ and His love, Tell of His
3. Give as 'twas giv-en to you in your need, Love as the
wea-ry and sad; . . . . . Car-ry the sunshine where darkness is rife,
are wea-ry and sad;
pow'r to for-give; . . . . . Oth-ers will trust Him if on-ly you prove
His pow'r to for-give;
Mas-ter loved you; . . . . . Be to the help-less a help-er in-deed,
the Mas-ter loved you;
rit.
CHORUS Men or Unison
Mak-ing the sor-row-ing glad. . . .
True, ev-'ry mo-ment you live. . . . . Make me a bless-ing,
Un-to your mis-sion be true. . . .
Women
Make me a bless-ing, Out of my life . . . . may Je-
Out of my life
Men
rit.
Unison
Women
sus shine; . . Make me a bless-ing, O Sav-ior,

Make Me a Blessing
Parts ad lib.
I pray, . . . Make me a bless - ing to some one to - day.
I pray Thee, my Sav - ior,
Tenors
9
Jesus Never Fails
A. A. L.
A. A. LUTHER
1. Earth-ly friends may prove un - true, Doubts and fears as - sail;
2. Tho' the sky be dark and drear, Fierce and strong the gale,
3. In life's dark and bit - ter hour Love will still pre - vail;
One still loves and cares for you: Je - sus nev - er fails.
nev - er fails.
Just re - mem - ber He is near, And He will not fail.
will not fail.
Trust His ev - er - last - ing pow'r, Je - sus will not fail.
will not fail.
CHORUS
Je - sus nev - er fails, Je - sus nev - er fails;
Heav'n and earth may pass a - way But Je - sus nev - er fails.

10 The God of Abraham Praise

Thomas Olivers — Hebrew Melody. Arr. by Meyer Leoni

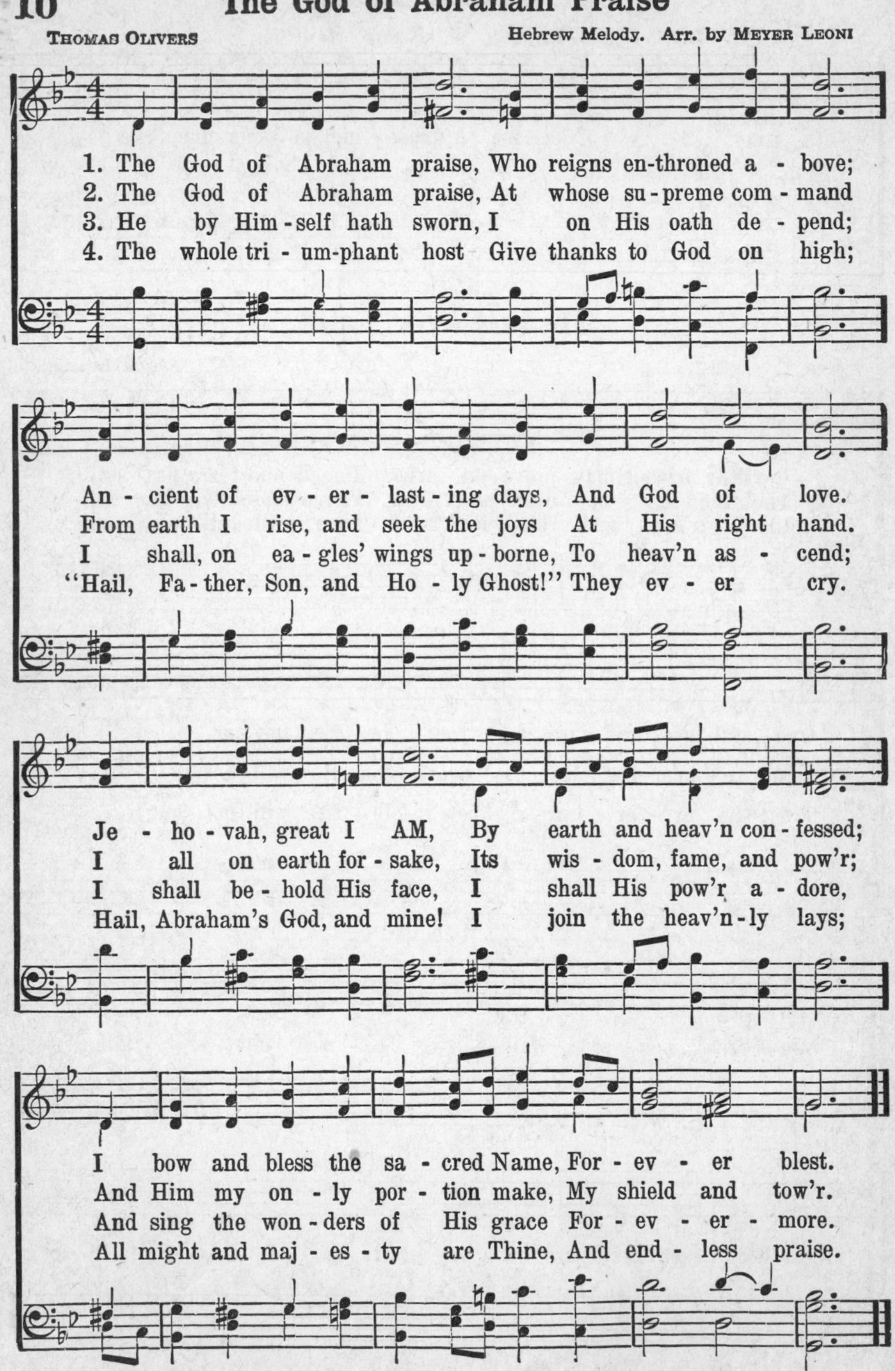
1. The God of Abraham praise, Who reigns en-throned a - bove;
2. The God of Abraham praise, At whose su - preme com - mand
3. He by Him - self hath sworn, I on His oath de - pend;
4. The whole tri - um-phant host Give thanks to God on high;
An - cient of ev - er - last - ing days, And God of love.
From earth I rise, and seek the joys At His right hand.
I shall, on ea - gles' wings up - borne, To heav'n as - cend;
"Hail, Fa - ther, Son, and Ho - ly Ghost!" They ev - er cry.
Je - ho - vah, great I AM, By earth and heav'n con - fessed;
I all on earth for - sake, Its wis - dom, fame, and pow'r;
I shall be - hold His face, I shall His pow'r a - dore,
Hail, Abraham's God, and mine! I join the heav'n - ly lays;
I bow and bless the sa - cred Name, For - ev - er blest.
And Him my on - ly por - tion make, My shield and tow'r.
And sing the won - ders of His grace For - ev - er - more.
All might and maj - es - ty are Thine, And end - less praise.

11

Songs of Praises

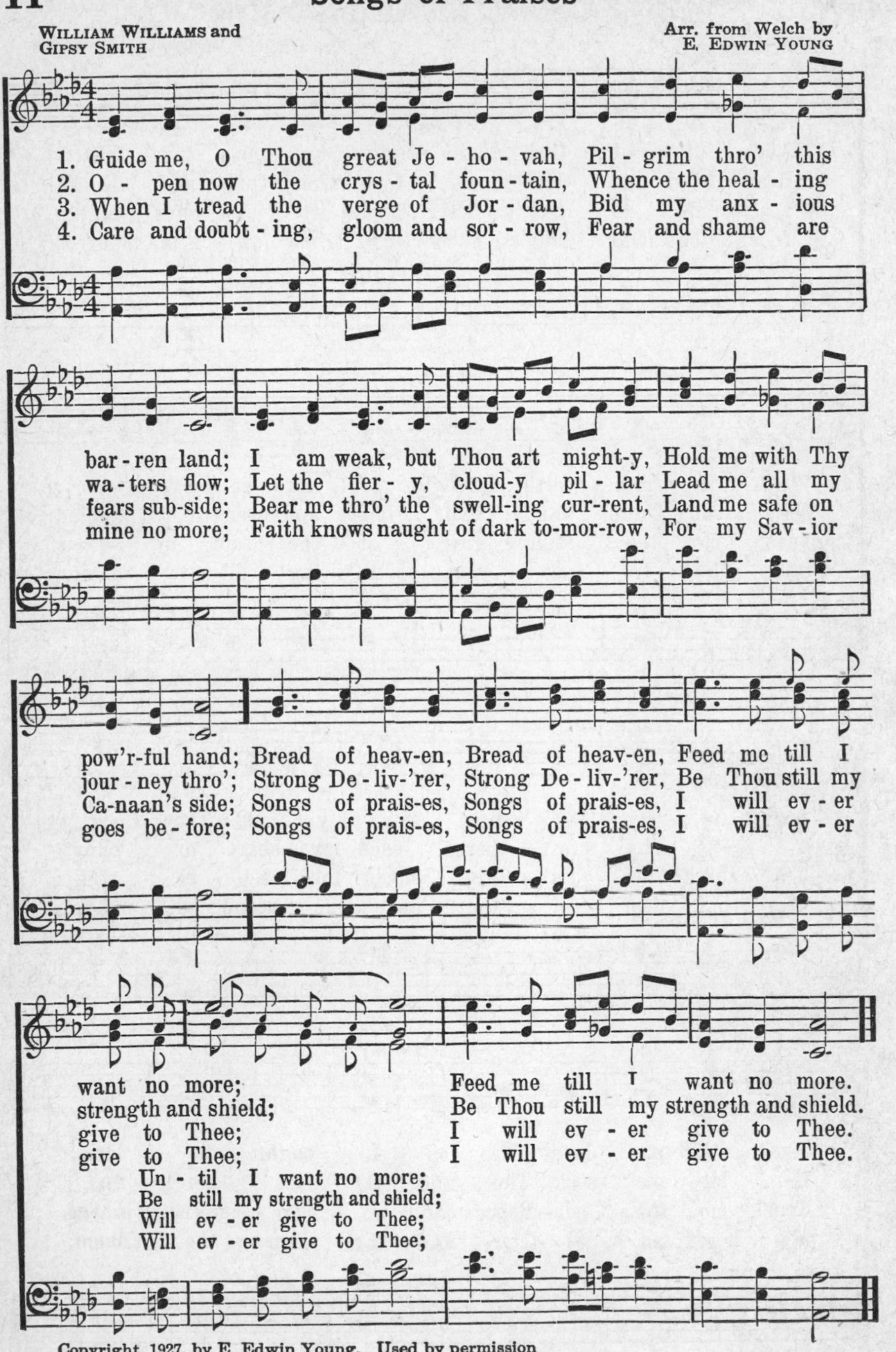

WILLIAM WILLIAMS and
GIPSY SMITH
Arr. from Welch by
E. EDWIN YOUNG
1. Guide me, O Thou great Je - ho - vah, Pil - grim thro' this
2. O - pen now the crys - tal foun - tain, Whence the heal - ing
3. When I tread the verge of Jor - dan, Bid my anx - ious
4. Care and doubt - ing, gloom and sor - row, Fear and shame are
bar - ren land; I am weak, but Thou art might - y, Hold me with Thy
wa - ters flow; Let the fier - y, cloud - y pil - lar Lead me all my
fears sub - side; Bear me thro' the swell - ing cur - rent, Land me safe on
mine no more; Faith knows naught of dark to - mor - row, For my Sav - ior
pow'r - ful hand; Bread of heav - en, Bread of heav - en, Feed me till I
jour - ney thro'; Strong De - liv - 'rer, Strong De - liv - 'rer, Be Thou still my
Ca - naan's side; Songs of prais - es, Songs of prais - es, I will ev - er
goes be - fore; Songs of prais - es, Songs of prais - es, I will ev - er
want no more; Feed me till I want no more.
strength and shield; Be Thou still my strength and shield.
give to Thee; I will ev - er give to Thee.
give to Thee; I will ev - er give to Thee.
Un - til I want no more;
Be still my strength and shield;
Will ev - er give to Thee;
Will ev - er give to Thee;

12 Spirit of God, Descend Upon My Heart

GEORGE CROLY
FREDERICK C. ATKINSON
1. Spir - it of God, de - scend up - on my heart;
2. Hast Thou not bid us love Thee, God and King?
3. Teach me to feel that Thou art al - ways nigh;
4. Teach me to love Thee as Thine an - gels love,
Wean it from earth, through all its puls - es move;
All, all Thine own, soul, heart and strength and mind;
Teach me the strug - gles of the soul to bear,
One ho - ly pas - sion fill - ing all my frame;
Stoop to my weak - ness, might - y as Thou art,
I see Thy cross— there teach my heart to cling:
To check the ris - ing doubt, the reb - el sigh;
The bap - tism of the heav'n - de - scend - ed Dove,
And make me love Thee as I ought to love.
O let me seek Thee, and O let me find.
Teach me the pa - tience of un - an - swered prayer.
My heart an al - tar, and Thy love the flame.

13 Walking In the Sunlight

R. J. O. RICHARD J. OLIVER

Do not hurry
1. Once my heart was dark with sin and sad-ness, Heav'nly hope destroyed by
2. Won-drous joy di-vine! I've found His fa - vor! Christ my Joy and Crown, my
3. Rich - est bless-ings He is dai - ly bring-ing; With all needs sup-plied my
world-ly mad-ness, Je-sus shed the light of joy and glad-ness; Now He dwells with-
Song, my Sav-ior, Gives His life, a life that lasts for - ev - er, Guides and keeps se-
soul keeps singing; In my heart the bells of joy are ring-ing; Guid - ed by His
REFRAIN.
in me night and day.
cure-ly all the way. Walk-ing in the sun-light with Je-sus, my Je - sus,
hand I can - not stray.
Dark-ness turns to daylight with Jesus, my Je-sus; He is Strength for my weakness,
Joy for my sor-row; Safe-ly I rest in His might-y arms: He's mighty arms.
1
2

14

He is Mine

C. AUSTIN MILES J. LINCOLN HALL

Parts
1. There is a Shepherd who cares for His own, And He is mine; Nothing am
2. Je - sus left heaven my Sav-ior to be, And He is mine; I am not
3. There is a Com-fort-er come from a-bove, He, too, is mine, Com-ing to
Tenor and Basses, or all in unison, or solo.
I, He's a King on a throne, But He is mine; How He can love such a
worth all He suffered for me, But He is mine; Tho' I'm not wor-thy He
me to re-veal Je-sus' love, And that is mine; Shepherd and Savior, and
sin-ner as I, Tho' He is mine, I can-not fath-om tho' oft-en I try,
dwells in my heart, And He is mine; From Him I'll never, no, nev-er de-part,
Com-fort-er, too, They all are mine; That's why I know the old sto-ry is true,
CHORUS
But He is mine. He is mine,....... He
For He is mine.
They all are mine. He is mine,
Tho' all un-wor-thy, I know He is mine, He
is mine; Tho' it is won-der-ful, yet it is true, That He is mine.
yes, He is mine;
is mine;

15 Wonderful Jesus

Annie B. Russell
Ernest O. Sellers
1. There is nev - er a day so drear - y, There is nev - er a night so long (so long), But the soul that is trust - ing Je - sus Will some-where find a song (a song).
2. There is nev - er a cross so heav - y, There is nev - er a weight of woe (of woe), But that Je - sus will help to car - ry Be- cause He lov - eth so (loves so).
3. There is nev - er a care or bur - den, There is nev - er a grief or loss (or loss), But that Je - sus in love will light - en When car - ried to the cross (the cross).
4. There is nev - er a guilt - y sin - ner, There is nev - er a wan-d'ring one (not one), But that God can in mer - cy par - don Thro' Je - sus Christ, His Son (His Son).
Chorus.
Won - der-ful, won-der - ful Je - sus,
In the heart He im-plant-eth a song: . . . .
He plant-eth a song,
A song of de-liv-'rance, of cour - age, of strength, In the heart He im-plant - eth a song (a song).

16 Throw Out the Life-Line

EDWARD S. UFFORD
E. S. U. Arr. by GEO. C. STEBBINS
1. Throw out the Life-Line a-cross the dark wave, There is a broth-er whom
2. Throw out the Life-Line with hand quick and strong: Why do you tar-ry, why
3. Throw out the Life-Line to dan-ger-fraught men, Sink-ing in an-guish where
4. Soon will the sea-son of res-cue be o'er, Soon will they drift to e-
some one should save; Some-bod-y's broth-er! oh, who then will dare To
lin-ger so long? See! he is sink-ing; oh, has-ten to-day—And
you've nev-er been: Winds of temp-ta-tion and bil-lows of woe Will
ter-ni-ty's shore, Haste then, my broth-er, no time for de-lay, But
CHORUS
throw out the Life-Line, his per-il to share?
out with the Life-Boat! a-way, then, a-way! Throw out the Life-Line!
soon hurl them out where the dark wa-ters flow.
throw out the Life-Line and save them to-day.
Throw out the Life-Line! Some-one is drift-ing a-way; Throw out the
Life-Line! Throw out the Life-Line! Some one is sink-ing to-day.
Copyright property of Hope Publishing Co.

17 I Need Jesus

George O. Webster — Chas. H. Gabriel

1. I need Je-sus, my need I now con-fess; No friend like Him in times of deep dis-tress; I need Je-sus, the need I glad-ly own; Tho' some may bear their load a-lone, Yet I need Je-sus.
2. I need Je-sus, I need a friend like Him, A friend to guide when paths of life are dim; I need Je-sus, when foes my soul assail; A-lone I know I can but fail, So I need Je-sus.
3. I need Je-sus, I need Him to the end; No one like Him, He is the sin-ner's Friend; I need Je-sus, no oth-er friend will do; So constant, kind, so strong and true, Yes, I need Je-sus.
Chorus
I need Je-sus, I need Je-sus,
I need Je-sus with me, I need Je-sus always,
I need Je-sus ev-'ry day; . . .
ev-'ry day;
Need Him in the sunshine hour,
Need Him when the storm-clouds low'r; Ev'ry day a-long my way, Yes, I need Je-sus.

18 Tell It Again

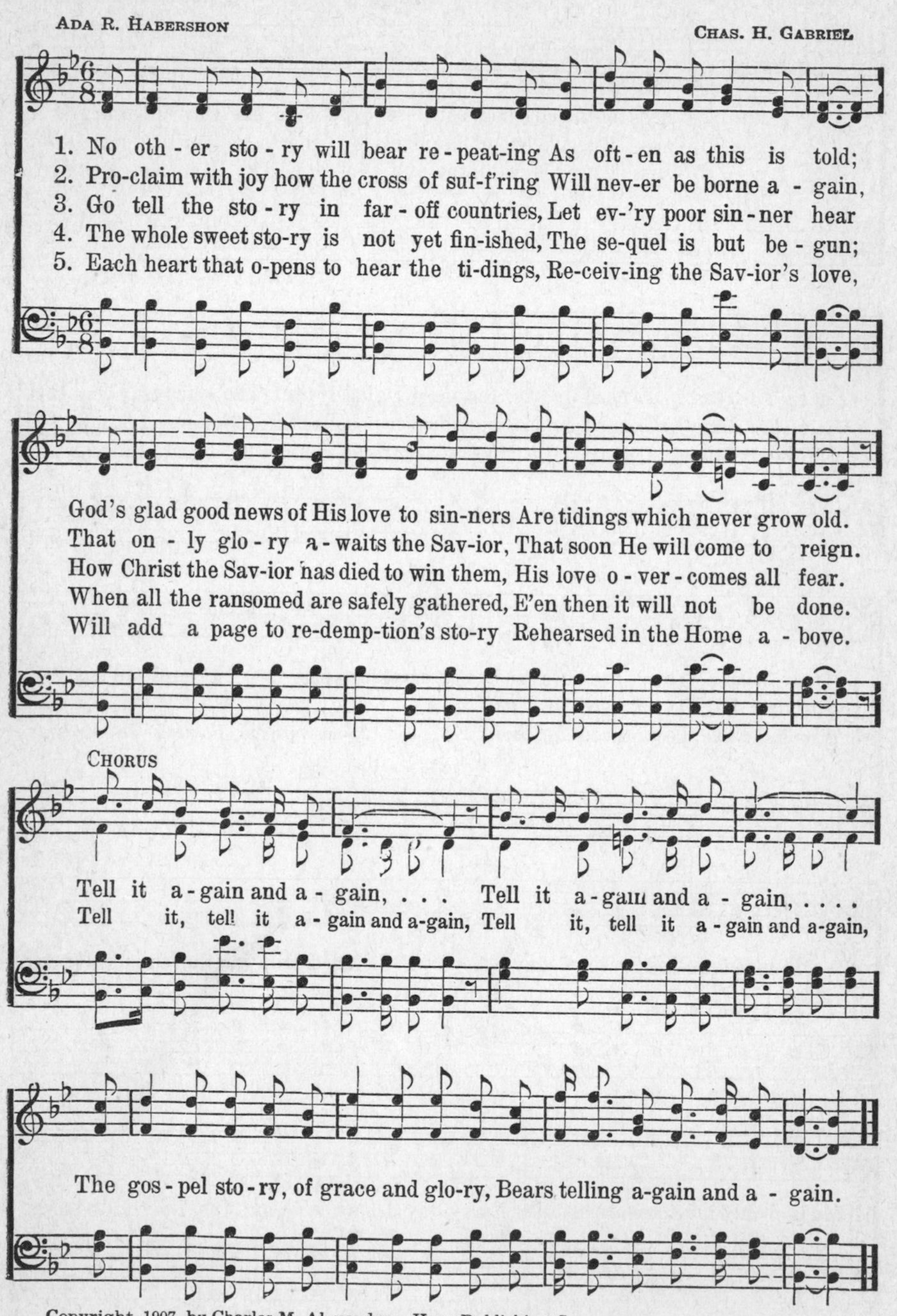
ADA R. HABERSHON
CHAS. H. GABRIEL
1. No oth - er sto - ry will bear re - peat-ing As oft - en as this is told;
2. Pro-claim with joy how the cross of suf-f'ring Will nev-er be borne a - gain,
3. Go tell the sto - ry in far - off countries, Let ev-'ry poor sin - ner hear
4. The whole sweet sto-ry is not yet fin-ished, The se-quel is but be - gun;
5. Each heart that o-pens to hear the ti-dings, Re-ceiv-ing the Sav-ior's love,
God's glad good news of His love to sin-ners Are tidings which never grow old.
That on - ly glo - ry a - waits the Sav-ior, That soon He will come to reign.
How Christ the Sav-ior has died to win them, His love o - ver - comes all fear.
When all the ransomed are safely gathered, E'en then it will not be done.
Will add a page to re-demp-tion's sto-ry Rehearsed in the Home a - bove.
CHORUS
Tell it a - gain and a - gain, . . . Tell it a - gain and a - gain, ...
Tell it, tell it a - gain and a-gain, Tell it, tell it a - gain and a-gain,
The gos - pel sto - ry, of grace and glo - ry, Bears telling a-gain and a - gain.

19 When Jesus Meets the Soul

J. V. R.
James V. Reid
1. When the cares of life sweep o'er me, And my heart with grief is torn, When I steal a-way and find a place to pray, Then Je-sus speaks and hope anew is born.
2. Ev-'ry day brings some new bur-den, And my faith is sore-ly tried; But the shad-ows flee when Je-sus speaks to me, As to the se-cret place I turn a-side.
3. When the sun of joy is shin-ing, And the day is bright and fair, In com-mun-ion sweet I tar-ry at His feet And tell Him how I love to meet Him there.
Chorus
O Je-sus, Wonder-ful is Je-sus Christ my Sav-ior,
In the hour of sweet com-mun-ion There is rest from ev-'ry earth-ly care;
There are depths of love and peace like heav'n above, When Jesus meets the soul in prayer.

20 No Disappointment in Heaven

F. M. L.

F. M. Lehman
Har. by Miss Claudia Lehman

1. There's no dis-ap-point-ment in heav-en, No wear-i-ness, sor-row or pain;
2. We'll nev-er pay rent for our man-sion, The tax-es will nev-er come due;
3. There'll nev-er be crepe on the door-knob, No fu-ner-al train in the sky;
No hearts that are bleeding and bro-ken, No song with a mi-nor re-frain.
Our garments will never grow threadbare, But al-ways be fade-less and new.
No graves on the hill-sides of glo-ry, For there we shall nev-er-more die.
The clouds of our earth-ly ho-ri-zon Will nev-er ap-pear in the sky,
We'll nev-er be hun-gry nor thirst-y, Nor lan-guish in pov-er-ty there,
The old will be young there for-ev-er, Transformed in a mo-ment of time;
For all will be sun-shine and gladness, With nev-er a sob nor a sigh.
For all the rich boun-ties of heav-en His sanc-ti-fied chil-dren will share.
Im-mor-tal we'll stand in His like-ness, The stars and the sun to out-shine.
Chorus
I'm bound for that beau-ti-ful cit-y My Lord has prepared for His own;

No Disappointment in Heaven

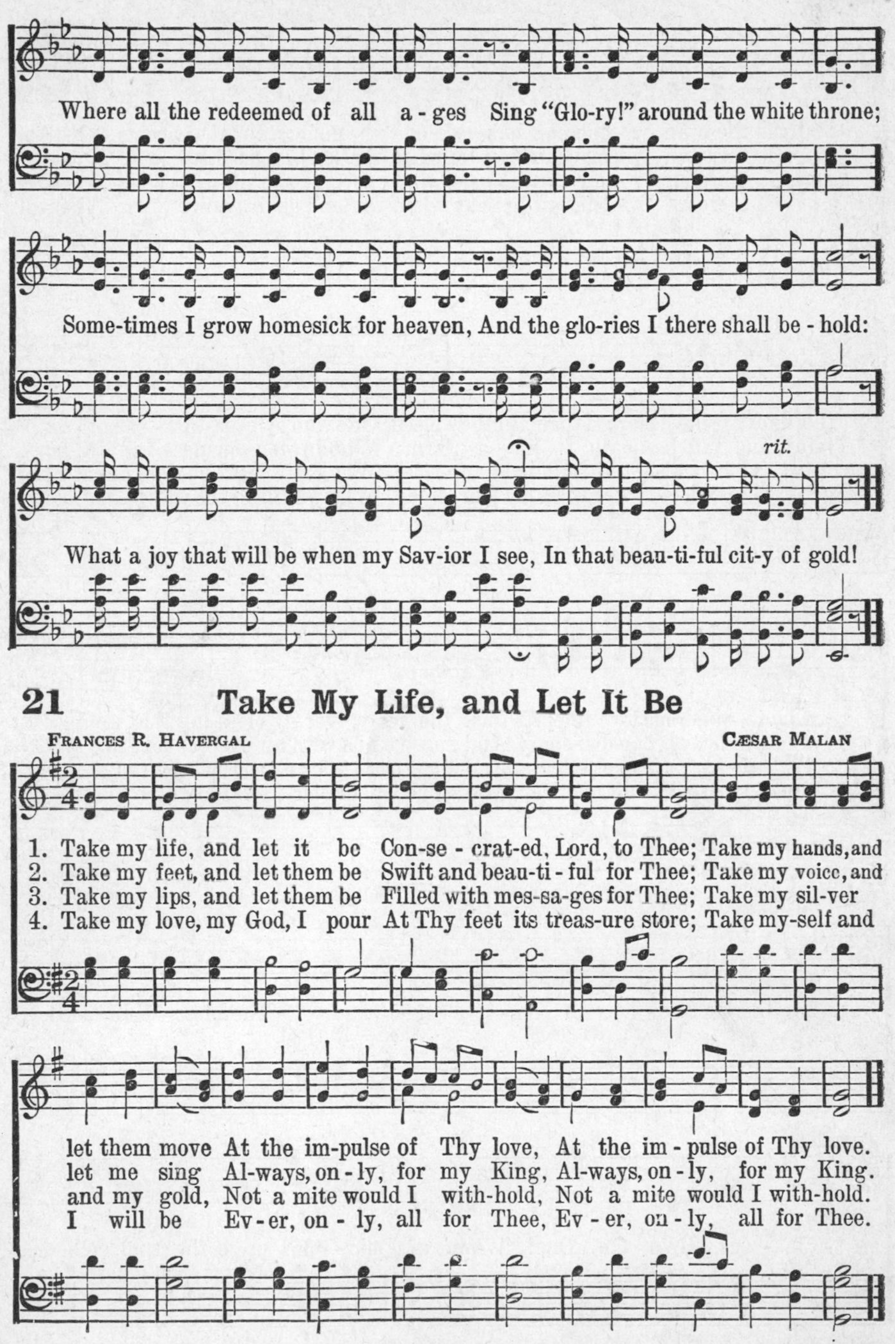
Where all the redeemed of all a-ges Sing "Glo-ry!" around the white throne;
Some-times I grow homesick for heaven, And the glo-ries I there shall be-hold:
rit.
What a joy that will be when my Sav-ior I see, In that beau-ti-ful cit-y of gold!
21 Take My Life, and Let It Be
Frances R. Havergal
Cæsar Malan
1. Take my life, and let it be Con-se-crat-ed, Lord, to Thee; Take my hands, and let them move At the im-pulse of Thy love, At the im-pulse of Thy love.
2. Take my feet, and let them be Swift and beau-ti-ful for Thee; Take my voice, and let me sing Al-ways, on-ly, for my King, Al-ways, on-ly, for my King.
3. Take my lips, and let them be Filled with mes-sa-ges for Thee; Take my sil-ver and my gold, Not a mite would I with-hold, Not a mite would I with-hold.
4. Take my love, my God, I pour At Thy feet its treas-ure store; Take my-self and I will be Ev-er, on-ly, all for Thee, Ev-er, on-ly, all for Thee.

He's the One

J. B. M.
J. B. Mackay
1. Is there an - y - one can help us—one who understands our hearts, When the
2. Is there an - y - one can help us when the load is hard to bear, And we
3. Is there an - y - one can help us who can give the sin-ner peace, When his
4. Is there an - y - one can help us when the end is draw-ing near, Who will
thorns of life have pierced them till they bleed; One who sym-pa-thiz - es with us,
faint and fall be-neath it in a - larm; Who in ten-der-ness will lift us,
heart is bur-dened down with pain and woe; Who can speak the word of par-don,
go thro' death's dark wa-ters by our side; Who will light the way be-fore us,
who in wondrous love imparts Just the ver-y, ver - y bless-ing that we need?
and the heav-y bur-den share, And sup-port us with an ev - er - last-ing arm?
that af - fords a sweet release, And whose blood can wash and make us white as snow?
and dis-pel all doubt and fear, And will bear our spir-its safe-ly o'er the tide?
Chorus
Yes, there's One! on - ly One! The bless-ed, bless-ed
Yes, there's One, on - ly One!
Je - sus, He's the One! When af - flic - tions press the soul, When

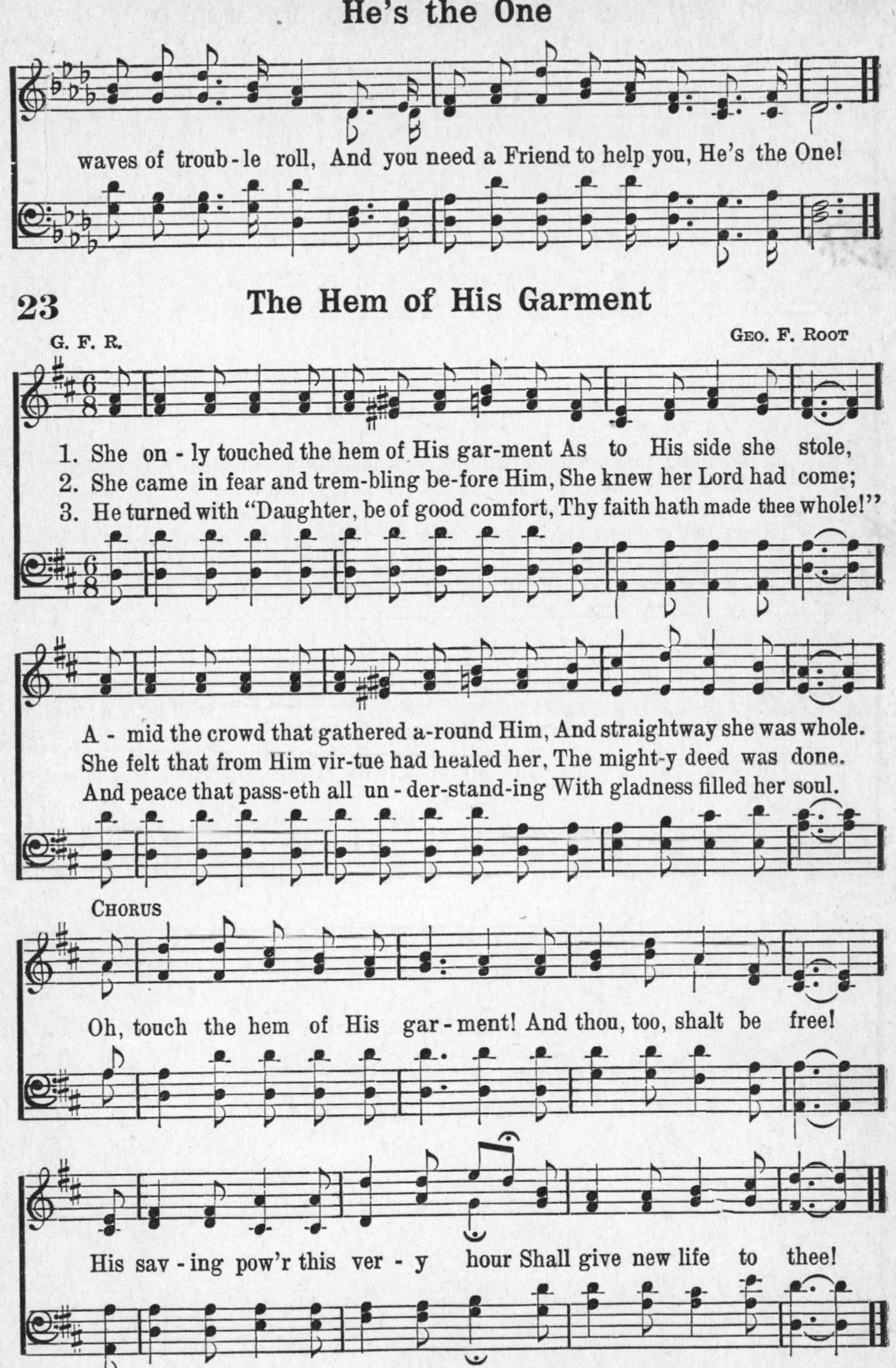
He's the One
waves of troub-le roll, And you need a Friend to help you, He's the One!
23 The Hem of His Garment
G. F. R.
Geo. F. Root
1. She on-ly touched the hem of His gar-ment As to His side she stole,
2. She came in fear and trem-bling be-fore Him, She knew her Lord had come;
3. He turned with "Daughter, be of good comfort, Thy faith hath made thee whole!"
A-mid the crowd that gathered a-round Him, And straightway she was whole.
She felt that from Him vir-tue had healed her, The might-y deed was done.
And peace that pass-eth all un-der-stand-ing With gladness filled her soul.
Chorus
Oh, touch the hem of His gar-ment! And thou, too, shalt be free!
His sav-ing pow'r this ver-y hour Shall give new life to thee!

24 Thy Word Have I Hid In My Heart

Adapted by E. O. S. — E. O. SELLERS

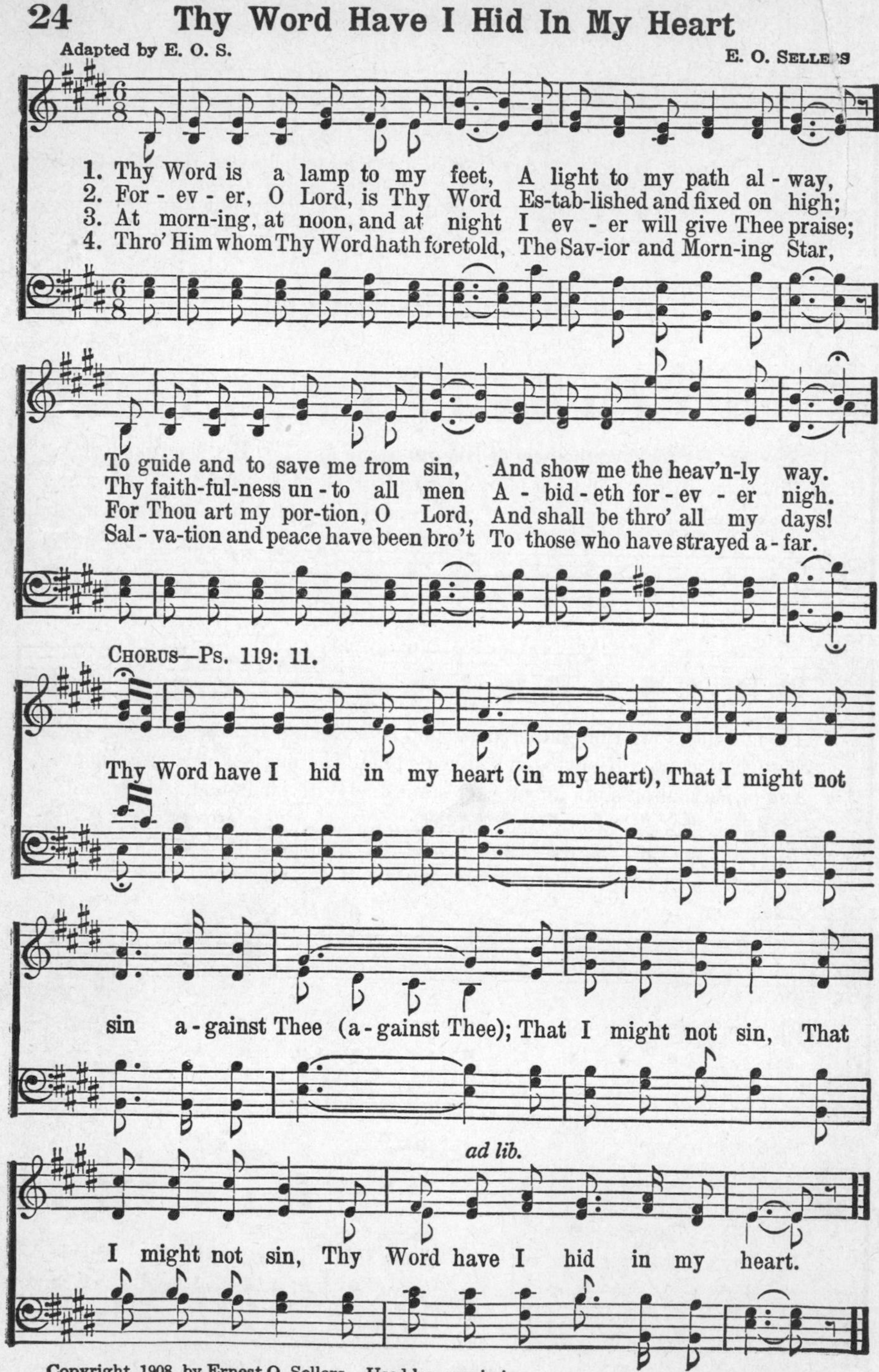
1. Thy Word is a lamp to my feet, A light to my path al - way,
2. For - ev - er, O Lord, is Thy Word Es-tab-lished and fixed on high;
3. At morn-ing, at noon, and at night I ev - er will give Thee praise;
4. Thro' Him whom Thy Word hath foretold, The Sav-ior and Morn-ing Star,
To guide and to save me from sin, And show me the heav'n-ly way.
Thy faith-ful-ness un - to all men A - bid - eth for - ev - er nigh.
For Thou art my por-tion, O Lord, And shall be thro' all my days!
Sal - va-tion and peace have been bro't To those who have strayed a - far.
CHORUS—Ps. 119: 11.
Thy Word have I hid in my heart (in my heart), That I might not
sin a - gainst Thee (a - gainst Thee); That I might not sin, That
ad lib.
I might not sin, Thy Word have I hid in my heart.

25 My Sins Are Blotted Out, I Know!

M. D. MERRILL DUNLOP

1. What a wondrous message in God's Word! My sins are blotted out, I know! If I trust in His redeeming blood, My sins are blotted out, I know!
2. Once my heart was black but now, what joy, My sins are blotted out, I know! I have peace that nothing can destroy, My sins are blotted out, I know!
3. I shall stand some day before my King, My sins all blotted out, I know! With the ransomed host I then shall sing: "My sins are blotted out, I know!"
CHORUS
My sins are blotted out, I know! I know! My sins are blotted out, I know! I know! They are buried in the depths of the deepest sea; My sins are blotted out, I know! I know!

When I See the Blood

J. F. G. and E. A. H. J. F. H.

1. Christ our Re-deem - er died on the cross, Died for the sin - ner, paid all his due; Sprin - kle your soul with the blood of the Lamb,
2. Chief-est of sin - ners, Je - sus will save; All He has prom-ised, that He will do; Wash in the foun - tain o - pened for sin,
3. Judg-ment is com - ing, all will be there, Each one re - ceiv - ing just - ly his due; Hide in the sav - ing sin-cleans-ing blood,
4. O great com-pas - sion! O bound-less love! O lov - ing kind - ness, faith - ful and true! Find peace and shel - ter un - der the blood,
And I will pass, will pass o - ver you.
CHORUS
When I see the blood, When I see the blood, When I see the blood, I will pass, I will pass o - ver you.
When I see the blood, When I see the blood, When I see the blood, o - ver you.
rit.

27 Precious Hiding Place

Avis B. Christiansen
Alto and Tenor Duet
Wendell P. Loveless
1. I was straying when Christ found me In the night so dark and cold;
2. With His nail-scarred hand He bro't me To the shel - ter of His love;
3. Tho' the night be dark a - round me, I am safe, for He is near;
Ten - der - ly His arm went round me And He bore me to His fold.
Of His grace and will He taught me, And of heav'n-ly rest a - bove.
Nev - er shall my foes con - found me, While the Sav-ior's voice I hear.
Chorus
Pre - cious hid - ing place, Pre - cious hid - ing place, In the
shel - ter of His love; Not a doubt or fear, Since my
rit.
Lord is near, And I'm shel - tered in His love.

28

I Am His, and He Is Mine

Rev. WADE ROBINSON

Rev. J. MOUNTAIN

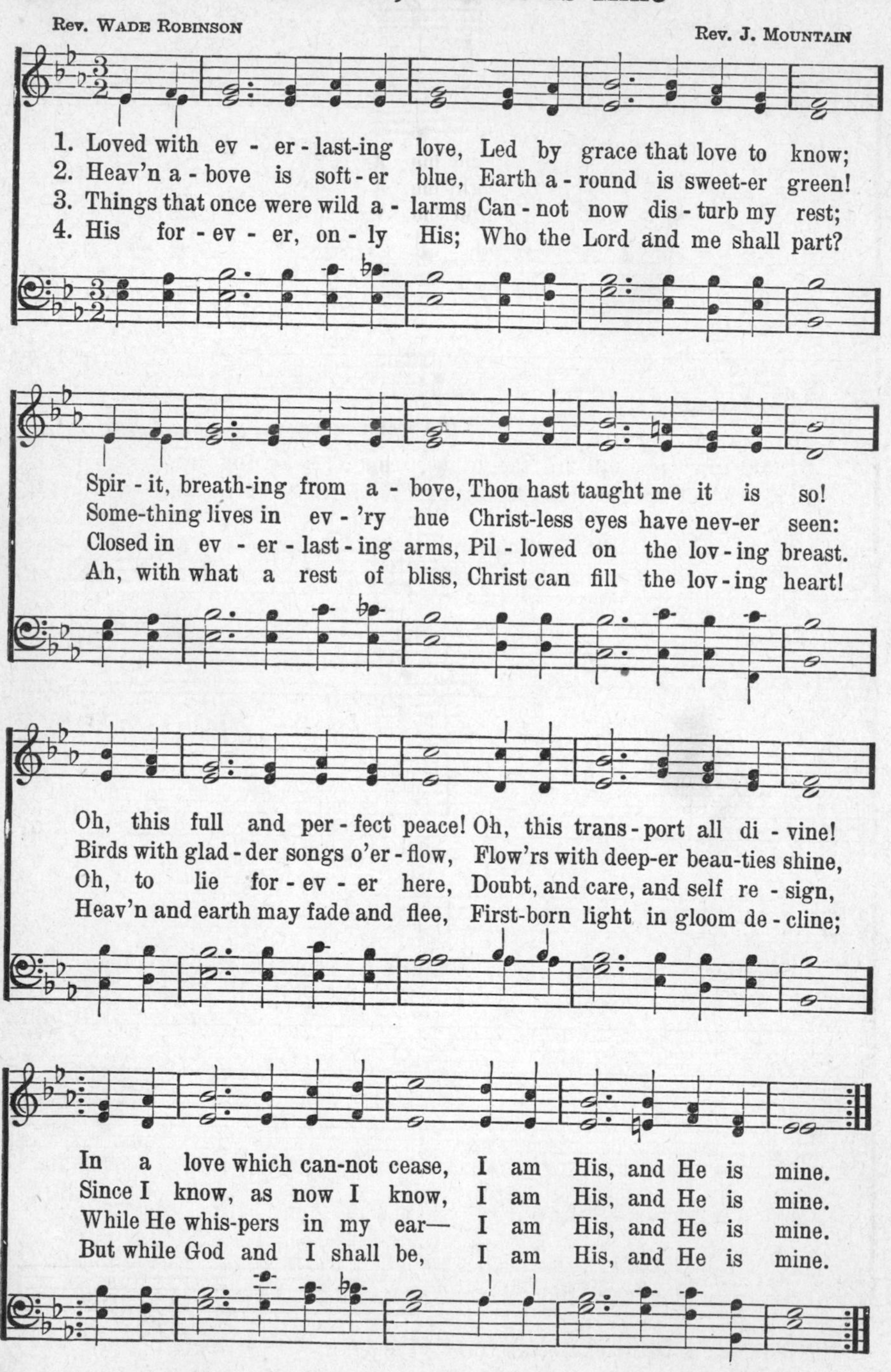

1. Loved with ev - er - last-ing love, Led by grace that love to know;
2. Heav'n a - bove is soft - er blue, Earth a - round is sweet-er green!
3. Things that once were wild a - larms Can - not now dis - turb my rest;
4. His for - ev - er, on - ly His; Who the Lord and me shall part?
Spir - it, breath-ing from a - bove, Thou hast taught me it is so!
Some-thing lives in ev - 'ry hue Christ-less eyes have nev-er seen:
Closed in ev - er - last - ing arms, Pil - lowed on the lov - ing breast.
Ah, with what a rest of bliss, Christ can fill the lov - ing heart!
Oh, this full and per - fect peace! Oh, this trans - port all di - vine!
Birds with glad - der songs o'er - flow, Flow'rs with deep-er beau-ties shine,
Oh, to lie for - ev - er here, Doubt, and care, and self re - sign,
Heav'n and earth may fade and flee, First-born light in gloom de - cline;
In a love which can-not cease, I am His, and He is mine.
Since I know, as now I know, I am His, and He is mine.
While He whis-pers in my ear— I am His, and He is mine.
But while God and I shall be, I am His, and He is mine.

29 Jesus Will!

INA DULEY OGDON
B. D. ACKLEY
1. Who will o-pen mer-cy's door? Je-sus will! Je-sus will!
2. Who can take a-way my sin? Je-sus will! Je-sus will!
3. Who can conquer doubts and fears? Je-sus will! Je-sus will!
4. Who will be my dear-est Friend? Je-sus will! Je-sus will!
Je-sus will! Je-sus will!
As for par-don I im-plore? Je-sus, bless-ed Je-sus will!
Make me pure, with-out, with-in? Je-sus, bless-ed Je-sus will!
Share my joys and dry my tears? Je-sus, bless-ed Je-sus will!
Love and keep me to the end? Je-sus, bless-ed Je-sus will!
REFRAIN
Je-sus will, Je-sus will! Yes, your lov-ing Sav-ior will;
sure-ly will;
He will each and ev'ry need ful-fill, Je-sus, bless-ed Je-sus will!

Still Sweeter Every Day

W. C. Martin — C. Austin Miles

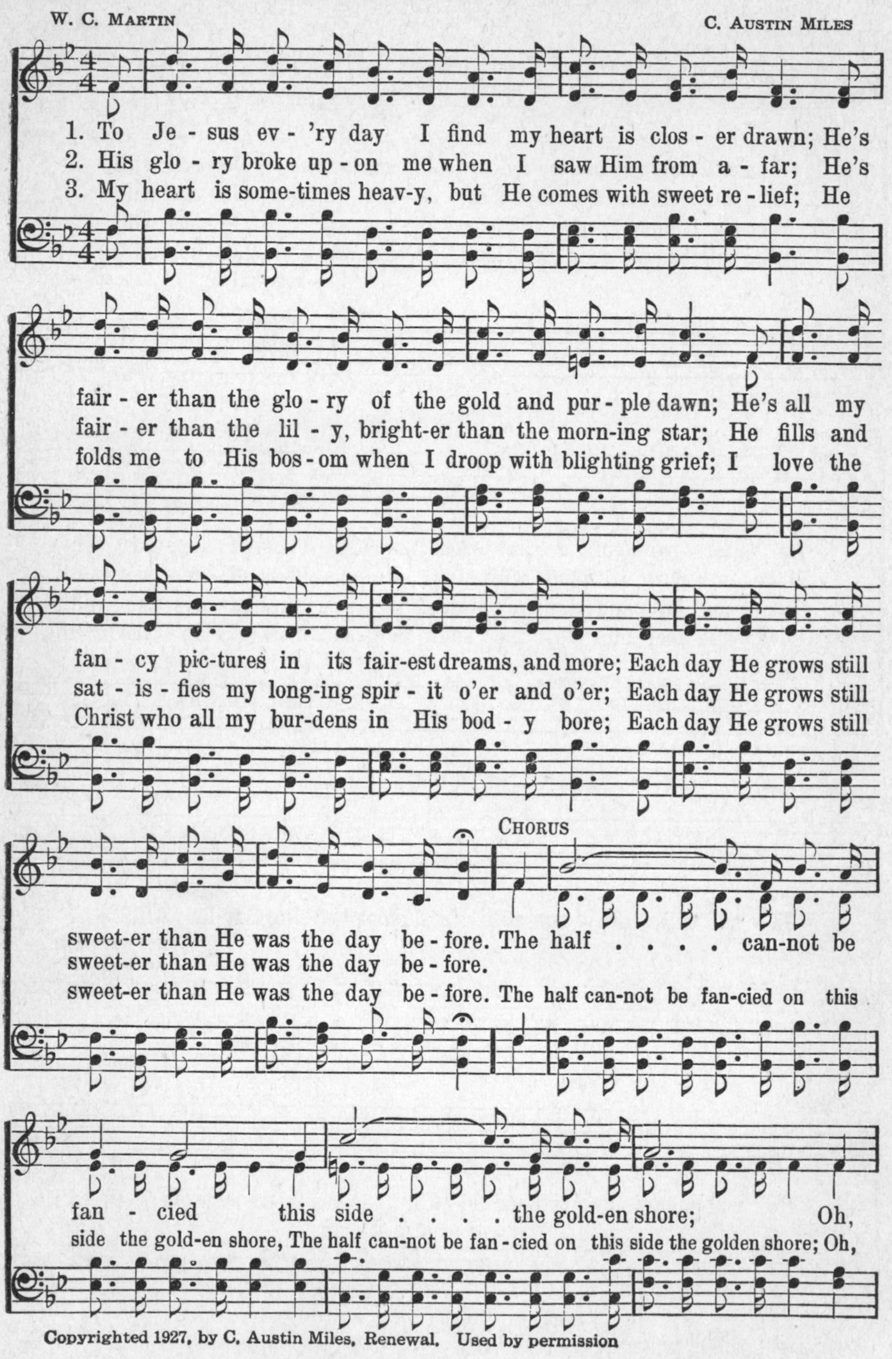

1. To Je - sus ev - 'ry day I find my heart is clos - er drawn; He's
2. His glo - ry broke up - on me when I saw Him from a - far; He's
3. My heart is some-times heav-y, but He comes with sweet re - lief; He
fair - er than the glo - ry of the gold and pur - ple dawn; He's all my
fair - er than the lil - y, bright-er than the morn-ing star; He fills and
folds me to His bos - om when I droop with blighting grief; I love the
fan - cy pic-tures in its fair-est dreams, and more; Each day He grows still
sat - is - fies my long-ing spir - it o'er and o'er; Each day He grows still
Christ who all my bur-dens in His bod - y bore; Each day He grows still
sweet-er than He was the day be - fore. The half . . . . can-not be
sweet-er than He was the day be - fore.
sweet-er than He was the day be - fore. The half can-not be fan-cied on this
CHORUS
fan - cied this side . . . . the gold-en shore; Oh,
side the gold-en shore, The half can-not be fan - cied on this side the golden shore; Oh,

Still Sweeter Every Day
there . . . . He'll be still sweet-er than He ev-er was be-fore.
there He'll be still sweeter than He ev-er was be-fore, than He ev-er was be-fore.
31
I Love Him
London Hymn Book
STEPHEN C. FOSTER
Arr. by D. B. TOWNER
1. Gone from my heart the world and all its charms; Now thro' the blood I'm saved from all a-larms; Down at the cross my heart is bend-ing low; The pre-cious blood of Je-sus cleanses white as snow.
2. Once I was lost, and 'way down deep in sin; Once was a slave to pas-sions fierce with-in; Once was a-fraid to meet an an-gry God, But now I'm cleansed from ev'ry stain thro' Jesus' blood.
3. Once I was bound, but now I am set free; Once I was blind, but now the light I see; Once I was dead, but now in Christ I live, To tell the world a-round the peace that He doth give.
CHORUS
I love Him, I love Him, Be-cause He first loved me, And purchased my sal-va-tion On Cal-v'ry's tree.

Over There

P. R. PAUL RADER

1. O-ver there where the heathen are dy-ing, O-ver there where the sin forc-es dwell. We must car-ry the great sal-va-tion, We must go and the glad sto-ry tell.
2. O-ver there where temp-ta-tion is call-ing, O-ver there where the vic-es a-bound, We must tell of the One who con-quers, We must tell of the Christ we have found.
3. O-ver there they are call-ing and dy-ing, O-ver there in the dark-ness they roam, They are wait-ing to hear of Je-sus, They are call-ing to us, "Won't you come?"
CHORUS
O-ver there where the mil-lions are dy-ing, o-ver there, O-ver there where God's tho'ts are turning, o-ver there; O-ver there dark-ened hearts are yearn-ing, o-ver there, We will pray for the souls o-ver there.
rit.

33 Take Your Burdens to Jesus

RICHARD J. OLIVER and M. D. MERRILL DUNLOP

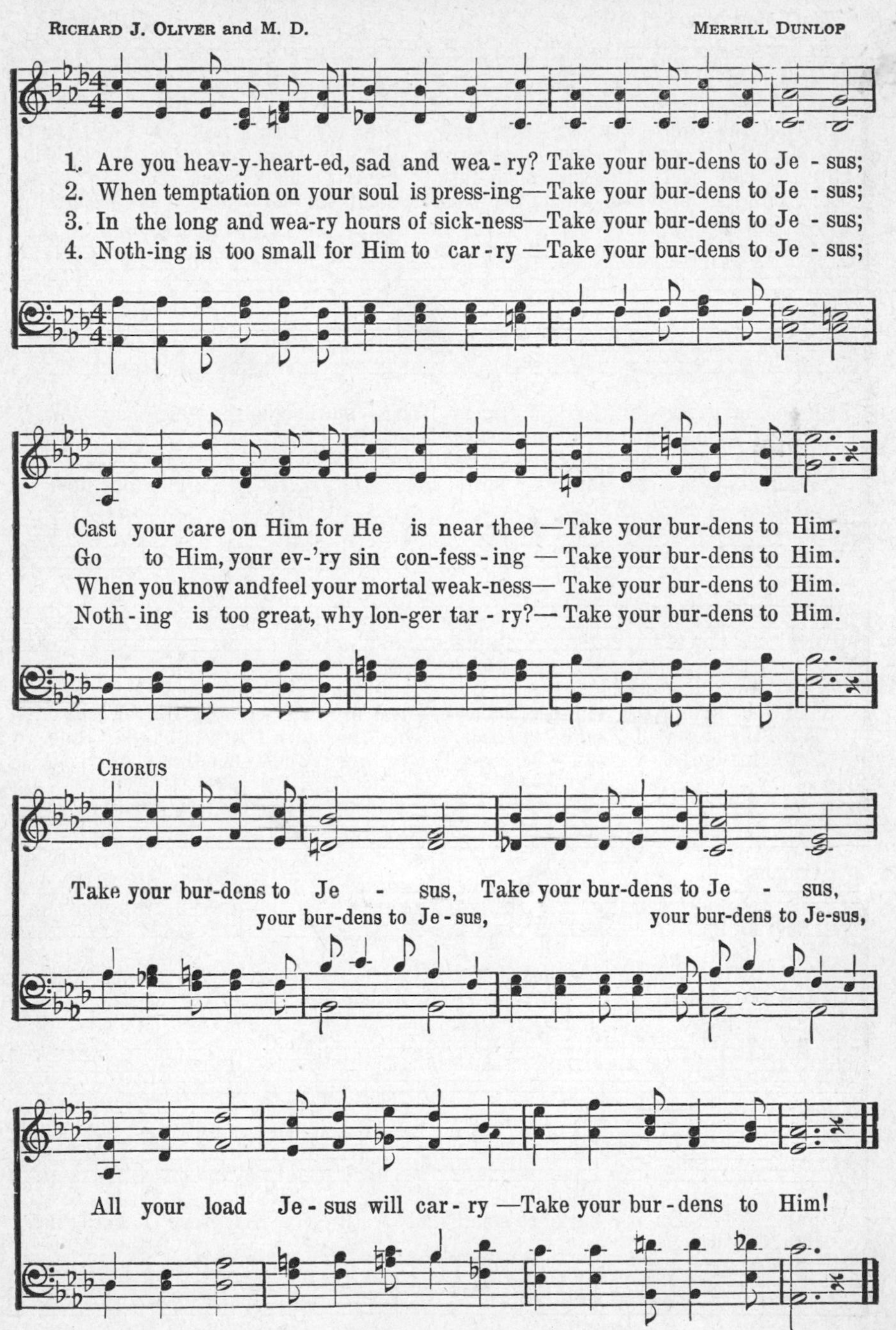
1. Are you heav-y-heart-ed, sad and wea - ry? Take your bur-dens to Je - sus;
2. When temptation on your soul is press-ing—Take your bur-dens to Je - sus;
3. In the long and wea-ry hours of sick-ness—Take your bur-dens to Je - sus;
4. Noth-ing is too small for Him to car - ry —Take your bur-dens to Je - sus;
Cast your care on Him for He is near thee —Take your bur-dens to Him.
Go to Him, your ev-'ry sin con-fess - ing — Take your bur-dens to Him.
When you know andfeel your mortal weak-ness— Take your bur-dens to Him.
Noth - ing is too great, why lon-ger tar - ry?— Take your bur-dens to Him.
CHORUS
Take your bur-dens to Je - sus, Take your bur-dens to Je - sus,
your bur-dens to Je-sus, your bur-dens to Je-sus,
All your load Je - sus will car - ry —Take your bur - dens to Him!

34

My Anchor Holds

W. C. Martin, arr. D. B. Towner

1. Tho' the an - gry sur - ges roll On my tem - pest-driv - en soul,
2. Might-y tides a - bout me sweep, Per - ils lurk with - in the deep,
3. I can feel the an - chor fast As I meet each sud - den blast,
4. Troub-les al - most 'whelm the soul; Griefs like bil - lows o'er me roll;
I am peace - ful, for I know, Wild - ly though the winds may blow,
An - gry clouds o'er-shade the sky, And the tem - pest ris - es high;
And the ca - ble, though un - seen, Bears the heav - y strain be - tween;
Tempters seek to lure a - stray; Storms ob - scure the light of day:
I've an an - chor safe and sure, That can ev - er - more en - dure.
Still I stand the tem-pest's shock, For my an - chor grips the Rock.
Thro' the storm I safe - ly ride, Till the turn - ing of the tide.
But in Christ I can be bold, I've an an - chor that shall hold.
Chorus
And it holds, my an - chor holds; Blow your wild - est, then, O
And it holds,....... my an - chor holds; Blow your wild - - - est,
gale, On my bark so small and frail: By His grace I shall not
then, O gale,

My Anchor Holds

fail, For my an - chor holds, my an - chor holds.
For my an - chor holds, it firm - ly holds,
35
Have Thine Own Way, Lord
A. A. P.
Geo. C. Stebbins
Slowly
1. Have Thine own way, Lord! Have Thine own way!.. Thou art the
2. Have Thine own way, Lord! Have Thine own way!.. Search me and
3. Have Thine own way, Lord! Have Thine own way!.. Wound-ed and
4. Have Thine own way, Lord! Have Thine own way!.. Hold o'er my
Pot - ter; I am the clay... Mould me and make me Aft - er Thy
try me, Mas-ter, to - day!... Whit - er than snow, Lord, Wash me just
wea - ry, Help me, I pray! Pow - er—all pow - er—Sure - ly is
be - ing Ab - so - lute sway!. Fill with Thy Spir - it Till all shall
will,... While I am wait - ing, Yield - ed and still...
now,... As in Thy pres - ence Hum - bly I bow...
Thine! Touch me and heal me, Sav - ior di - vine!..
see.... Christ on - ly, al - ways, Liv - ing in me!....

If Jesus Goes With Me

C. A. M. C. AUSTIN MILES

1. It may be in the val-ley, where countless dangers hide; It may be in the sun-shine that I, in peace, a - bide; But this one thing I know—if it be dark or fair, If Je - sus is with me, I'll go an - y - where!
2. It ma be I must car - ry the bless- ed word of life A-cross the burning des - erts to those in sin - ful strife; And tho' it be my lot to bear my col - ors there, If Je - sus goes with me, I'll go an - y - where!
3. But if it be my por- tion to bear my cross at home, While others bear their bur - dens be - yond the bil - low's foam, I'll prove my faith in Him—con-fess His judgments fair, And, if He stays with me, I'll stay an - y - where!
4. It is not mine to ques-tion the judg-ments of my Lord, It is but mine to fol - low the lead-ings of His Word; But if to go or stay, or wheth-er here or there, I'll be, with my Sav - ior, Con-tent an - y - where!
CHORUS
If Je-sus goes with me, I'll go.... An - y - where! 'Tis heaven to me, Wher-
I'll go
e'er I may be, If He is there! I count it a priv - i-lege here.. His
His cross, His

If Jesus Goes With Me

cross to bear;.. If Je-sus goes with me, I'll go... An - y - where!
cross, His cross to bear;
37
At Calvary
WM. R. NEWELL
D. B. TOWNER
1. Years I spent in van - i - ty and pride, Car - ing not my Lord was cru - ci - fied, Know-ing not it was for me He died On Cal - va - ry.
2. By God's Word at last my sin I learned; Then I trem-bled at the law I'd spurned, Till my guilt-y soul im-plor-ing turned To Cal - va - ry.
3. Now I've giv'n to Je - sus ev - 'ry - thing, Now I glad - ly own Him as my King, Now my raptured soul can on - ly sing Of Cal - va - ry.
4. Oh, the love that drew sal - va - tion's plan! Oh, the grace that bro't it down to man! Oh, the might-y gulf that God did span At Cal - va - ry!
CHORUS
Mer - cy there was great, and grace was free; Par - don there was mul - ti - plied to me; There my burdened soul found lib-er - ty, At Cal - va - ry.

38 **Under His Wings**

WILLIAM O. CUSHING — IRA D. SANKEY

1. Un-der His wings I am safe-ly a-bid-ing; Tho' the night deep-ens and tem-pests are wild, Still I can trust Him; I know He will keep me; He has re-deemed me, and I am His child.
2. Un-der His wings, what a ref-uge in sor-row! How the heart yearn-ing-ly turns to His rest! Oft-en when earth has no balm for my heal-ing, There I find com-fort, and there I am blest.
3. Un-der His wings, O what pre-cious en-joy-ment! There will I hide till life's tri-als are o'er; Shel-tered, pro-tect-ed, no e-vil can harm me; Rest-ing in Je-sus I'm safe ev-er-more.
CHORUS
Un-der His wings, un-der His wings, Who from His love can sev-er?
Un-der His wings my soul shall a-bide, Safe-ly a-bide for-ev-er.

Christ Receiveth Sinful Men

Arr. from NEUMASTER, 1671 JAMES MCGRANAHAN

1. Sin - ners Je - sus will re - ceive; Sound this word of grace to all
2. Come, and He will give you rest; Trust Him, for His word is plain;
3. Now my heart con-demns me not, Pure be - fore the law I stand;
4. Christ re - ceiv - eth sin - ful men, E - ven me with all my sin;
Who the heav'n - ly path-way leave, All who lin - ger, all who fall.
He will take the sin - ful - est; Christ re - ceiv - eth sin - ful men.
He who cleansed me from all spot, Sat - is - fied its last de-mand.
Purged from ev - 'ry spot and stain, Heav'n with Him I en - ter in.
REFRAIN
Sing it o'er. . . . . . . and o'er a - gain; . . . . . . Christ re-
Sing it o'er a-gain, Sing it o'er a-gain; Christ re-
ceiv - - - eth sin-ful men; . . . . . Make the mes - - - sage
ceiv-eth sin - ful men, Christ re-ceiv - eth sin - ful men; Make the message plain,
clear and plain: . . . . . . Christ re - ceiv - eth sin - ful men.
Make the mes-sage plain:

40 Pray, Pray

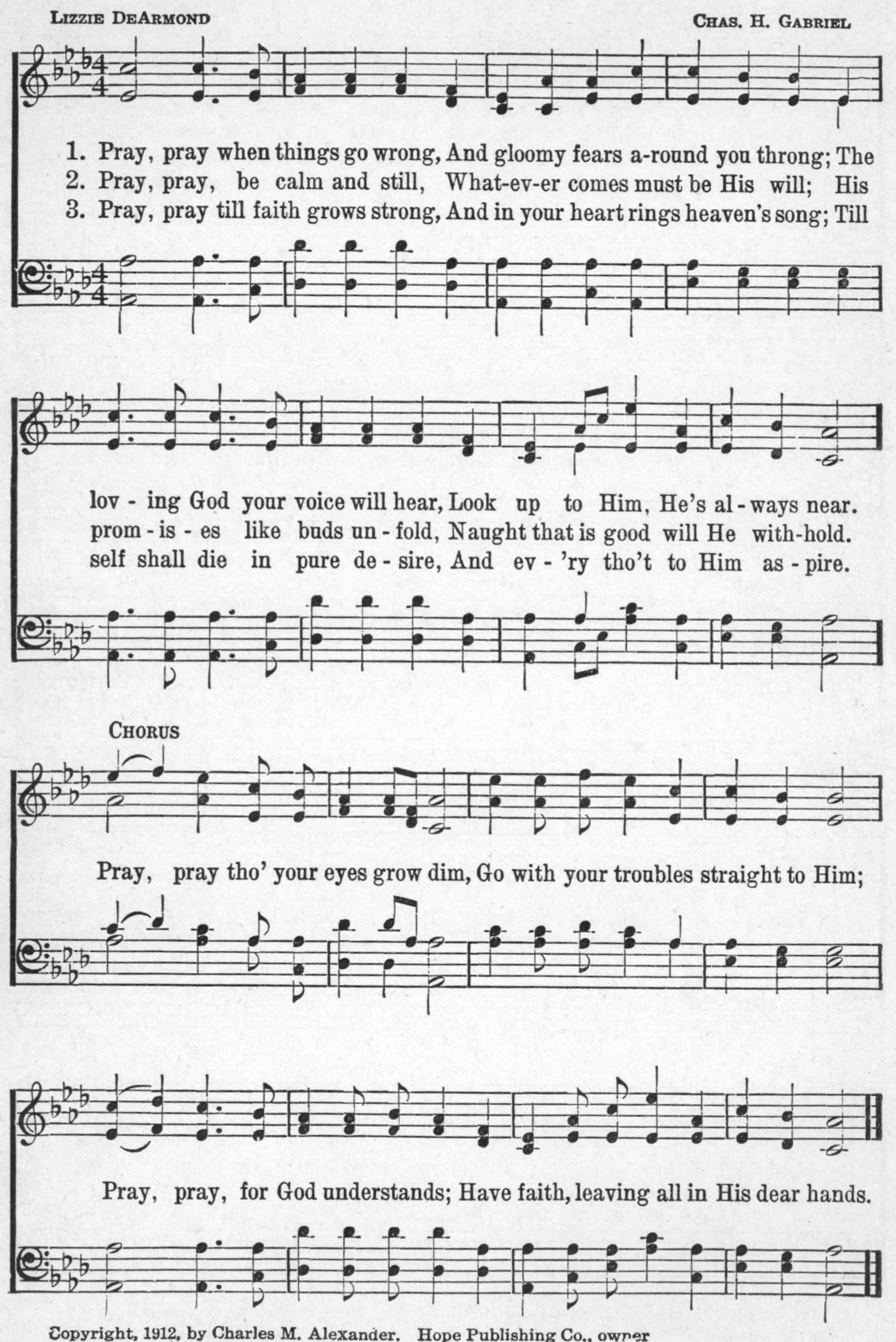
LIZZIE DEARMOND
CHAS. H. GABRIEL
1. Pray, pray when things go wrong, And gloomy fears a-round you throng; The
2. Pray, pray, be calm and still, What-ev-er comes must be His will; His
3. Pray, pray till faith grows strong, And in your heart rings heaven's song; Till
lov - ing God your voice will hear, Look up to Him, He's al - ways near.
prom - is - es like buds un - fold, Naught that is good will He with-hold.
self shall die in pure de - sire, And ev - 'ry tho't to Him as - pire.
CHORUS
Pray, pray tho' your eyes grow dim, Go with your troubles straight to Him;
Pray, pray, for God understands; Have faith, leaving all in His dear hands.

41 The Old-Time Way

R. H. ROBERT HARKNESS

1. Do you love the bless - ed Sav - ior In the old - time way?
2. Are you keep - ing close to Je - sus In the old - time way?
3. Have you made a full sur - ren - der In the old - time way?
4. Are you work - ing for His king - dom In the old - time way?
Is your heart a - glow with rap - ture In the old - time way?
Dai - ly walk - ing in His pres - ence In the old - time way?
Giv - en all to fol - low Je - sus In the old - time way?
Are you lead - ing oth - ers to Him In the old - time way?
CHORUS
In the old - time way, In the old - time way, We must
claim the old - time bless - ing, In the old - time way.

Constantly Abiding

Mrs. W. L. M. — Mrs. Will L. Murphy

1. There's a peace in my heart that the world nev-er gave, A peace it can not take a-way; Tho' the tri-als of life may surround like a cloud, I've a peace that has come there to stay!
2. All the world seemed to sing of a Sav-ior and King, When peace sweetly came to my heart; Troubles all fled a-way and my night turned to day, Bless-ed Je-sus, how glorious Thou art!
3. This treas-ure I have in a tem-ple of clay, While here on His foot-stool I roam; But He's coming to take me some glo-ri-ous day, O-ver there to my heav-en-ly home!
CHORUS
Con - - - stant-ly a- bid - - - - ing, Je - - - sus is mine;........
Con-stant-ly a-bid - ing, con-stant-ly a-bid-ing, Je - sus is mine, yes, Je - sus is mine;
Con - - - stant-ly a - bid - - - - ing, rap - - ture di-
Con-stant-ly a - bid - ing, con-stant-ly a - bid-ing, rap-ture di-vine, O

Constantly Abiding

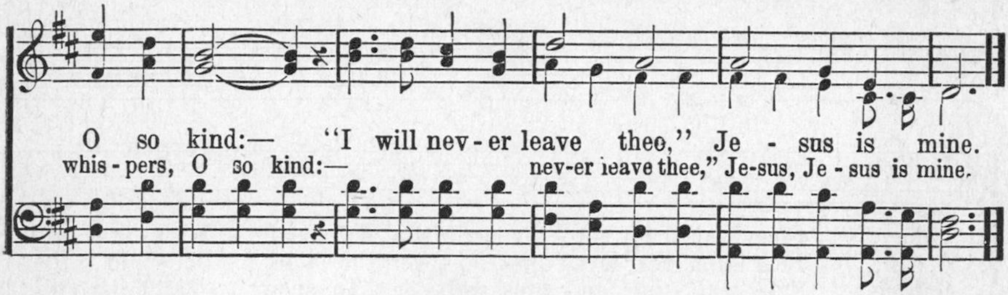

vine; He nev-er leaves me lone - - - ly, whis-pers,
rap-ture di-vine; He nev-er leaves me, nev-er leaves me lone-ly, whis-pers,

O so kind:— "I will nev-er leave thee," Je - sus is mine.
whis-pers, O so kind:— nev-er leave thee," Je-sus, Je - sus is mine.

43 Sometime!

R. H. ROBERT HARKNESS

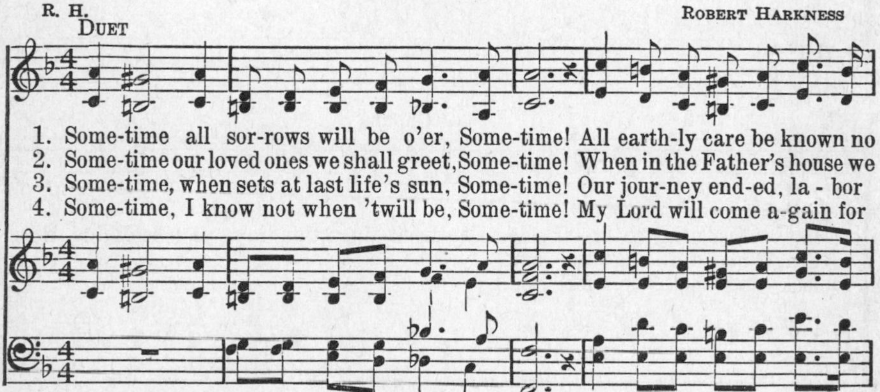

DUET

1. Some-time all sor-rows will be o'er, Some-time! All earth-ly care be known no more! Oh, what rejoicing on the golden shore,
2. Some-time our loved ones we shall greet, Some-time! When in the Father's house we meet, On - ly to sit for - ev - er at His feet, Sometime, sometime soon!
3. Some-time, when sets at last life's sun, Some-time! Our jour-ney end-ed, la - bor done, Oh, what a crown for ev-'ry vict'ry won, some-time soon!
4. Some-time, I know not when 'twill be, Some-time! My Lord will come a-gain for me, Then I shall reign with Him eternally,

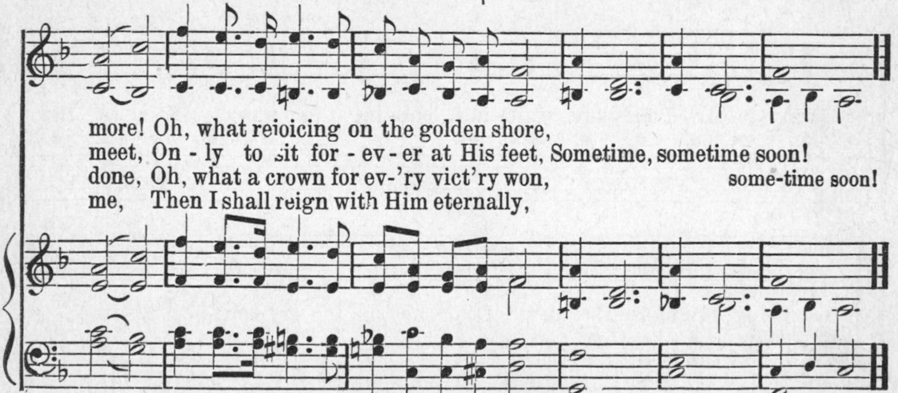

Looking This Way

J. W. V. J. W. Van De Venter

Solo or Duet

1. O - ver the riv - er, fa - ces I see, Fair as the morn-ing, look-ing for me; Free from their sor - row, grief and de - spair, Wait - ing and watch-ing pa - tient - ly there.
2. Fa - ther and moth-er, safe in the vale, Watch for the boatman, wait for the sail, Bear-ing the loved ones o - ver the tide, In - to the har - bor, near to their side.
3. Broth-er and sis - ter, gone to that clime, Wait for the oth - ers, coming some-time, Safe with the an - gels, whit - er than snow, Watch-ing for dear ones wait-ing be - low.
4. Sweet lit - tle dar-ling, light of the home, Look-ing for some one, beck-on-ing come; Bright as a sun-beam, pure as the dew, Anx - ious - ly look - ing, moth - er, for you.

Chorus

Look - ing this way, yes, look - ing this way; Loved ones are wait - ing, look - ing this way; Fair as the morn - ing, bright as the day, Dear ones in glo - ry, look-ing this way.

45 Nothing Between

Words and Music by C. A. Tindley
Arr. by F. A. Clark
1. Noth-ing be-tween my soul and the Sav-ior, Naught of this world's de-
2. Noth-ing be-tween, like world - ly pleas-ure, Hab-its of life though
3. Noth-ing be-tween, like pride or sta-tion, Self or friends shall
4. Noth-ing be-tween, e'en man-y hard tri-als, Tho' the whole world a-
lu - sive dream; I have re-nounced all sin - ful pleas-ure,
harm-less they seem, Must not my heart from Him e'er sev-er,
not in-ter-vene, Tho' it may cost me much trib-u-la-tion,
gainst me con-vene; Watching with prayer and much self-de-ni-al, I'll
Je-sus is mine; there's noth-ing be-tween.
He is my all; there's noth-ing be-tween.
I am re-solved; there's noth-ing be-tween.
tri-umph at last, with noth-ing be-tween.
CHORUS
Noth-ing be-tween my
soul and the Sav-ior, So that His bless-ed face may be seen; Noth-ing pre-
vent-ing the least of His fa-vor, Keep the way clear! Let nothing between.

46 There is Power in the Blood

L. E. J. L. E. Jones

1. Would you be free from the bur - den of sin? There's pow'r in the blood,
2. Would you be free from your pas-sion and pride? There's pow'r in the blood,
3. Would you be whit - er, much whiter than snow? There's pow'r in the blood,
4. Would you do serv - ice for Je - sus your King? There's pow'r in the blood,
pow'r in the blood; Would you o'er e - vil a vic - to - ry win? There's
pow'r in the blood; Come for a cleans-ing to Cal - va - ry's tide; There's
pow'r in the blood; Sin-stains are lost in its life - giv - ing flow; There's
pow'r in the blood; Would you live dai - ly His prais - es to sing? There's
won - der-ful pow'r in the blood.
Chorus.
There is pow'r, pow'r, Wonder-working pow'r
there is
In the blood of the Lamb;
In the blood of the Lamb;
There is pow'r, pow'r,
there is
Won - der - work - ing pow'r In the pre - cious blood of the Lamb.

47 Only Jesus

Avis B. Christiansen | Lance B. Latham

1. I've found a ref - uge from life's care in Je - sus, I am hid - ing in His love di - vine; He ful - ly un - der-stands my soul's deep long - ing, And He whis-pers soft - ly, "Thou art mine."
2. I've found a pre - cious joy in know-ing Je - sus, Nev - er dreamed of in this world of woe; No clouds, how-ev - er dark, can dim the ra - diance Of the heav'n-ly light He doth be - stow.
3. I've found a bless - ed hope di - vine in Je - sus, 'Tis a Day Star ev - er shin-ing bright; It fills my earth-ly way with heav'n-ly glo - ry, And it turns life's dark-ness in - to light.
Refrain
On - ly Je - sus! On - ly Je - sus! On - ly He can sat - is - fy;
Ev-'ry bur - den be-comes a bless - ing, When I know my Lord is nigh.

48 Grace Greater Than Our Sins

Julia H. Johnston — D. B. Towner

1. Mar-vel-ous grace of our lov-ing Lord, Grace that ex-ceeds our sin and our guilt, Yon-der on Cal-va-ry's mount out-poured, There where the blood of the Lamb was spilt.
2. Sin and de-spair like the sea waves cold, Threat-en the soul with in-fi-nite loss; Grace that is great-er, yes, grace un-told, Points to the Ref-uge, the Might-y Cross.
3. Dark is the stain that we can-not hide, What can a-vail to wash it a-way? Look! there is flow-ing a crim-son tide; Whit-er than snow you may be to-day.
4. Mar-vel-ous, in-fi-nite, match-less grace, Free-ly be-stowed on all who be-lieve; You that are long-ing to see His face, Will you this mo-ment His grace re-ceive?
Chorus
Grace, grace, God's grace, Grace that will par-don and cleanse with-in; Grace, grace, God's grace, Grace that is great-er than all our sin.
Mar-vel-ous grace, In-fi-nite grace,
Mar-vel-ous grace, In-fi-nite grace,

49 Thou Wilt Keep Him in Perfect Peace

R. J. O.
RICHARD J. OLIVER
1. In this world of trib - u - la - tion, With its storms of end - less strife,
2. Let us sing a - mid our sor-row, "He will wipe all tears a - way,"
3. Since the Ho - ly Spir - it sealed us, And thro' Je - sus' blood we're free,
There is peace, per - fect peace; Christ will be your con - so - la - tion,
There is peace, per - fect peace; Faith will bring a glad to - mor - row,
There is peace, per - fect peace; With God's hand out-stretched to shield us,
He is Life, E - ter - nal Life, He will keep you in per - fect peace.
Tho' the clouds hang low to - day, As He keeps us in per - fect peace.
We shall more than conqu'rors be, For He keeps us in per - fect peace.
CHORUS—Isaiah 26: 3
"Thou wilt keep him in per-fect peace, Whose mind is stayed on
in per-fect peace,
Thee, Be - cause he trust-eth, Because he trust-eth in Thee."
is stayed on Thee,

Count Your Blessings

Rev. JOHNSON OATMAN, JR. E. O. EXCELL

1. When up - on life's bil-lows you are tem - pest - tossed, When you are dis-
2. Are you ev - er bur-dened with a load of care? Does the cross seem
3. When you look at oth - ers with their lands and gold, Think that Christ has
4. So, a - mid the con-flict, whether great or small, Do not be dis-
cour-aged, think-ing all is lost, Count your man-y bless-ings, name them
heav - y you are called to bear? Count your man-y bless-ings, ev - 'ry
prom-ised you His wealth un - told; Count your man-y bless-ings, mon-ey
cour-aged, God is o - ver all; Count your man-y bless-ings, an - gels
one by one, And it will sur-prise you what the Lord hath done.
doubt will fly, And you will be sing-ing as the days go by.
can - not buy Your re-ward in Heav-en, nor your home on high.
will at - tend, Help and com-fort give you to your jour - ney's end.
CHORUS.
Count your bless-ings, Name them one by one; Count your
Count your man-y bless-ings, Name them one by one; Count your man-y
bless-ings, See what God hath done; Count your bless-ings,
bless - ings, See what God hath done; Count your man-y bless - ings,

Count Your Blessings

51 When We All Get to Heaven

rit.
a tempo
Name them one by one; Count your man-y blessings, See what God hath done.
E. E. Hewitt
Mrs. J. G. Wilson
1. Sing the won-drous love of Je - sus, Sing His mer-cy and His grace;
2. While we walk the pil - grim pathway, Clouds will o - ver-spread the sky;
3. Let us then be true and faith-ful, Trust-ing, serv-ing ev - 'ry day;
4. On-ward to the prize be - fore us! Soon His beau-ty we'll be - hold;
In the man-sions bright and blessed, He'll pre-pare for us a place.
But when trav'ling days are o - ver, Not a shad-ow, not a sigh.
Just one glimpse of Him in glo - ry Will the toils of life re - pay.
Soon the pearl - y gates will o - pen, We shall tread the streets of gold.
for us a place.
Chorus
When we all get to heaven, What a day of re-joicing that will be!
When we all What a day of re-joicing that will be!
When we all see Je-sus, We'll sing and shout the vic-to-ry . . . .
When we all and shout the vic-to-ry.

Just One Touch

BIRDIE BELL
J. HOWARD ENTWISTLE
SOLO Slow, with expression
1. Just one touch as He moves a - long, Pushed and pressed by the jostling throng,
2. Just one touch and He makes me whole, Speaks sweet peace to my sin-sick soul,
3. Just one touch! and the work is done, I am saved by the bless - ed Son,
4. Just one touch! and He turns to me, Oh, the love in His eyes I see!
5. Just one touch! by His mighty pow'r He can heal thee this bless-ed hour,
Just one touch and the weak was strong, Cured by the Heal-er di - vine.
At His feet all my bur - dens roll,—Cured by the Heal-er di - vine.
I will sing while the a - ges run, Cured by the Heal-er di - vine.
I am His, for He hears my plea, Cured by the Heal-er di - vine.
Thou canst hear tho' the tempests low'r, Cured by the Heal-er di - vine.
CHORUS
Just one touch as He pass - es by, He will list to the faint-est cry,
Come and be saved while the Lord is nigh, Christ is the Heal-er di-vine.
di-vine.

53 O Perfect Life of Love!

HENRY W. BAKER CLARENCE W. JONES

1. O per - fect life of love! All, all is fin - ished now;
2. No pain that we can share But He has felt its smart;
3. In per - fect love He dies; For me He dies, for me:
All that He left His throne a - bove To do for us be - low.
All forms of hu - man grief and care Have pierced that ten - der heart;
O all - a - ton - ing Sac - ri - fice, I cling by faith to Thee.
No work is left un - done Of all the Fa - ther willed;
And on His thorn-crowned head, And on His sin - less soul,
In ev - 'ry time of need, Be - fore Thy gra - cious throne,
His toil, His sor - rows, one by one, The Scrip - ture have ful-filled;
Our sins in all their guilt were laid, That He might make us whole;
Thy work, O Lamb of God, I'll plead, Thy mer - it, not my own;
His toil, His sor-rows, one by one, The Scrip - ture have ful-filled.
Our sins in all their guilt were laid, That He might make us whole.
Thy work. O Lamb of God, I'll plead, Thy mer - it, not my own.

54 Since the Fullness of His Love Came In

E. E. HEWITT B. D. ACKLEY

1. Once my way was dark and drear - y, For my heart was full of sin,
2. There is grace for all the low - ly, Grace to keep the trust-ing soul:
3. Let me spread a - broad the sto - ry, Oth - er souls to Je - sus win;
But the sky is bright and cheer-y, Since the full-ness of His love came in.
Pow'r to cleanse and make me ho - ly, Je - sus shall my yield-ed life con - trol.
For the cross is now my glo - ry, Since the full-ness of His love came in.
CHORUS
I can nev-er tell how much I love Him, I can nev-er tell His love for me;
For it pass-eth hu-man measure, Like a deep, unfathomed sea;
deep, unfathomed sea;
'Tis re-deeming love in Christ my Sav-ior, In my soul the heav'nly joys be-gin;

Since the Fullness of His Love Came In

And I live for Je - sus on - ly, Since the full-ness of His love came in.
55
Wonderful Words of Life
P. P. B.
P. P. Bliss
1. Sing them o - ver a - gain to me, Won-der - ful words of Life;
2. Christ, the bless - ed One, gives to all, Won-der - ful words of Life;
3. Sweet - ly ech - o the gos - pel call, Won-der - ful words of Life;
Let me more of their beau - ty see, Won-der-ful words of Life.
Sin - ner, list to the lov - ing call, Won-der-ful words of Life.
Of - fer par-don and peace to all, Won-der-ful words of Life.
Words of life and beau - ty, Teach me faith and du - ty:
All so free - ly giv - en, Woo - ing us to Heav - en:
Je - sus, on - ly Sav - ior, Sanc - ti - fy for - ev - er:
Refrain
1
2
Beau - ti - ful words, won-der-ful words, Won-der-ful words of Life. Life.

Prayer Changes Things

M. A. S.
May Agnew Stephens
1. Man - y prob-lems meet us on our heav'n-ly way; If we had no
2. "What-so - ev - er ye de - sire when ye pray;" Hear His lov - ing
3. While you plead His might-y name you can - not fail, Heed-ing not the
Help - er we would sure - ly stray; But our lov - ing Sav - ior bids us
prom - ise, 'tis for you to - day; Stand up - on His faith - ful-ness; fresh
dark-ness, nor the fierc - est gale; Shad-ows at His word will flee, and
seek His face, Meets us at the throne of grace.
cour - age take: "All is yours"—for His dear sake.
storms be calm, Sor-rows turn to joy - ful psalm.
Chorus
Prayer chan - ges
things; Prayer chan-ges things. No mat - ter how heav - y the
bur - den you bear, If you cast it on Je - sus He'll car - ry your care;

Prayer Changes Things

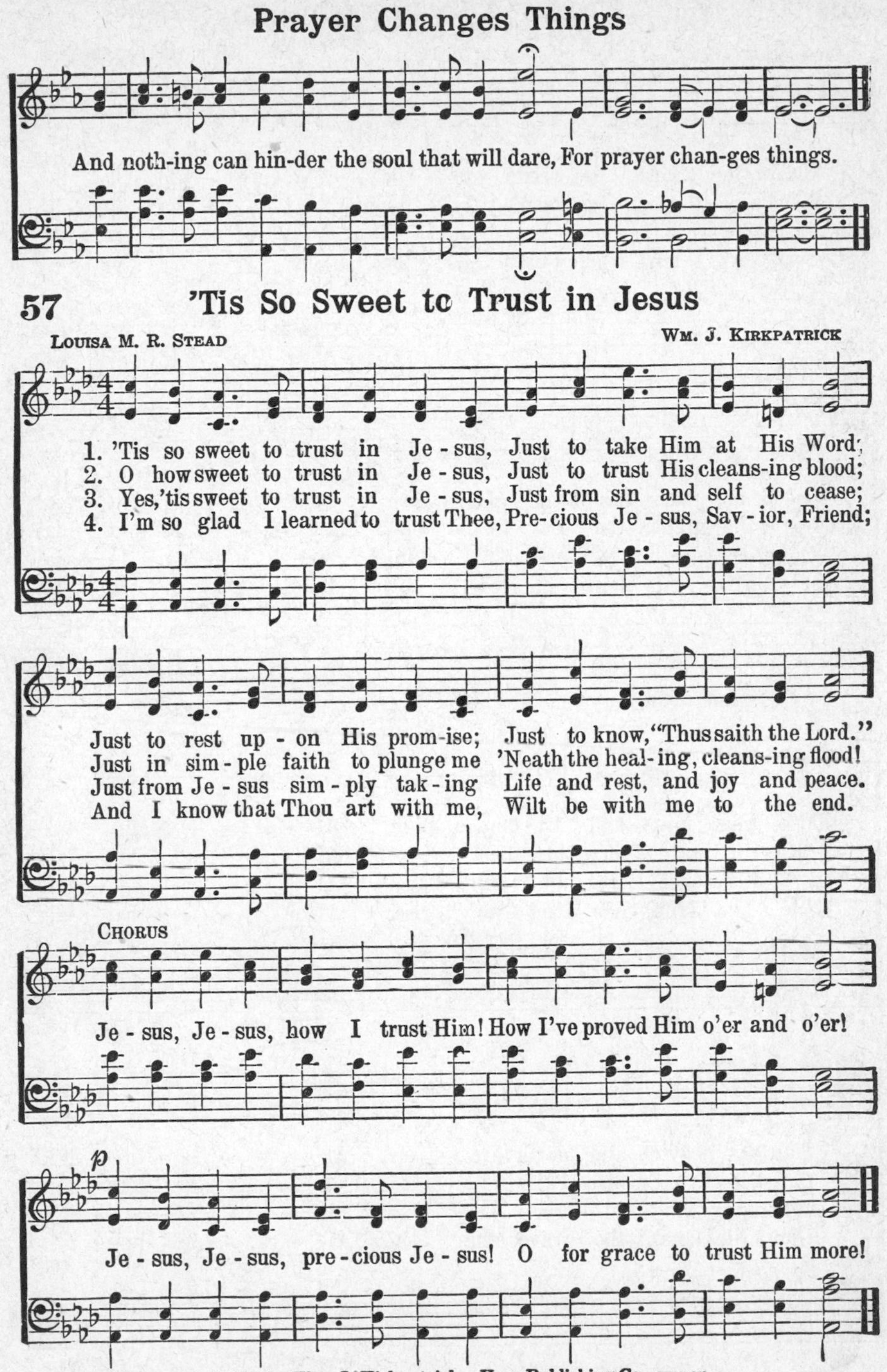

And noth-ing can hin-der the soul that will dare, For prayer chan-ges things.

57 'Tis So Sweet to Trust in Jesus

Louisa M. R. Stead
Wm. J. Kirkpatrick

1. 'Tis so sweet to trust in Je-sus, Just to take Him at His Word;
2. O how sweet to trust in Je-sus, Just to trust His cleans-ing blood;
3. Yes, 'tis sweet to trust in Je-sus, Just from sin and self to cease;
4. I'm so glad I learned to trust Thee, Pre-cious Je-sus, Sav-ior, Friend;

Just to rest up-on His prom-ise; Just to know, "Thus saith the Lord."
Just in sim-ple faith to plunge me 'Neath the heal-ing, cleans-ing flood!
Just from Je-sus sim-ply tak-ing Life and rest, and joy and peace.
And I know that Thou art with me, Wilt be with me to the end.

Chorus
Je-sus, Je-sus, how I trust Him! How I've proved Him o'er and o'er!
p
Je-sus, Je-sus, pre-cious Je-sus! O for grace to trust Him more!

58 Christ the Lord is Risen To-day

CHARLES WESLEY

Lyra Davidica

1. Christ the Lord is ris'n to - day, Al - - le - lu - ia!
2. Love's re - deem - ing work is done, Al - - le - lu - ia!
3. Lives a - gain our glo - rious King; Al - - le - lu - ia!
4. Soar we now, where Christ has led, Al - - le - lu - ia!
Sons of men and an - gels say: Al - - - le - lu - ia!
Fought the fight, the bat - tle won; Al - - - le - lu - ia!
Where, O death, is now thy sting? Al - - - le - lu - ia!
Fol - l'wing our ex - alt - ed Head; Al - - - le - lu - ia!
Raise your joys and tri - umphs high, Al - - - le - lu - ia!
Death in vain for - bids Him rise; Al - - - le - lu - ia!
Dy - ing once, He all doth save: Al - - - le - lu - ia!
Made like Him, like Him we rise; Al - - - le - lu - ia!
Sing, ye heav'ns, and earth re - ply. Al - - - le - lu - ia!
Christ has o - pened Par - a - dise. Al - - - le - lu - ia!
Where thy vic - to - ry, O grave? Al - - - le - lu - ia!
Ours the cross, the grave, the skies. Al - - - le - lu - ia!

59 The Story of Jesus Can Never Grow Old

Maj. D. W. WHITTLE — MAY WHITTLE MOODY

1. They tell me the sto - ry of Je - sus is old, And they ask that we preach something new; They say that the Babe, and the Man of the cross, For the wise of this world will not do.
2. Yet the sto - ry is old, as the sun-light is old, Tho' it's new ev - 'ry morn all the same; As it floods all the world with its glad-ness and light, Kindling far - a - way stars by its flame.
3. For what can we tell to the wea - ry of heart, If we preach not sal- va - tion from sin? And how can we com-fort the souls that de - part, If we tell not how Christ rose a - gain?
4. So with sor - row we turn from the wise of this world, To the wan - der - ers far from the fold; With hearts for the mes-sage they'll join in our song, That the sto - ry can nev - er grow old.

REFRAIN

It can nev-er grow old, It can nev-er grow old, Tho' a million times o-ver the sto - ry is told; While sin lives un- vanquished, And death rules the world, The sto - ry of Je - sus can nev-er grow old.

rit.

Who Could It Be?

FRED P. MORRIS ROBERT HARKNESS

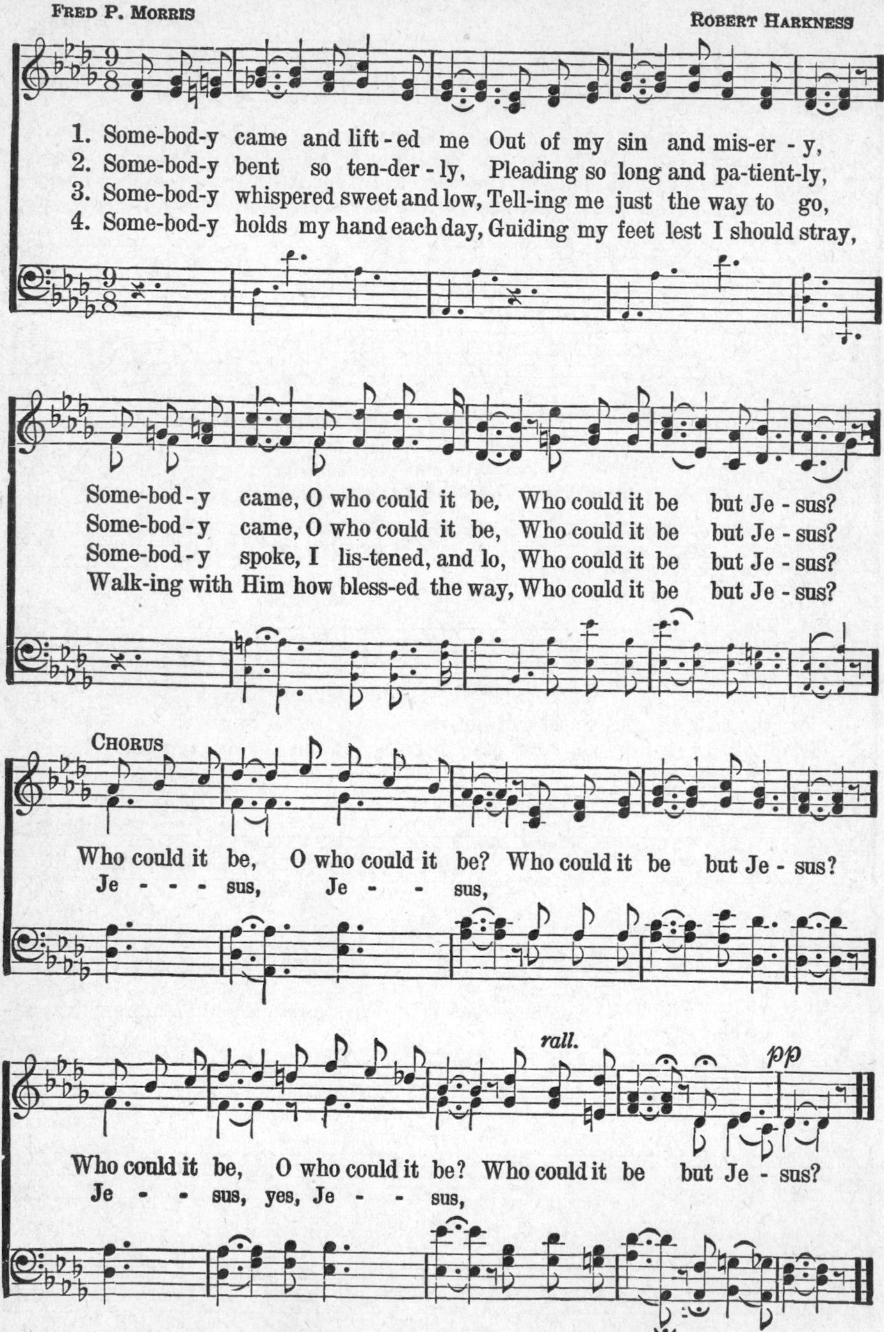
1. Some-bod-y came and lift-ed me Out of my sin and mis-er-y,
2. Some-bod-y bent so ten-der-ly, Pleading so long and pa-tient-ly,
3. Some-bod-y whispered sweet and low, Tell-ing me just the way to go,
4. Some-bod-y holds my hand each day, Guiding my feet lest I should stray,
Some-bod-y came, O who could it be, Who could it be but Je-sus?
Some-bod-y came, O who could it be, Who could it be but Je-sus?
Some-bod-y spoke, I lis-tened, and lo, Who could it be but Je-sus?
Walk-ing with Him how bless-ed the way, Who could it be but Je-sus?
CHORUS
Who could it be, O who could it be? Who could it be but Je-sus?
Je - - - sus, Je - - sus,
rall.
pp
Who could it be, O who could it be? Who could it be but Je-sus?
Je - - sus, yes, Je - - sus,

How Can I Be Lonely?

H. L.

Haldor Lillenas

With expression
1. One is walk-ing with me o - ver life's un - e - ven way, Con-stant-ly sup-port - ing me each mo-ment of the day; How can I be lone - ly when such fel-low-ship is mine, With my blessed Lord di - vine!
2. Days may bring their burdens and their tri-als as I go, But my Lord is near and helps to make them lighter grow. Life may have its cross-es, or its loss - es, or increase, Je-sus meets them all with peace.
3. In the hour of sad be-reave-ment or of bit - ter loss, I can find sup-port and con - so - la - tion at the cross; Want or woe or suf-f'ring all seem glo - ri-fied when He Dai-ly walks and talks with me.
4. In life's ros - y morn-ing when the skies a - bove are clear, In its noon-tide hours with many cares and problems near, Or when eve-ning shad-ows fall at clos-ing of my day Je - sus will be there al - way.
Refrain
How can I be lone - ly When I've Je - sus on - ly To be my com-pan - ion and un-fail-ing guide?
rit.
Why should I be wea-ry, Or my path seem dreary, When He's walking by my side!

62 He Is Coming Again

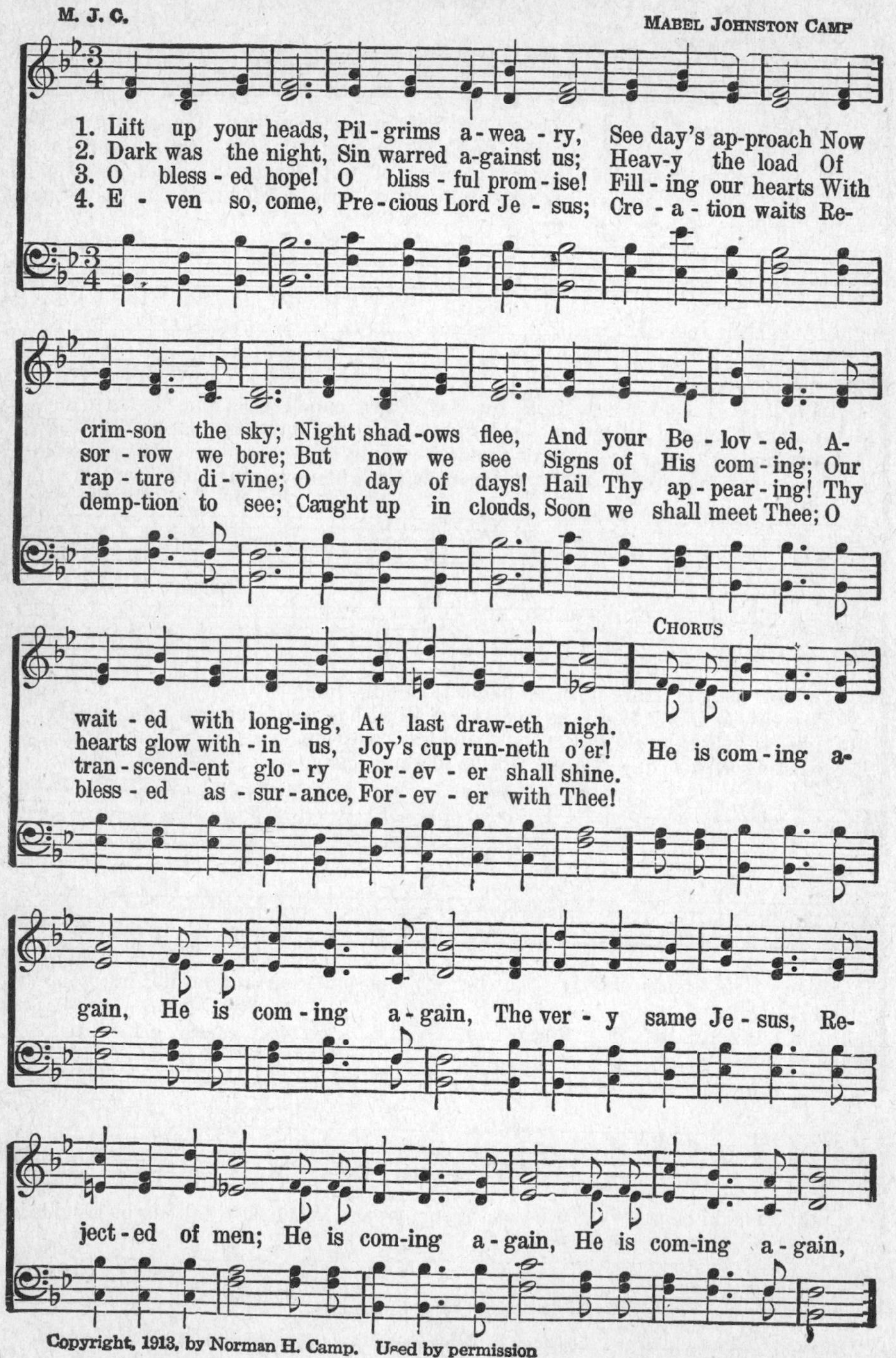
M. J. C.
Mabel Johnston Camp
1. Lift up your heads, Pil-grims a-wea-ry, See day's ap-proach Now crim-son the sky; Night shad-ows flee, And your Be-lov-ed, A-wait-ed with long-ing, At last draw-eth nigh.
2. Dark was the night, Sin warred a-gainst us; Heav-y the load Of sor-row we bore; But now we see Signs of His com-ing; Our hearts glow with-in us, Joy's cup run-neth o'er!
3. O bless-ed hope! O bliss-ful prom-ise! Fill-ing our hearts With rap-ture di-vine; O day of days! Hail Thy ap-pear-ing! Thy tran-scend-ent glo-ry For-ev-er shall shine.
4. E-ven so, come, Pre-cious Lord Je-sus; Cre-a-tion waits Re-demp-tion to see; Caught up in clouds, Soon we shall meet Thee; O bless-ed as-sur-ance, For-ev-er with Thee!
Chorus
He is com-ing a-gain, He is com-ing a-gain, The ver-y same Je-sus, Re-ject-ed of men; He is com-ing a-gain, He is com-ing a-gain, He is com-ing a-gain,

He Is Coming Again

With pow'r and great glo - ry, He is com-ing a-gain!
is com-ing a - gain!

63

Fill Me Now

E. R. STOKES, JNO. R. SWENEY

1. Hov - er o'er me, Ho - ly Spir - it, Bathe my trem-bling heart and brow;
2. Thou canst fill me, gra-cious Spir - it, Though I can - not tell Thee how;
3. I am weak-ness, full of weak-ness, At Thy sa - cred feet I bow;
4. Cleanse and com-fort, bless and save me, Bathe, O bathe my heart and brow;
Fill me with Thy hal-lowed pres-ence, Come, O come and fill me now.
But I need Thee, great-ly need Thee, Come, O come and fill me now.
Blest, di - vine, e - ter - nal Spir - it, Fill with pow'r, and fill me now.
Thou art com-fort - ing and sav - ing, Thou art sweet - ly fill - ing now.
CHORUS
Fill me now, fill me now, Je - sus, come and fill me now;
Fill me with Thy hal-lowed pres-ence, Come, O come and fill me now.

Lead Me, Savior

F. M. D. FRANK M. DAVIS

1. Sav - ior, lead me, lest I stray, Gen - tly lead me all the way;
2. Thou the ref-uge of my soul When life's storm-y bil-lows roll;
3. Sav - ior, lead me, then at last, When the storm of life is past,
1. Sav - ior, lead me, lest I stray, Gen - tly lead me all the way;
I am safe when by Thy side, I would in Thy love a-bide.
I am safe when Thou art nigh, All my hopes on Thee re-ly.
To the land of end-less day, Where all tears are wiped away.
I am safe when by Thy side, I would in Thy love a-bide.
CHORUS
Lead me, lead me, Sav - ior, lead me, lest I stray;.....
lest I stray;
Gen-tly down the stream of time, Lead me, Sav-ior, all the way.
stream of time,
all the way.

He Keeps Me Singing

L. B. B. L. B. Bridgers

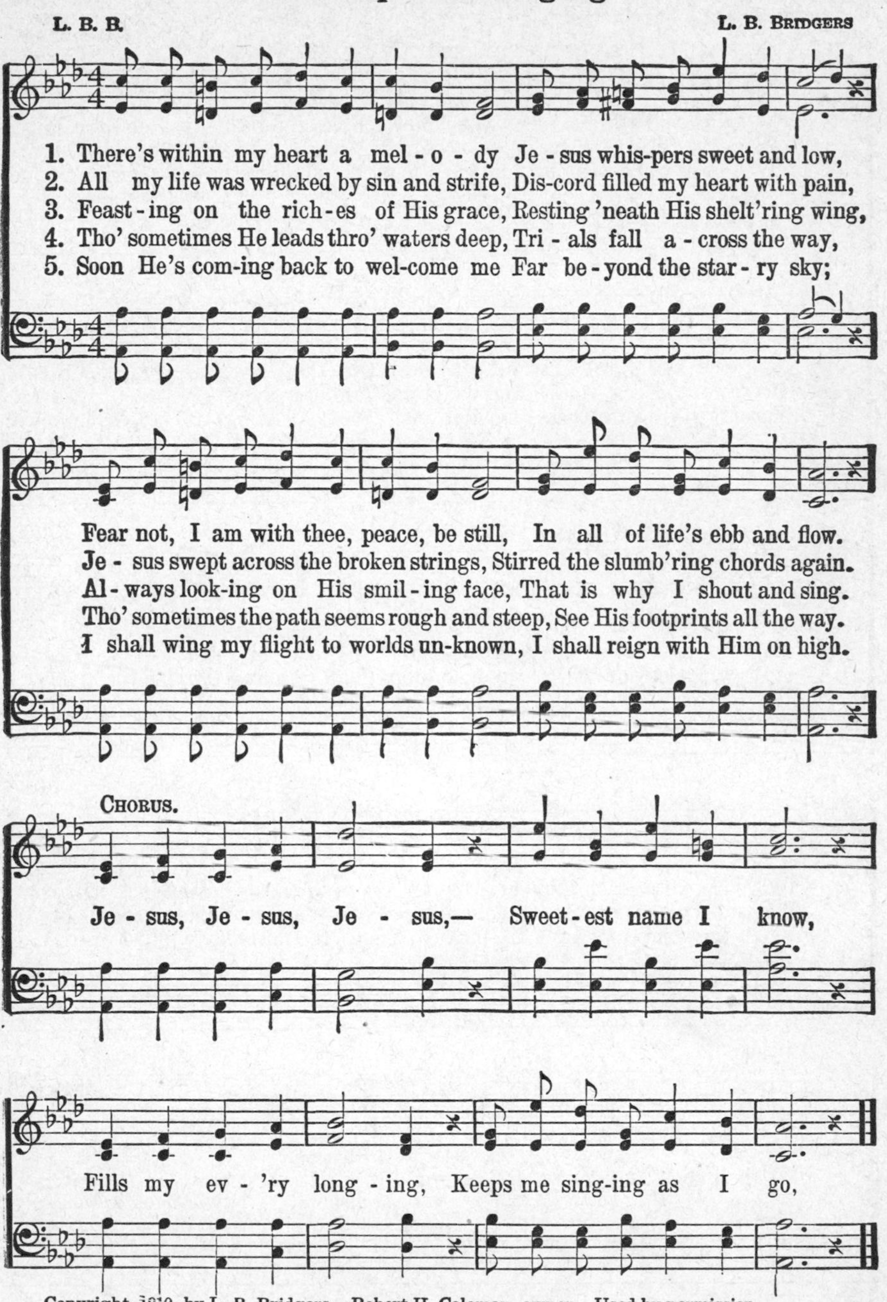
1. There's within my heart a mel - o - dy Je - sus whis-pers sweet and low,
2. All my life was wrecked by sin and strife, Dis-cord filled my heart with pain,
3. Feast - ing on the rich - es of His grace, Resting 'neath His shelt'ring wing,
4. Tho' sometimes He leads thro' waters deep, Tri - als fall a - cross the way,
5. Soon He's com-ing back to wel-come me Far be - yond the star - ry sky;
Fear not, I am with thee, peace, be still, In all of life's ebb and flow.
Je - sus swept across the broken strings, Stirred the slumb'ring chords again.
Al - ways look-ing on His smil - ing face, That is why I shout and sing.
Tho' sometimes the path seems rough and steep, See His footprints all the way.
I shall wing my flight to worlds un-known, I shall reign with Him on high.
Chorus.
Je - sus, Je - sus, Je - sus,— Sweet - est name I know,
Fills my ev - 'ry long - ing, Keeps me sing-ing as I go,

66 When the Mists Have Rolled Away

ANNIE HERBERT. ARR. IRA D. SANKEY

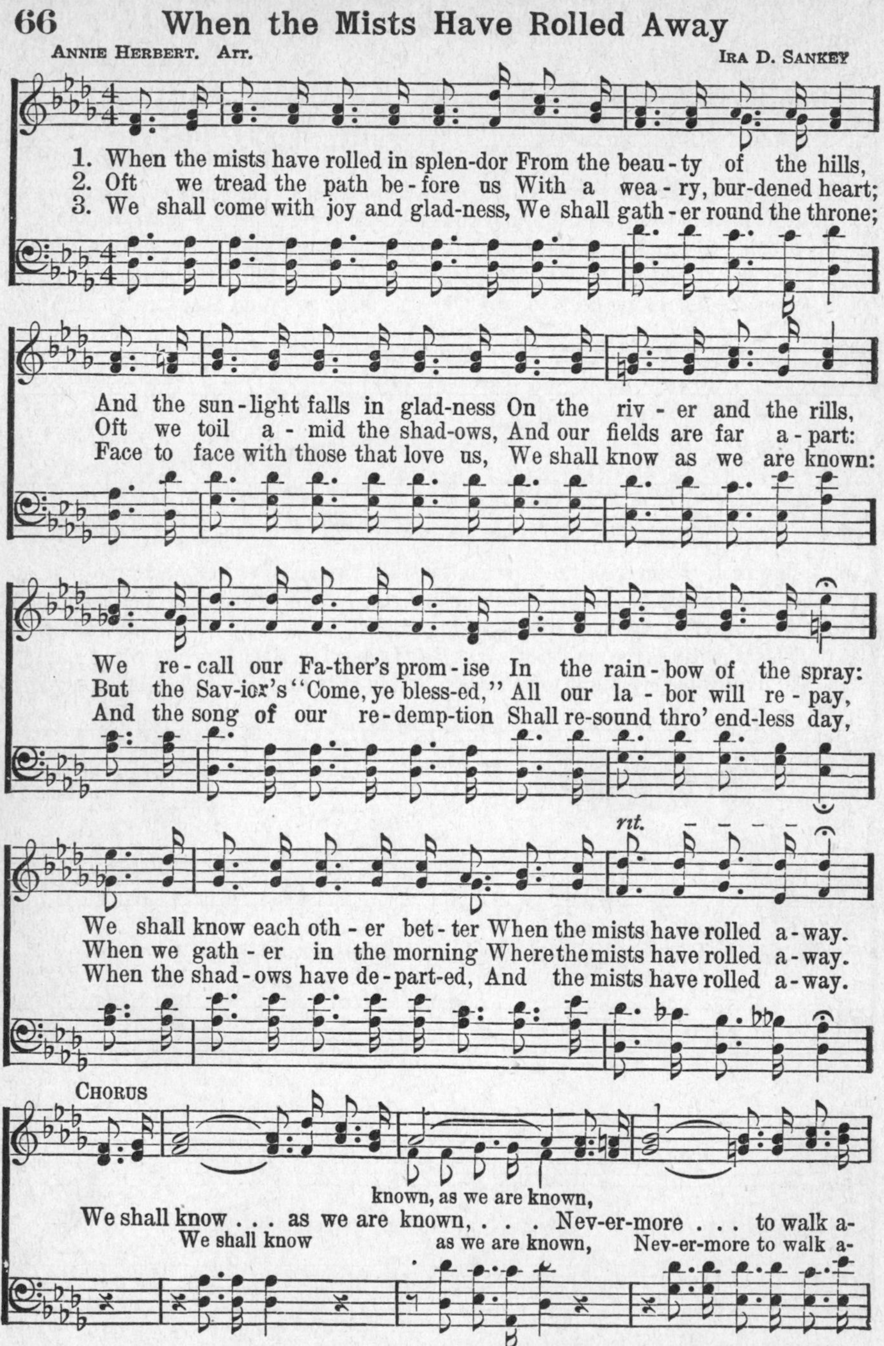

1. When the mists have rolled in splen-dor From the beau-ty of the hills,
2. Oft we tread the path be-fore us With a wea-ry, bur-dened heart;
3. We shall come with joy and glad-ness, We shall gath-er round the throne;
And the sun-light falls in glad-ness On the riv-er and the rills,
Oft we toil a-mid the shad-ows, And our fields are far a-part:
Face to face with those that love us, We shall know as we are known:
We re-call our Fa-ther's prom-ise In the rain-bow of the spray:
But the Sav-ior's "Come, ye bless-ed," All our la-bor will re-pay,
And the song of our re-demp-tion Shall re-sound thro' end-less day,
rit.
We shall know each oth-er bet-ter When the mists have rolled a-way.
When we gath-er in the morning Where the mists have rolled a-way.
When the shad-ows have de-part-ed, And the mists have rolled a-way.
CHORUS
known, as we are known,
We shall know . . . as we are known, . . . Nev-er-more . . . to walk a-
We shall know as we are known, Nev-er-more to walk a-

When the Mists Have Rolled Away

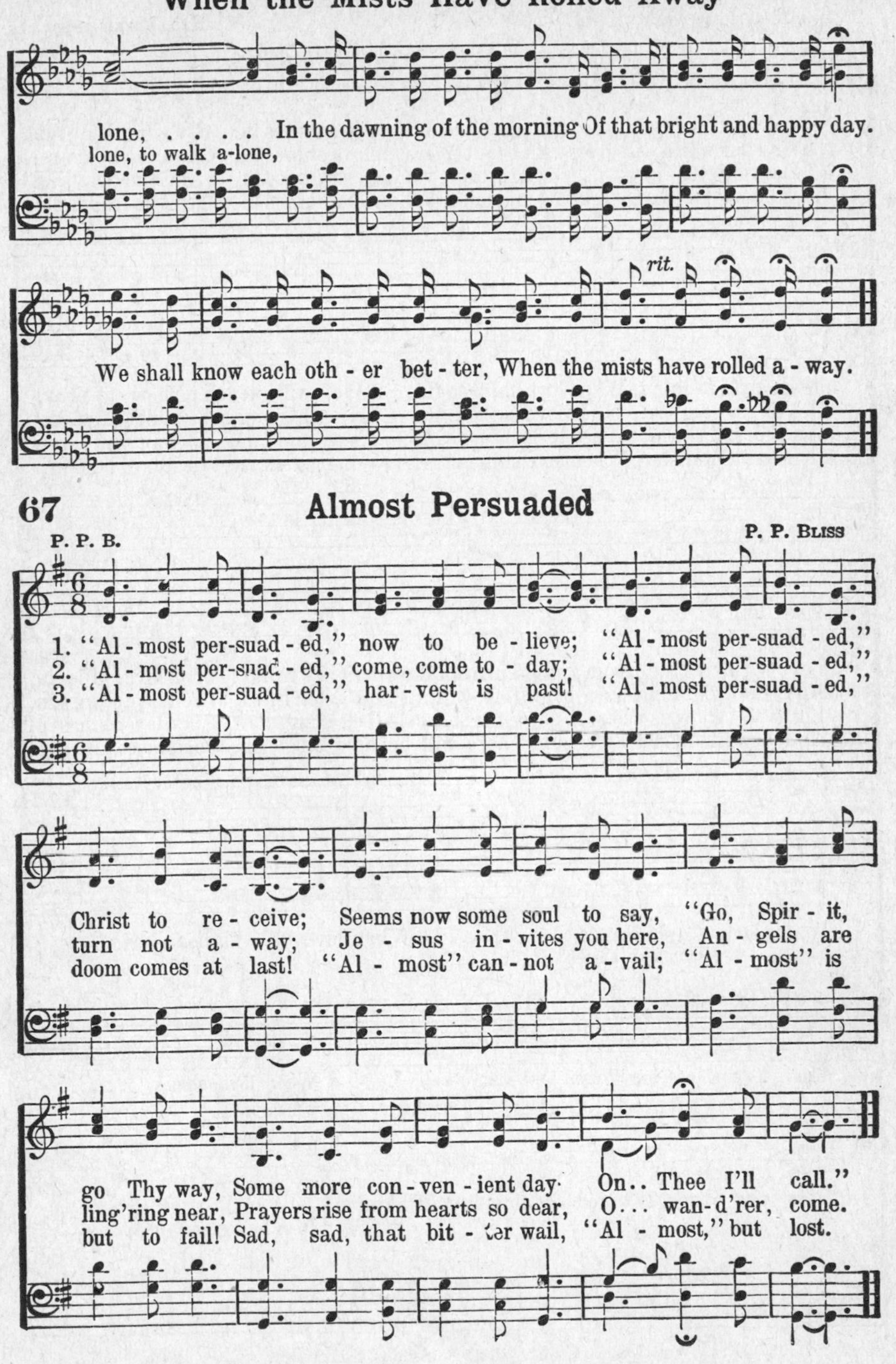

lone, ... In the dawning of the morning Of that bright and happy day.
lone, to walk a-lone,
rit.
We shall know each oth - er bet - ter, When the mists have rolled a - way.
67
Almost Persuaded
P. P. B.
P. P. Bliss
1. "Al - most per-suad - ed," now to be - lieve; "Al - most per-suad - ed,"
2. "Al - most per-suad - ed," come, come to - day; "Al - most per-suad - ed,"
3. "Al - most per-suad - ed," har - vest is past! "Al - most per-suad - ed,"
Christ to re - ceive; Seems now some soul to say, "Go, Spir - it,
turn not a - way; Je - sus in - vites you here, An - gels are
doom comes at last! "Al - most" can - not a - vail; "Al - most" is
go Thy way, Some more con - ven - ient day On.. Thee I'll call."
ling'ring near, Prayers rise from hearts so dear, O... wan - d'rer, come.
but to fail! Sad, sad, that bit - ter wail, "Al - most," but lost.

68 When Love Shines In

Mrs. Frank A. Breck — Wm. J. Kirkpatrick

1. Je-sus comes with pow'r to gladden, When love shines in, Ev-'ry life that woe can sad-den, When love shines in. Love will teach us how to pray,
2. How the world will grow with beauty, When love shines in, And the heart re-joice in du-ty, When love shines in. Tri-als may be sanc-ti-fied,
3. Dark-est sor-row will grow brighter, When love shines in, And the heav-iest bur-den light-er, When love shines in. 'Tis the glo-ry that will throw
4. We may have un-fad-ing splendor, When love shines in, And a friend-ship true and ten-der, When love shines in. When earth vic-t'ries shall be won,
Love will drive the gloom away, Turn our darkness in-to day, When love shines in.
And the soul in peace a-bide, Life will all be glo-ri-fied, When love shines in.
Light to show us where to go; O, the heart shall blessing know, When love shines in.
And our life in Heav'n begun, There will be no need of sun, When love shines in.
CHORUS
When love shines in,....... When love shines in,...
When love shines in,........
When love shines in, When love shines in, When love shines in,....
How the heart is tuned to sing-ing, When love.. shines in;.....
When love shines in;.......

When Love Shines In

When love shines in,....... When love shines in,..
When love shines in,........
When love shines in, When love shines in, When love shines in,...
Joy and peace to oth-ers bring-ing, When love shines in...
When love, when love shines in....
69
Don't Stop Praying
E. R. W.
Edna R. Worrell
1. Don't stop pray-ing, the Lord is nigh; Don't stop praying, He'll hear your cry;
2. Don't stop pray-ing for ev-'ry need; Don't stop praying, the Lord will heed;
3. Don't stop pray-ing when led to sin; Don't stop praying that good may win;
4. Don't stop pray-ing when bowed with grief; Don't stop praying, you'll find re-lief;
5. Don't stop pray-ing but have more trust; Don't stop praying, for pray we must;
God has prom-ised, and He is true, Don't stop praying, He'll an-swer you.
No pe-ti-tion to Him is small; Dont' stop praying, He'll give you all.
Christ was tempted and un-der-stands; Don't stop praying, He'll hold your hands.
Troub-les nev-er es-cape God's sight; Don't stop praying, He'll make it right.
Faith will ban-ish a mount of care; Don't stop praying, God an-swers prayer.

I Know Whom I Have Believed

Maj. D. W. WHITTLE (El Nathan) JAMES MCGRANAHAN

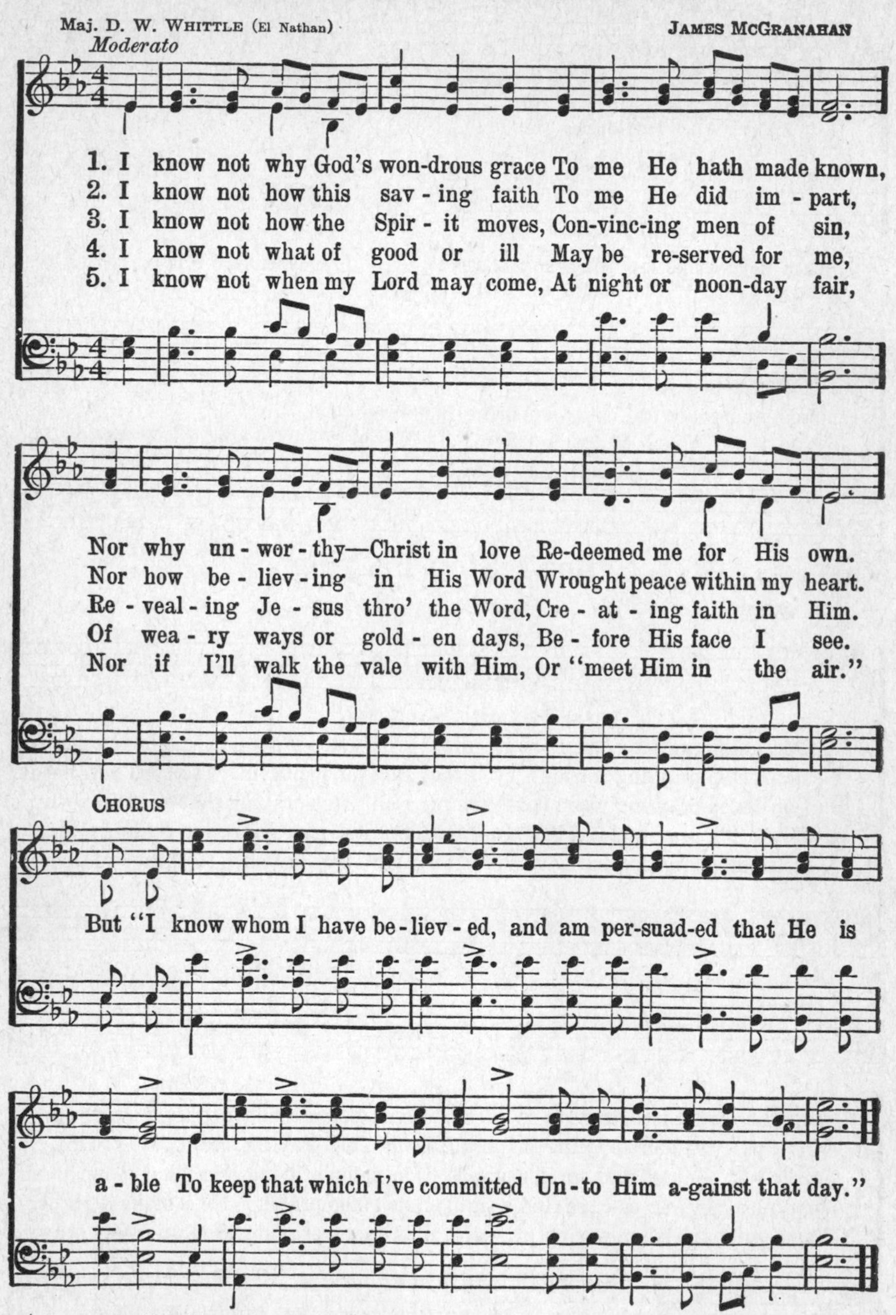
Moderato
1. I know not why God's won-drous grace To me He hath made known,
2. I know not how this sav - ing faith To me He did im - part,
3. I know not how the Spir - it moves, Con-vinc-ing men of sin,
4. I know not what of good or ill May be re-served for me,
5. I know not when my Lord may come, At night or noon-day fair,
Nor why un - wor - thy—Christ in love Re-deemed me for His own.
Nor how be - liev - ing in His Word Wrought peace within my heart.
Re - veal - ing Je - sus thro' the Word, Cre - at - ing faith in Him.
Of wea - ry ways or gold - en days, Be - fore His face I see.
Nor if I'll walk the vale with Him, Or "meet Him in the air."
CHORUS
But "I know whom I have be - liev - ed, and am per-suad-ed that He is
a - ble To keep that which I've committed Un - to Him a-gainst that day."

71 Harvest Time

Paul Rader — Lance B. Latham

1. The har-vest fields are bending With precious, ripened grain; More reapers now are need-ed, Ere Christ comes back again.
2. The call must now be heed-ed, We can-not say Him nay; Since He has died to save them, We must go forth to-day.
3. We'll come a-gain re-joic-ing, A reap-er's crown to gain; The Har-vest Home is com-ing, When Christ comes back again.
Chorus
Harvest time! Harvest time! Pre-cious gos-pel seed is sown.
Pre-cious gos-pel seed is sown.
Reap-ers go! Reap-ers go! Je-sus, King, must have His own, His loved ones; Soon He'll come! Soon He'll come! Come and catch away His Bride. His own! His own! His own!......
His own! His own! His own!

I Must Tell Jesus

E. A. H. E. A. Hoffman

1. I must tell Jesus all of my trials; I cannot bear these burdens alone; In my distress He kindly will help me; He ever loves and cares for His own.

2. I must tell Jesus all of my troubles; He is a kind, compassionate Friend; If I but ask Him, He will deliver, Make of my troubles quickly an end.

3. Tempted and tried I need a great Savior, One who can help my burdens to bear; I must tell Jesus, I must tell Jesus; He all my cares and sorrows will share.

4. O how the world to evil allures me! O how my heart is tempted to sin! I must tell Jesus, and He will help me Over the world the vict'ry to win.

Chorus

I must tell Jesus! I must tell Jesus! I cannot bear my burdens alone; I must tell Jesus! I must tell Jesus! Jesus can help me, Jesus alone.

73 I Am Happy in Him

E. O. E. E. O. EXCELL

1. My soul is so happy in Je - sus, For He is so precious to me; . . . .
2. He sought me so long ere I knew Him, When wand'ring afar from the fold; . .
3. His love and His mercy surround me, His grace like a riv-er doth flow; . . .
4. They say I shall some day be like Him, My cross and my burden lay down; . .
His voice it is mu-sic to hear it, His face it is heav-en to see. . . .
Safe home in His arms He hath bro't me, To where there are pleasures untold.
His Spir - it, to guide and to com-fort, Is with me wher-ev-er I go. . . .
Till then I will ev-er be faith - ful, In gath - er-ing gems for His crown.
CHORUS
I am hap-py in Him, ... I am hap-py in Him; . . . .
I . . . . am hap-py in Him, I . . . . am hap-py in Him;
My soul with de-light He fills day and night, For I am hap-py in Him.

74 Shadows

R. H. ROBERT HARKNESS

SOLO
1. When we cross the val - ley there need be no shad - ows, When life's day is end - ed and its sor - rows o'er; When the sum - mons comes to meet the bless-ed Sav - ior, When we rise to dwell with Him for - ev - er - more.
2. When our loved ones leave us there need be no shad - ows, If their faith is fixed in Je - sus as their Lord; For they go to be with Him who died to save them, To be with the One whom they have long a-dored.
3. When He comes to meet us there need be no shad - ows, When He comes in all His glo - ri - ous ar - ray; When the trump of God shall sound and loved ones waken, When He leads us on-ward with tri-um-phant sway.
CHORUS
Shad-ows! no need of shad-ows When at last we lay life's burden down;

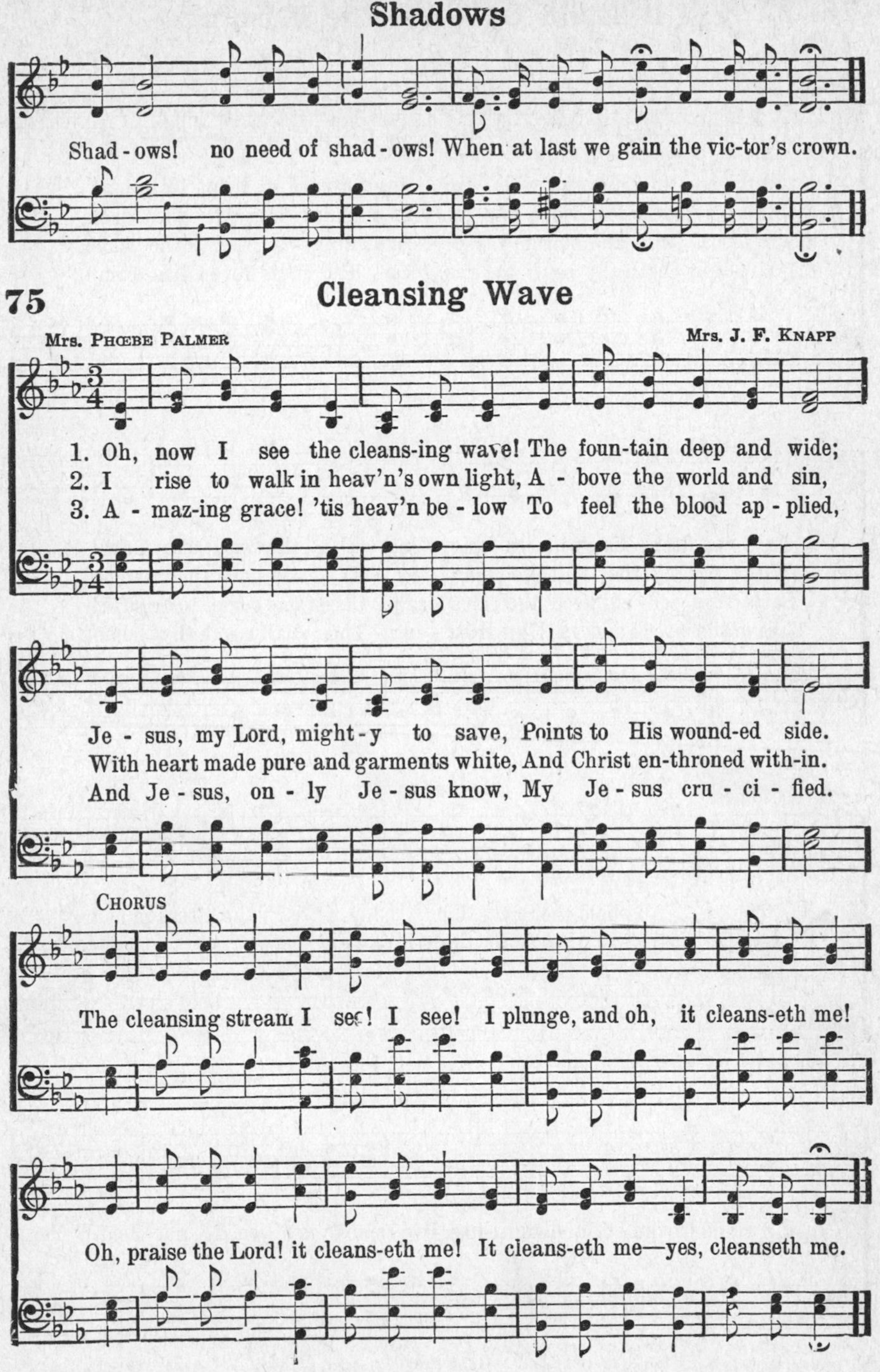
Shadows
Shad-ows! no need of shad-ows! When at last we gain the vic-tor's crown.
75
Cleansing Wave
Mrs. Phœbe Palmer
Mrs. J. F. Knapp
1. Oh, now I see the cleans-ing wave! The foun-tain deep and wide;
2. I rise to walk in heav'n's own light, A - bove the world and sin,
3. A - maz-ing grace! 'tis heav'n be - low To feel the blood ap - plied,
Je - sus, my Lord, might - y to save, Points to His wound-ed side.
With heart made pure and garments white, And Christ en-throned with-in.
And Je - sus, on - ly Je - sus know, My Je - sus cru - ci - fied.
Chorus
The cleansing stream I see! I see! I plunge, and oh, it cleans-eth me!
Oh, praise the Lord! it cleans-eth me! It cleans-eth me—yes, cleanseth me.

I'll Stand By Until the Morning

W. W. D. JAMES McGRANAHAN

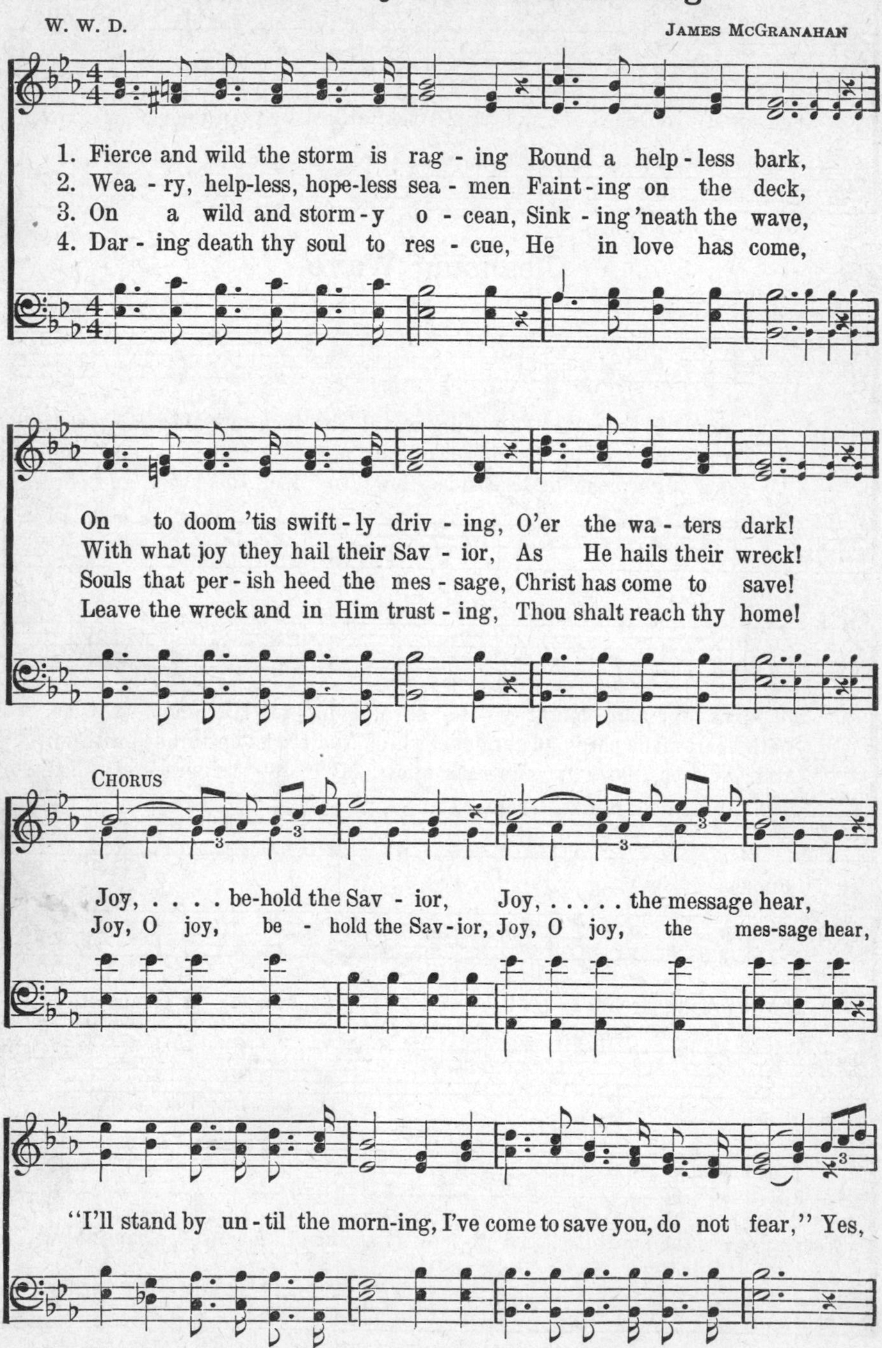
1. Fierce and wild the storm is rag - ing Round a help - less bark,
2. Wea - ry, help-less, hope-less sea - men Faint - ing on the deck,
3. On a wild and storm - y o - cean, Sink - ing 'neath the wave,
4. Dar - ing death thy soul to res - cue, He in love has come,
On to doom 'tis swift - ly driv - ing, O'er the wa - ters dark!
With what joy they hail their Sav - ior, As He hails their wreck!
Souls that per - ish heed the mes - sage, Christ has come to save!
Leave the wreck and in Him trust - ing, Thou shalt reach thy home!
CHORUS
Joy, ... be-hold the Sav - ior, Joy, ... the message hear,
Joy, O joy, be - hold the Sav - ior, Joy, O joy, the mes-sage hear,
"I'll stand by un - til the morn-ing, I've come to save you, do not fear," Yes,

I'll Stand By Until the Morning

I'll stand by un - til the morn-ing, I've come to save you, do not fear (do not fear).

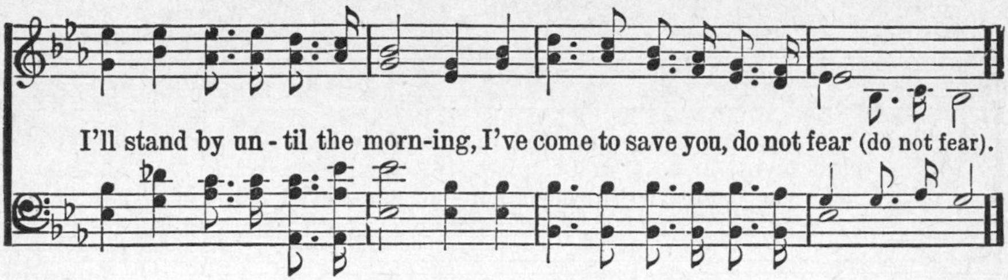

77 Sweet Hour of Prayer

W. W. WALFORD — WM. B. BRADBURY

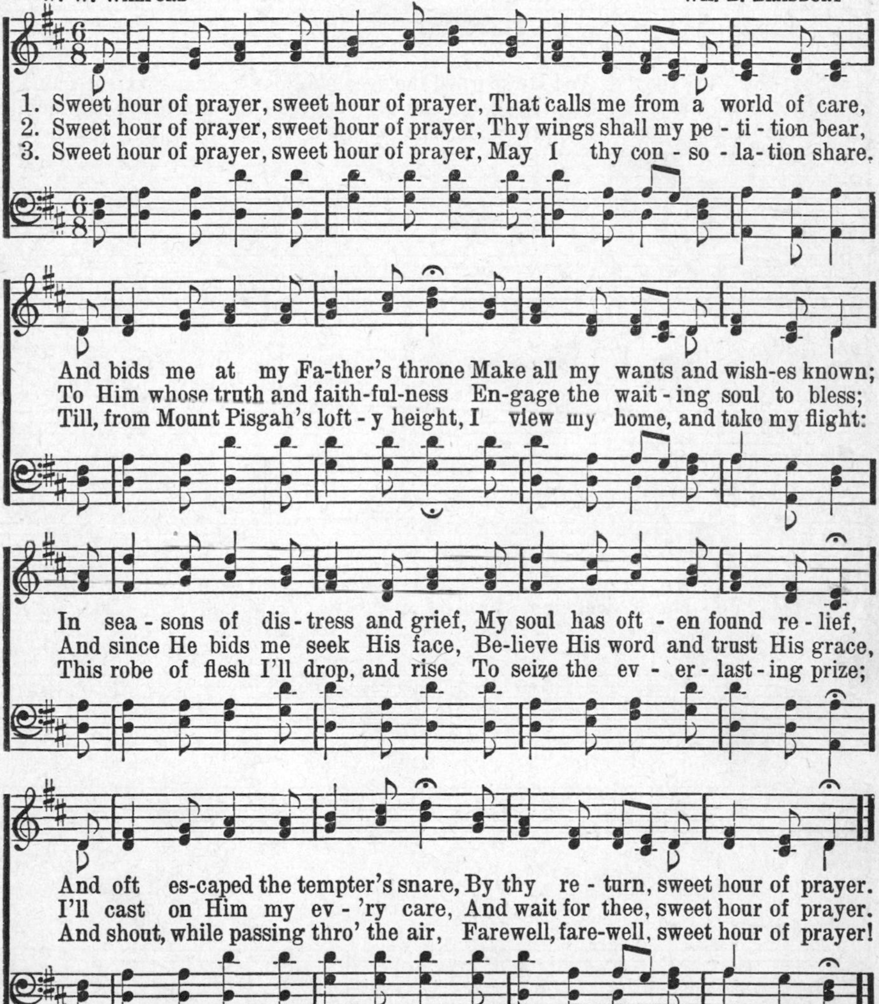

1. Sweet hour of prayer, sweet hour of prayer, That calls me from a world of care,
2. Sweet hour of prayer, sweet hour of prayer, Thy wings shall my pe - ti - tion bear,
3. Sweet hour of prayer, sweet hour of prayer, May I thy con - so - la - tion share.

And bids me at my Fa-ther's throne Make all my wants and wish-es known;
To Him whose truth and faith-ful-ness En-gage the wait - ing soul to bless;
Till, from Mount Pisgah's loft - y height, I view my home, and take my flight:

In sea - sons of dis - tress and grief, My soul has oft - en found re - lief,
And since He bids me seek His face, Be-lieve His word and trust His grace,
This robe of flesh I'll drop, and rise To seize the ev - er - last - ing prize;

And oft es-caped the tempter's snare, By thy re - turn, sweet hour of prayer.
I'll cast on Him my ev - 'ry care, And wait for thee, sweet hour of prayer.
And shout, while passing thro' the air, Farewell, fare-well, sweet hour of prayer!

78 The Savior for Me

W. M. R. — WILLIAM M. RUNYAN

DUET

1. From heav-en a-bove, in His in-fi-nite love, Came Je-sus, a Sav-ior to be; And He scorned the deep pain our ran-som to gain, O He is the Sav-ior for me. . . . . . . the Sav-ior for me.
2. The birds had their nest and the peo-ple their rest, While Je-sus all night made His plea; On the moun-tain a-lone was the Fa-ther's dear Son,
3. For sil-ver be-trayed, in mock pur-ple ar-rayed, Con-demned to a death on the tree; Then they led Him a-way on that Won-der-ful Day,

CHORUS

O Je-sus is will-ing to be . . . . . and wait-ing to be A Sav-ior for sin-ners like me, ... e-ven me, And the bur-den will roll From the

The Savior for Me
poor troub-led soul That to Je - sus the Sav - ior will flee.
79
In the Hollow of His Hand
William M. Runyan
George S. Schuler
Alto Solo or Trio
1. Our God hath giv - en prom - ise—And His grace for this hath planned:
2. O soul, be thou not troub - led, Tho' thou dost not un - der - stand;
3. E'en tho' stern du - ty call thee, And each day make full de - mand,
4. The joy that pass-eth knowl-edge, Peace that none can un - der - stand,
His child shall rest se - cure - ly In the hol - low of His hand.
No tur - moil shall mo - lest thee In the hol - low of His hand.
The soul may find its shel - ter In the hol - low of His hand.
For thee, for thee are wait - ing In the hol - low of His hand.
Chorus
Let come what may— or wave, or tem-pest—"Peace, be still!" 'tis His command;
My soul is held in peace e - ter - nal In the hol - low of His hand.

80 Speed the Light

E. A. H. ELISHA A. HOFFMAN

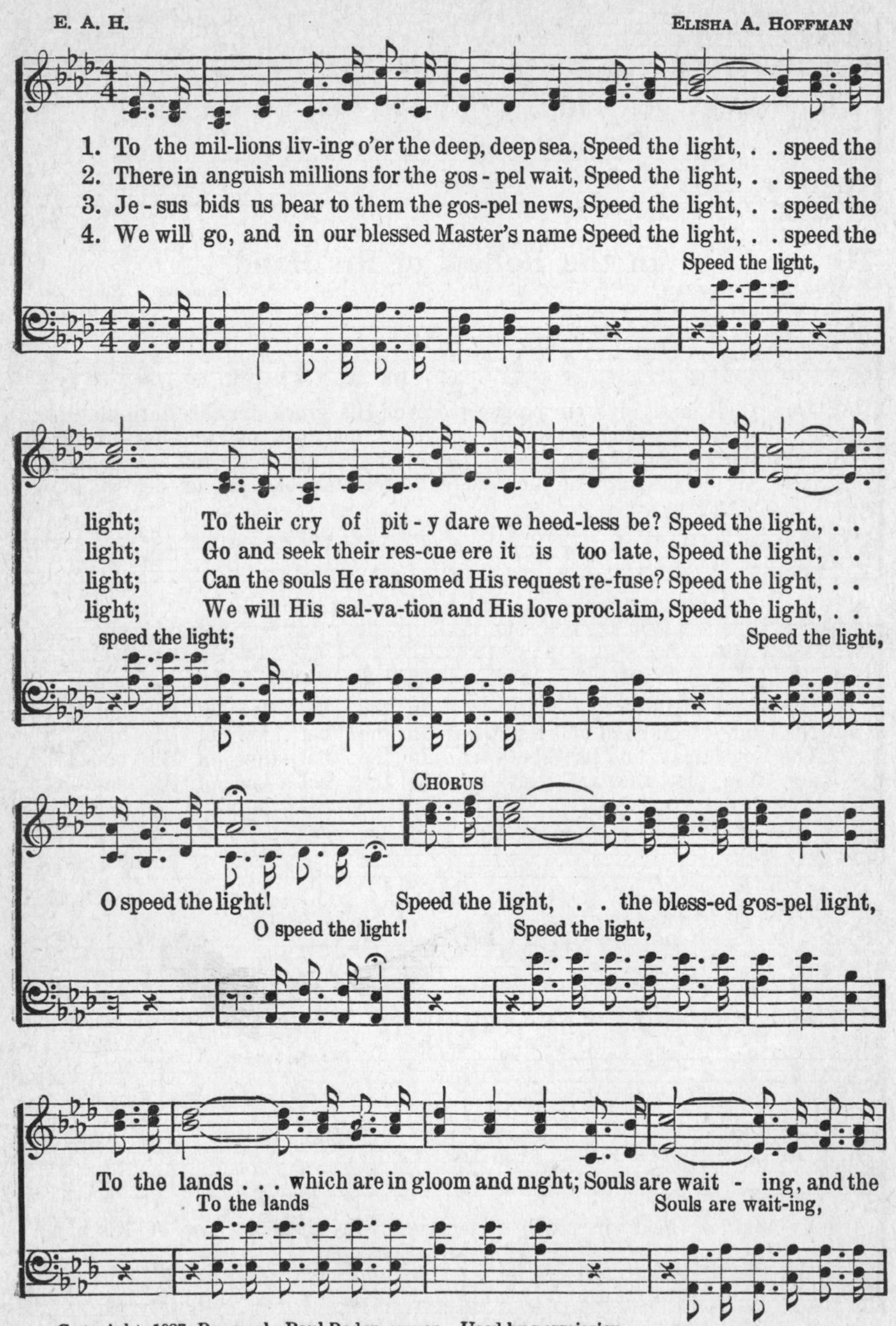
1. To the mil-lions liv-ing o'er the deep, deep sea, Speed the light, . . speed the light; To their cry of pit - y dare we heed-less be? Speed the light, . . O speed the light!
2. There in anguish millions for the gos - pel wait, Speed the light, . . speed the light; Go and seek their res-cue ere it is too late, Speed the light, . .
3. Je - sus bids us bear to them the gos-pel news, Speed the light, . . speed the light; Can the souls He ransomed His request re-fuse? Speed the light, . .
4. We will go, and in our blessed Master's name Speed the light, . . speed the light; We will His sal-va-tion and His love proclaim, Speed the light, . .
Speed the light,
speed the light;
Speed the light,
O speed the light!
CHORUS
Speed the light, . . the bless-ed gos-pel light,
Speed the light,
To the lands . . . which are in gloom and night; Souls are wait - ing, and the
To the lands
Souls are wait-ing,

Speed the Light

fields are white, Speed the light, ... O speed the light!
Speed the light! O speed the light!
81 Where Jesus Is, 'Tis Heaven
C. F. Butler
J. M. Black
1. Since Christ my soul from sin set free, This world has been a Heav'n to me;
2. Once Heav-en seemed a far-off place, Till Je-sus showed His smil-ing face;
3. What mat-ters where on earth we dwell? On moun-tain top, or in the dell,
And 'mid earth's sorrows and its woe, 'Tis Heav'n my Je-sus here to know.
Now it's be-gun with-in my soul, 'Twill last while end-less a-ges roll.
In cot-tage, or a man-sion fair, Where Je-sus is, 'tis Heav-en there.
Chorus
O hal-le-lu-jah, yes, 'tis Heav'n, 'Tis Heav'n to know my sins for-giv'n;
On land or sea, what matters where? Where Je-sus is, 'tis Heav-en there.

82 Some Time We'll Understand

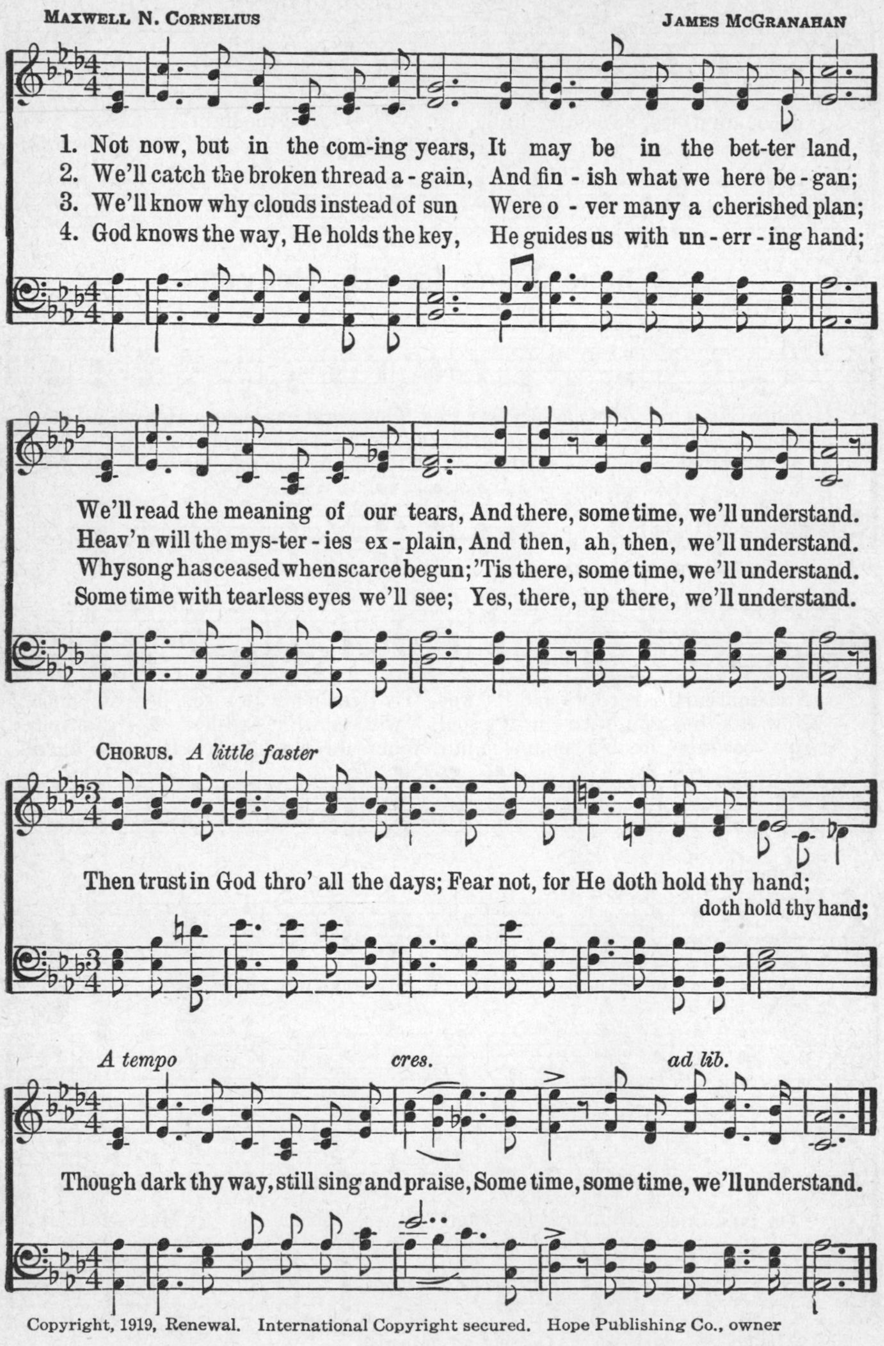
MAXWELL N. CORNELIUS
JAMES MCGRANAHAN
1. Not now, but in the com-ing years, It may be in the bet-ter land,
2. We'll catch the broken thread a-gain, And fin-ish what we here be-gan;
3. We'll know why clouds instead of sun Were o-ver many a cherished plan;
4. God knows the way, He holds the key, He guides us with un-err-ing hand;
We'll read the meaning of our tears, And there, some time, we'll understand.
Heav'n will the mys-ter-ies ex-plain, And then, ah, then, we'll understand.
Why song has ceased when scarce begun; 'Tis there, some time, we'll understand.
Some time with tearless eyes we'll see; Yes, there, up there, we'll understand.
CHORUS. A little faster
Then trust in God thro' all the days; Fear not, for He doth hold thy hand;
doth hold thy hand;
A tempo
cres.
ad lib.
Though dark thy way, still sing and praise, Some time, some time, we'll understand.

83 The Victory

P. R. PAUL RADER

1. No more need fear, and no more need doubt-ing, No more need pride con-trol in my life. I may be free from all con-dem-na-tion, I can have vic-to-ry now in the strife.
2. There is a place, praise God, I have found it! There is a place where we may be free; Free from de-feat, with pow-er sur-round-ed; Yes, there is vic-to-ry, Je-sus, in Thee.
3. Pre-cious pro-vi-sion, won-der-ful pros-pect, Je-sus will rule and Je-sus will lead; He is my Shep-herd, He is my Keep-er, He is my Bread of Life, on Him I feed.
CHORUS
I take the life of vic-to-ry, Not I, but Christ Him-self in me;
He con-quers now, He sets me free; I take, He gives—the vic-to-ry.

His Eye is On the Sparrow

Mrs. C. D. Martin — Chas. H. Gabriel

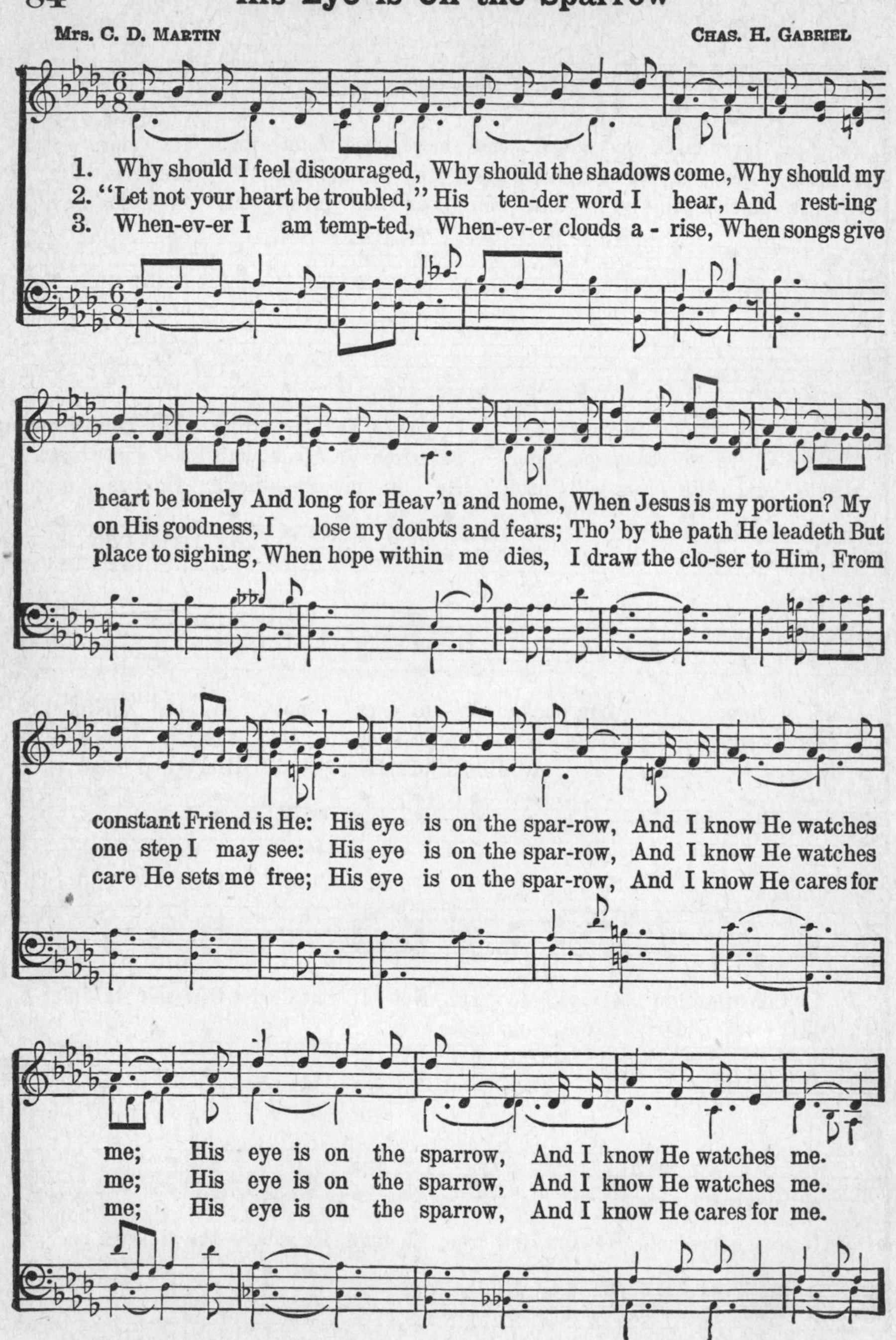
1. Why should I feel discouraged, Why should the shadows come, Why should my
2. "Let not your heart be troubled," His ten-der word I hear, And rest-ing
3. When-ev-er I am temp-ted, When-ev-er clouds a - rise, When songs give
heart be lonely And long for Heav'n and home, When Jesus is my portion? My
on His goodness, I lose my doubts and fears; Tho' by the path He leadeth But
place to sighing, When hope within me dies, I draw the clo-ser to Him, From
constant Friend is He: His eye is on the spar-row, And I know He watches
one step I may see: His eye is on the spar-row, And I know He watches
care He sets me free; His eye is on the spar-row, And I know He cares for
me; His eye is on the sparrow, And I know He watches me.
me; His eye is on the sparrow, And I know He watches me.
me; His eye is on the sparrow, And I know He cares for me.

His Eye is On the Sparrow

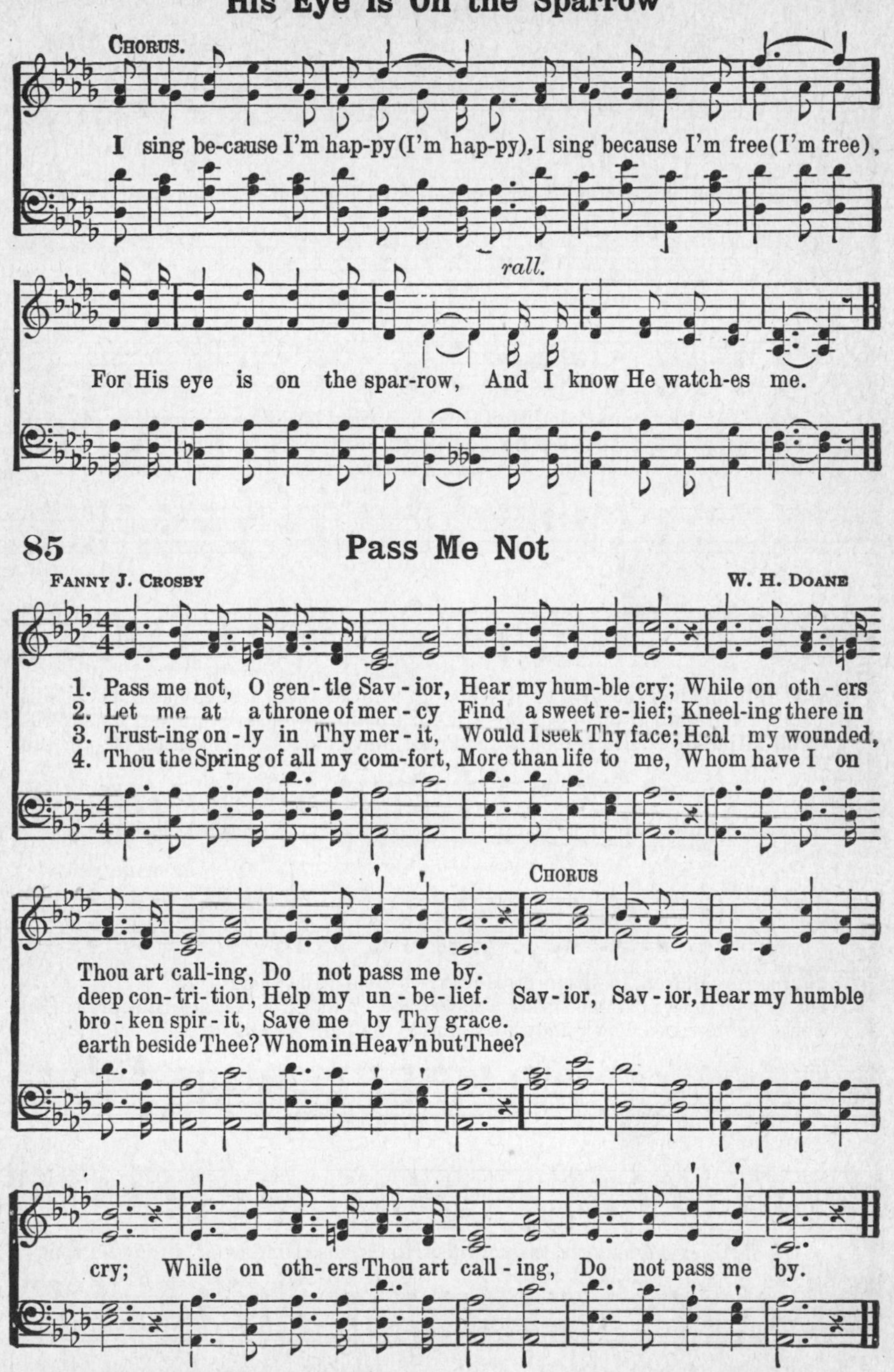
CHORUS.
I sing be-cause I'm hap-py (I'm hap-py), I sing because I'm free (I'm free),
rall.
For His eye is on the spar-row, And I know He watch-es me.
85
Pass Me Not
FANNY J. CROSBY
W. H. DOANE
1. Pass me not, O gen-tle Sav-ior, Hear my hum-ble cry; While on oth-ers
2. Let me at a throne of mer-cy Find a sweet re-lief; Kneel-ing there in
3. Trust-ing on-ly in Thy mer-it, Would I seek Thy face; Heal my wounded,
4. Thou the Spring of all my com-fort, More than life to me, Whom have I on
CHORUS
Thou art call-ing, Do not pass me by.
deep con-tri-tion, Help my un-be-lief. Sav-ior, Sav-ior, Hear my humble
bro-ken spir-it, Save me by Thy grace.
earth beside Thee? Whom in Heav'n but Thee?
cry; While on oth-ers Thou art call-ing, Do not pass me by.

86 Praise Him! Praise Him!

FANNY J. CROSBY
CHESTER G. ALLEN
1. Praise Him! praise Him! Je-sus, our bless-ed Re-deem-er! Sing, O Earth, His
2. Praise Him! praise Him! Je-sus, our bless-ed Re-deem-er! For our sins He
3. Praise Him! praise Him! Je-sus, our bless-ed Re-deem-er! Heav'nly por - tals
won-der-ful love pro-claim! Hail Him! hail Him! highest archangels in glo-ry;
suffered, and bled, and died; He our Rock, our hope of e - ter-nal sal-va-tion,
loud with ho-san-nas ring! Je - sus, Sav - ior, reigneth for-ev - er and ev - er;
Strength and hon - or give to His ho - ly name! Like a shep-herd, Je-sus will
Hail Him! hail Him! Je-sus the Cru - ci - fied. Sound His praises! Je-sus who
Crown Him! crown Him! Prophet, and Priest, and King! Christ is com-ing! o-ver the
REFRAIN
guard His children, In His arms He carries them all day long:
bore our sorrows, Love unbounded, wonderful, deep and strong: Praise Him! praise Him!
world vic-to-rious, Pow'r and glo-ry un - to the Lord be-long:
tell of His ex-cel-lent greatness; Praise Him! praise Him! ev-er in joy-ful song!

87 The Cross Is Not Greater

B. B.
BALLINGTON BOOTH
1. The cross that He gave may be heav-y, But it ne'er outweighs His grace;
2. The thorns in my path are not sharp-er Than composed His crown for me;
3. The light of His love shin-eth brighter As it falls on paths of woe,
4. His will I have joy in ful-fill-ing, As I'm walk-ing in His sight;
The storm that I feared may surround me, But it ne'er ex-cludes His face.
The cup that I drink not more bit-ter Than He drank in Geth-sem-a-ne.
The toil of my work groweth light-er As I stoop to raise the low.
My all to the blood I am bring-ing, It a - lone can keep me right.
CHORUS
The cross is not great-er than His grace, The storm can - not
hide His bless - ed face; I am sat - is - fied to know
That with Je - sus here be - low, I can con - quer ev - 'ry foe.

88 Sunshine In the Soul

E. E. HEWITT — JNO. R. SWENEY

1. There's sun-shine in my soul to-day, More glo-ri-ous and bright
2. There's mu-sic in my soul to-day, A car-ol to my King,
3. There's springtime in my soul to-day, For, when the Lord is near,
4. There's glad-ness in my soul to-day, And hope and praise and love,

Than glows in an-y earth-ly sky, For Je-sus is my light.
And Je-sus, lis-ten-ing, can hear The songs I can-not sing.
The dove of peace sings in my heart, The flow'rs of grace ap-pear.
For bless-ings which He gives me now, For joys "laid up" a-bove.

REFRAIN

O there's sun - - - shine, bless-ed sun - - - shine,
O there's sun-shine in the soul, bless-ed sun-shine in the soul,
When the peace-ful, hap-py mo-ments roll;
hap-py mo-ments roll;
When Je-sus shows His smil-ing face, There is sun-shine in the soul.

89 Let Jesus Come Into Your Heart

C. H. M. — Mrs. C. H. Morris

1. If you are tired of the load of your sin, Let Je - sus come
2. If 'tis for pu - ri - ty now that you sigh, Let Je - sus come
3. If there's a tem - pest your voice can - not still, Let Je - sus come
4. If you would join the glad songs of the blest, Let Je - sus come
in - to your heart; If you de - sire a new life to be - gin,
in - to your heart; Fountains for cleans-ing are flow - ing near by,
in - to your heart; If there's a void this world nev - er can fill,
in - to your heart; If you would en - ter the man-sions of rest,
Let Je - sus come in - to your heart.
CHORUS
Just now, your
doubt-ings give o'er; Just now, re - ject Him no more; Just now, throw
o - pen the door; Let Je - sus come in - to your heart.

90 Jesus Loves Even Me

P. P. B. P. P. Bliss

1. I am so glad that our Father in heav'n Tells of His love in the Book He has giv'n, Wonder-ful things in the Bible I see; This is the dear-est, that Je-sus loves me.
2. Tho' I for-get Him and wan-der a-way, Still He doth love me wher-ev-er I stray; Back to His dear lov-ing arms would I flee, When I re-mem-ber that Je-sus loves me.
3. Oh, if there's on-ly one song I can sing, When in His beau-ty I see the great King, This shall my song in e-ter-ni-ty be: "Oh, what a won-der that Je-sus loves me."
Chorus
I am so glad that Je-sus loves me, Je-sus loves me, Je-sus loves me,
I am so glad that Je-sus loves me, Je-sus loves e-ven me.

91 In My Heart There Rings a Melody

E. M. R. ELTON M. ROTH

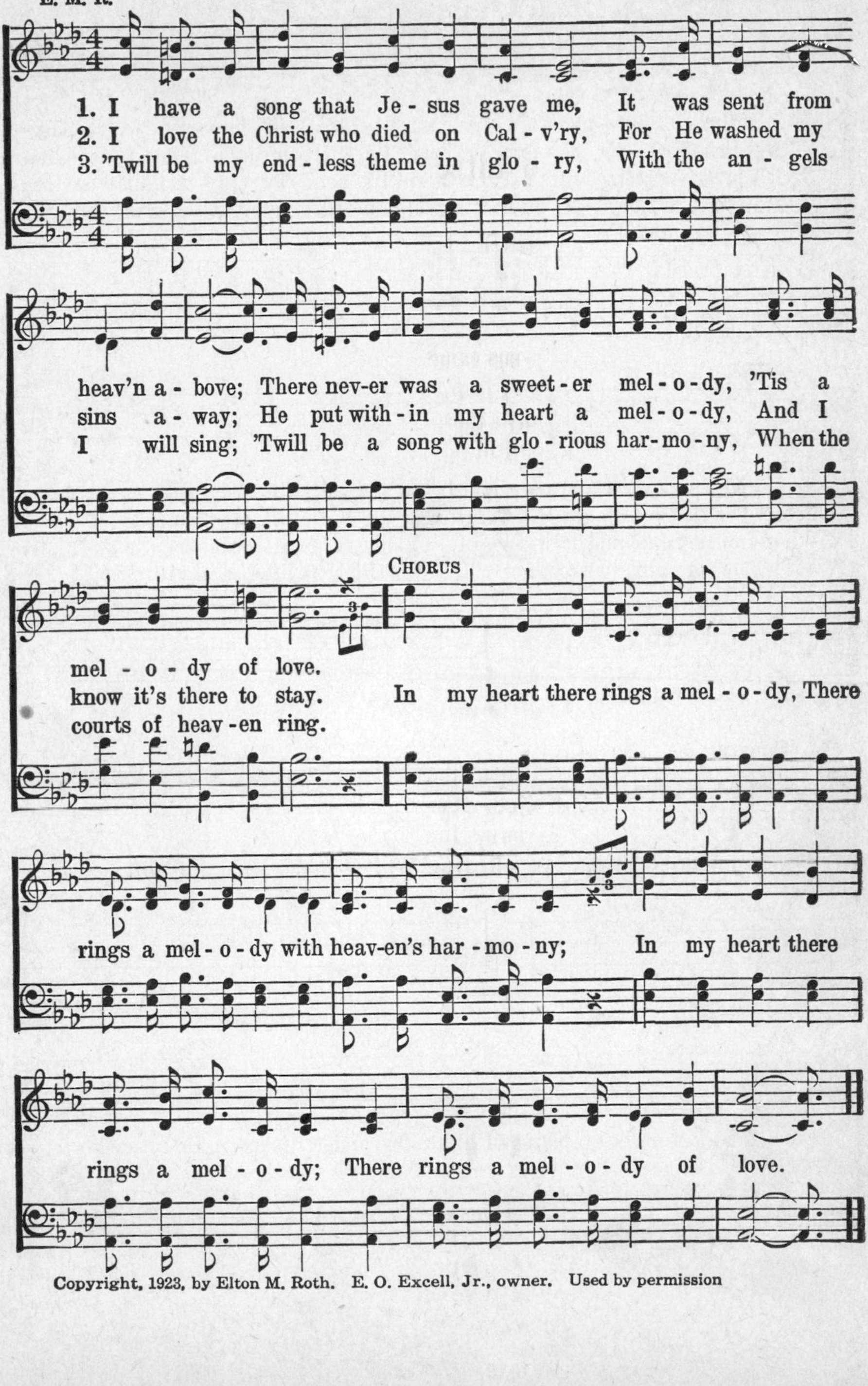

1. I have a song that Je - sus gave me, It was sent from
2. I love the Christ who died on Cal - v'ry, For He washed my
3. 'Twill be my end - less theme in glo - ry, With the an - gels

heav'n a - bove; There nev-er was a sweet - er mel - o - dy, 'Tis a
sins a - way; He put with - in my heart a mel - o - dy, And I
I will sing; 'Twill be a song with glo - rious har - mo - ny, When the

mel - o - dy of love.
know it's there to stay.
courts of heav - en ring.

CHORUS

In my heart there rings a mel - o - dy, There
rings a mel - o - dy with heav-en's har - mo - ny;
In my heart there
rings a mel - o - dy; There rings a mel - o - dy of love.

92 He Lifted Me

CHARLOTTE G. HOMER — CHAS. H. GABRIEL

1. In lov-ing-kind-ness Je-sus came My soul in mer-cy to re-claim,
2. He called me long be-fore I heard, Be-fore my sin-ful heart was stirred,
3. His brow was pierced with many a thorn, His hands by cru-el nails were torn,
4. Now on a high-er plane I dwell, And with my soul I know 'tis well;
And from the depths of sin and shame Thro' grace He lift-ed me. . . . . .
But when I took Him at His word, For-giv'n He lift-ed me. . . . . .
When from my guilt and grief, forlorn, In love He lift-ed me. . . . . .
Yet how or why, I can-not tell, He should have lift-ed me. . . . . .
He lift-ed me.
CHORUS.
From sink-ing sand He lift-ed me, With ten-der hand He lift-ed me,
From shades of night to plains of light, Oh, praise His name, He lift-ed me!

93 Our Great Savior

J. WILBUR CHAPMAN

ARR. by ROBERT HARKNESS

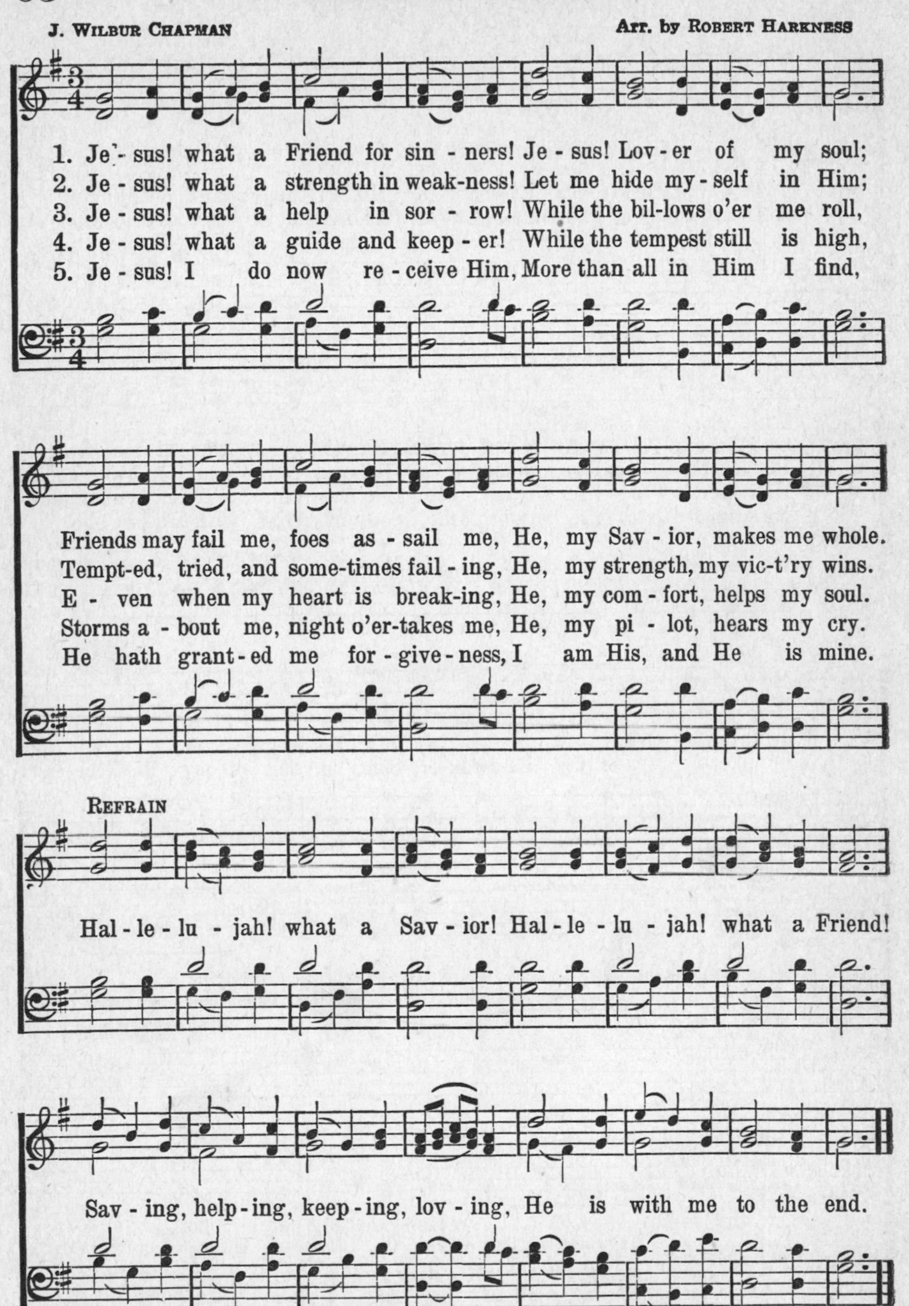
1. Je - sus! what a Friend for sin - ners! Je - sus! Lov - er of my soul;
2. Je - sus! what a strength in weak-ness! Let me hide my - self in Him;
3. Je - sus! what a help in sor - row! While the bil-lows o'er me roll,
4. Je - sus! what a guide and keep - er! While the tempest still is high,
5. Je - sus! I do now re - ceive Him, More than all in Him I find,
Friends may fail me, foes as - sail me, He, my Sav - ior, makes me whole.
Tempt-ed, tried, and some-times fail - ing, He, my strength, my vic-t'ry wins.
E - ven when my heart is break-ing, He, my com - fort, helps my soul.
Storms a - bout me, night o'er-takes me, He, my pi - lot, hears my cry.
He hath grant-ed me for - give - ness, I am His, and He is mine.
REFRAIN
Hal - le - lu - jah! what a Sav - ior! Hal - le - lu - jah! what a Friend!
Sav - ing, help - ing, keep - ing, lov - ing, He is with me to the end.

94 My Redeemer

P. P. Bliss
James McGranahan
1. I will sing of my Re-deem-er, And His won-drous love to me;
2. I will tell the won-drous sto-ry, How my lost es-tate to save,
3. I will praise my dear Re-deem-er, His tri-um-phant pow'r I'll tell,
4. I will sing of my Re-deem-er, And His heav'n-ly love to me;
On the cru-el cross He suf-fered, From the curse to set me free.
In His bound-less love and mer-cy, He the ran-som free-ly gave.
How the vic-to-ry He giv-eth O-ver sin, and death, and hell.
He from death to life hath bro't me, Son of God with Him to be.
Chorus
Sing, oh, sing . . . . of my Re-deem - er,
of my Re-deem-er, Sing, oh, sing of my Re-deem-er,
With His blood . . . . He pur-chased me, ...
He pur-chased me, With His blood He pur-chased me,
On the cross . . . . He sealed my par - don,
He sealed my par-don, On the cross He sealed my par-don,

My Redeemer

Paid the debt, ... and made me free. . . . .
and made me free, and made me free.

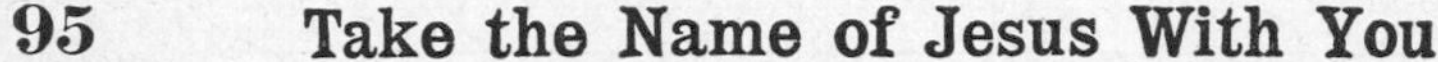

95 Take the Name of Jesus With You

Mrs. Lydia Baxter W. H. Doane

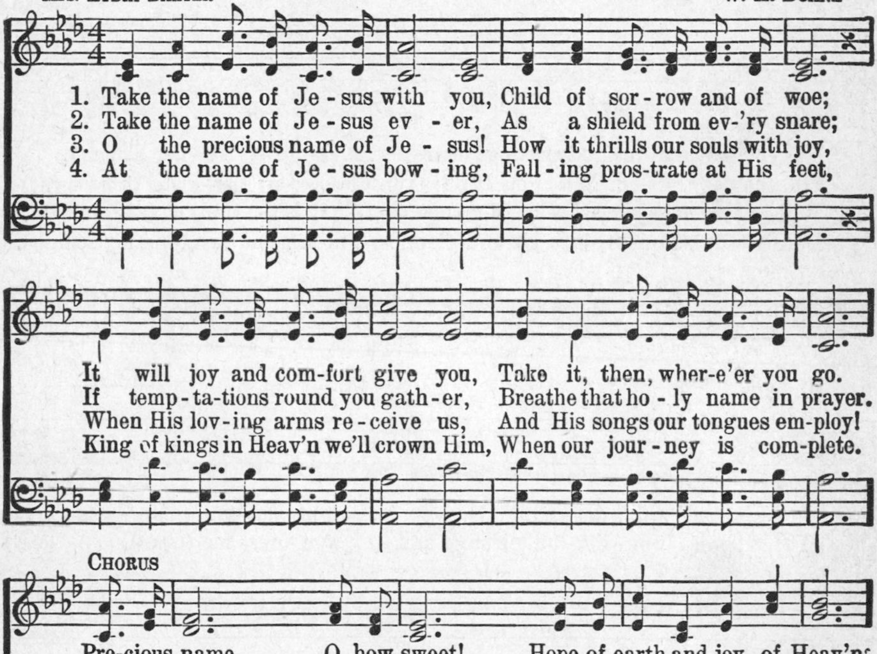

1. Take the name of Je - sus with you, Child of sor - row and of woe;
2. Take the name of Je - sus ev - er, As a shield from ev-'ry snare;
3. O the precious name of Je - sus! How it thrills our souls with joy,
4. At the name of Je - sus bow - ing, Fall - ing pros-trate at His feet,

It will joy and com-fort give you, Take it, then, wher-e'er you go.
If temp - ta-tions round you gath - er, Breathe that ho - ly name in prayer.
When His lov-ing arms re - ceive us, And His songs our tongues em-ploy!
King of kings in Heav'n we'll crown Him, When our jour - ney is com-plete.

Chorus

Pre-cious name, O how sweet! Hope of earth and joy of Heav'n;
Precious name, O how sweet!
Pre-cious name, O how sweet!... Hope of earth and joy of Heav'n.
Precious name, O how sweet, how sweet!

96 Is It Not Wonderful?

E. A. H. E. A. Hoffman

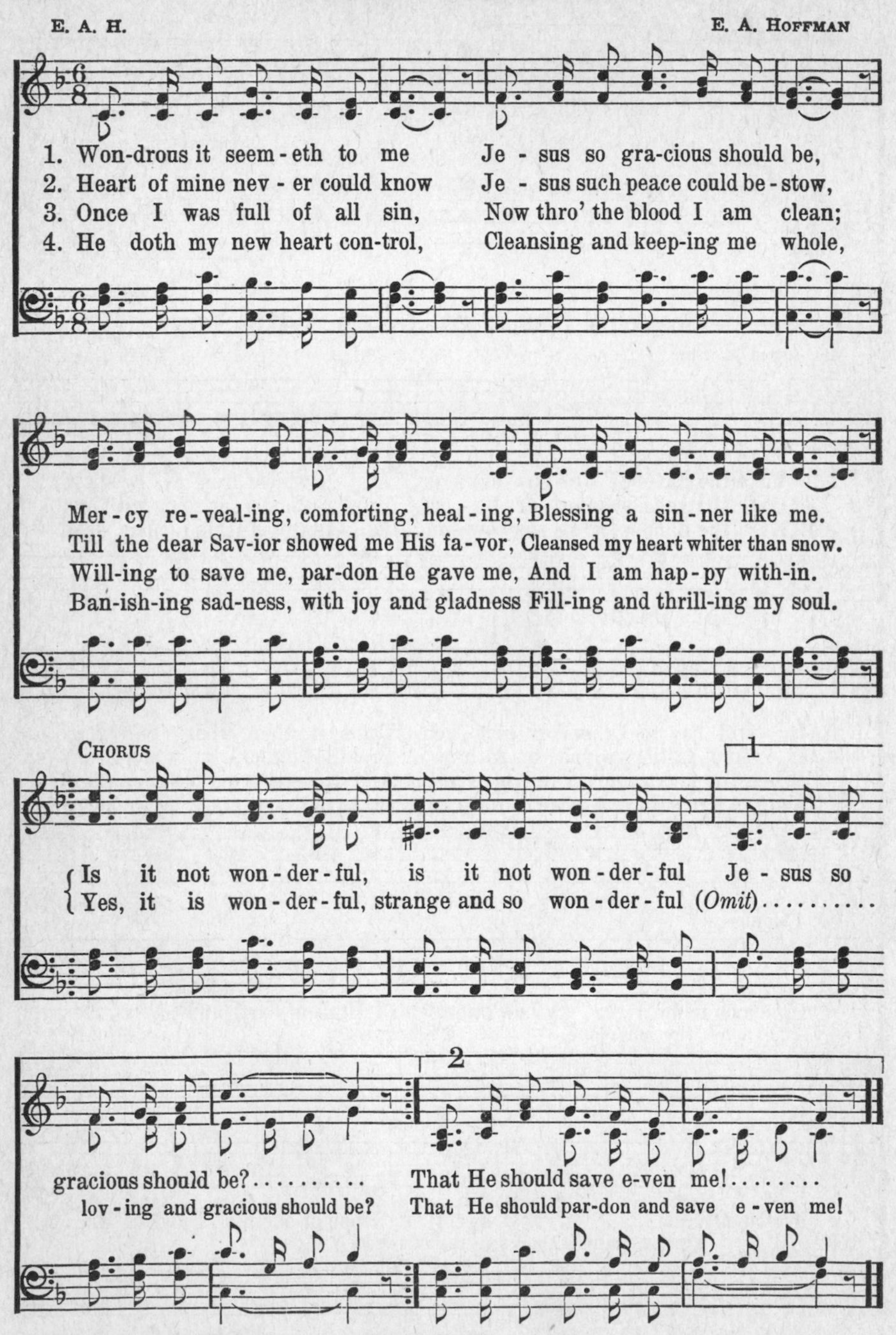
1. Won-drous it seem-eth to me Je - sus so gra-cious should be,
2. Heart of mine nev - er could know Je - sus such peace could be - stow,
3. Once I was full of all sin, Now thro' the blood I am clean;
4. He doth my new heart con-trol, Cleansing and keep-ing me whole,
Mer-cy re-veal-ing, comforting, heal-ing, Blessing a sin-ner like me.
Till the dear Sav-ior showed me His fa-vor, Cleansed my heart whiter than snow.
Will-ing to save me, par-don He gave me, And I am hap-py with-in.
Ban-ish-ing sad-ness, with joy and gladness Fill-ing and thrill-ing my soul.
Chorus
1
Is it not won-der-ful, is it not won-der-ful Je - sus so
Yes, it is won-der-ful, strange and so won-der-ful (Omit)..........
gracious should be?..........
lov-ing and gracious should be?
2
That He should save e-ven me!........
That He should par-don and save e - ven me!

97 Higher Ground

Johnson Oatman, Jr. — Chas. H. Gabriel

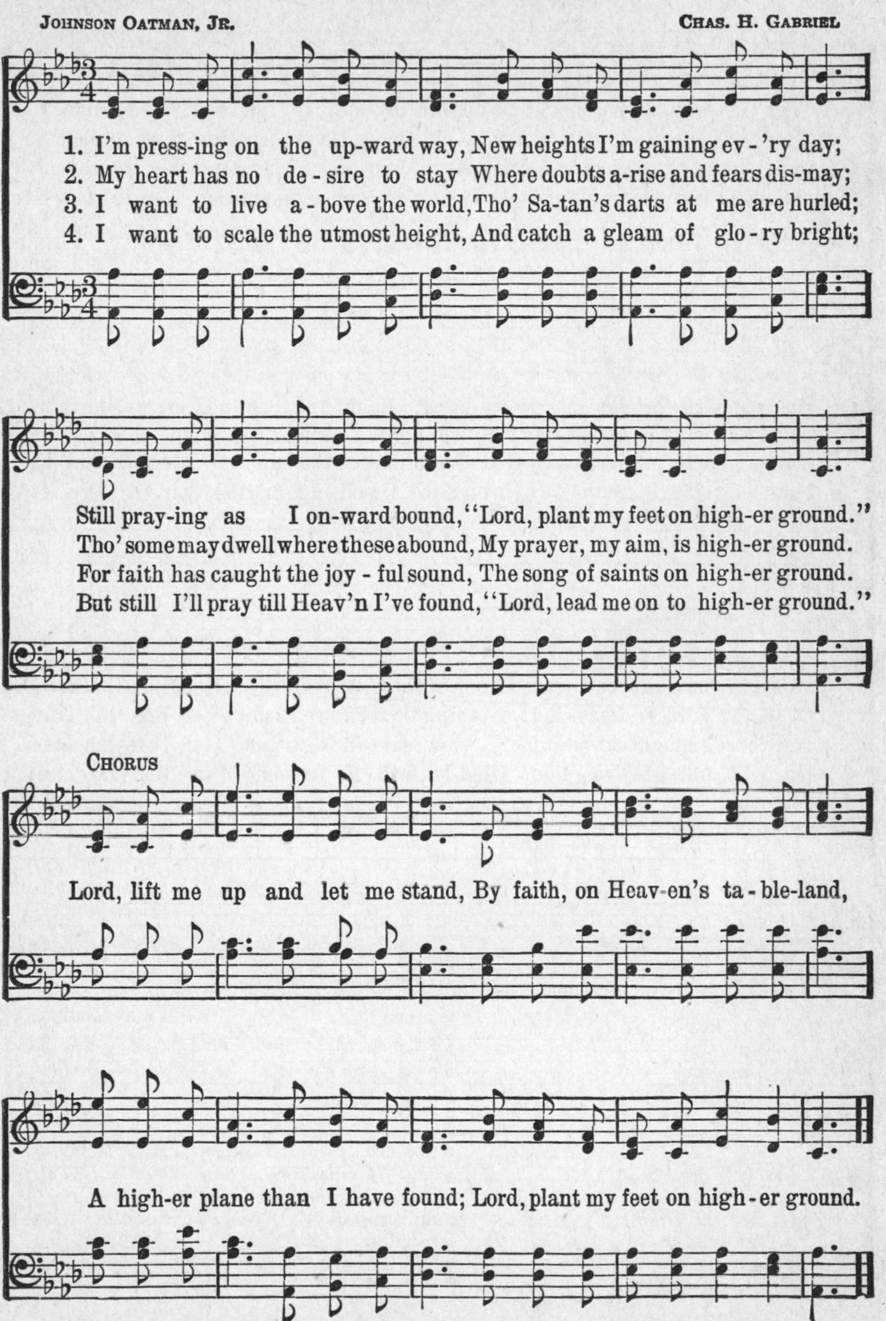

1. I'm press-ing on the up-ward way, New heights I'm gaining ev - 'ry day;
2. My heart has no de - sire to stay Where doubts a-rise and fears dis-may;
3. I want to live a - bove the world, Tho' Sa-tan's darts at me are hurled;
4. I want to scale the utmost height, And catch a gleam of glo - ry bright;
Still pray-ing as I on-ward bound, "Lord, plant my feet on high-er ground."
Tho' some may dwell where these abound, My prayer, my aim, is high-er ground.
For faith has caught the joy - ful sound, The song of saints on high-er ground.
But still I'll pray till Heav'n I've found, "Lord, lead me on to high-er ground."
Chorus
Lord, lift me up and let me stand, By faith, on Heav-en's ta - ble-land,
A high-er plane than I have found; Lord, plant my feet on high - er ground.

98 Dwelling in Beulah Land

C. A. M. C. Austin Miles

1. Far a-way the noise of strife up-on my ear is fall-ing, Then I know the
2. Far be-low the storm of doubt up-on the world is beat-ing, Sons of men in
3. Let the storm-y breez-es blow, their cry can-not a-larm me; I am safe-ly
4. Viewing here the works of God, I sink in con-tem-pla-tion, Hearing now His
sins of earth be-set on ev-'ry hand: Doubt and fear and things of earth in
bat-tle long the en-e-my with-stand: Safe am I with-in the cas-tle
sheltered here, pro-tect-ed by God's hand: Here the sun is al-ways shin-ing,
bless-ed voice, I see the way He planned: Dwell-ing in the Spir-it, here I
vain to me are call-ing, None of these shall move me from Beu-lah Land.
of God's word re-treat-ing, Nothing then can reach me—'tis Beu-lah Land.
here there's naught can harm me, I am safe for-ev-er in Beu-lah Land.
learn of full sal-va-tion, Glad-ly will I tar-ry in Beu-lah Land.
Chorus
I'm liv-ing on the moun-tain, un-der-neath a cloud-less sky, I'm
Praise God!
drink-ing at the foun-tain that never shall run dry; O yes! I'm feasting on the

Dwelling in Beulah Land
man-na from a boun-ti - ful sup-ply, For I am dwell-ing in Beu - lah Land.
99
Does Jesus Care?
Frank E. Graeff
J. Lincoln Hall
1. Does Je - sus care when my heart is pained Too deep-ly for mirth and song;
2. Does Je - sus care when my way is dark With a name - less dread and fear?
3. Does Je - sus care when I've tried and failed To re-sist some temp-ta - tion strong;
4. Does Je - sus care when I've said "good-by" To the dear-est on earth to me,
As the burdens press, and the cares distress, And the way grows wea-ry and long?
As the daylight fades into deep night shades, Does He care e-nough to be near?
When for my deep grief I find no re - lief, Tho' my tears flow all the night long?
And my sad heart aches till it nearly breaks–Is it aught to Him? Does He see?
Chorus
O yes, He cares; I know He cares, His heart is touched with my grief;
ad lib.
rit.
When the days are wea-ry, the long nights dreary, I know my Sav - ior cares.
He cares.

100 Coming Again

A. S. Reitz — A. W. McKee

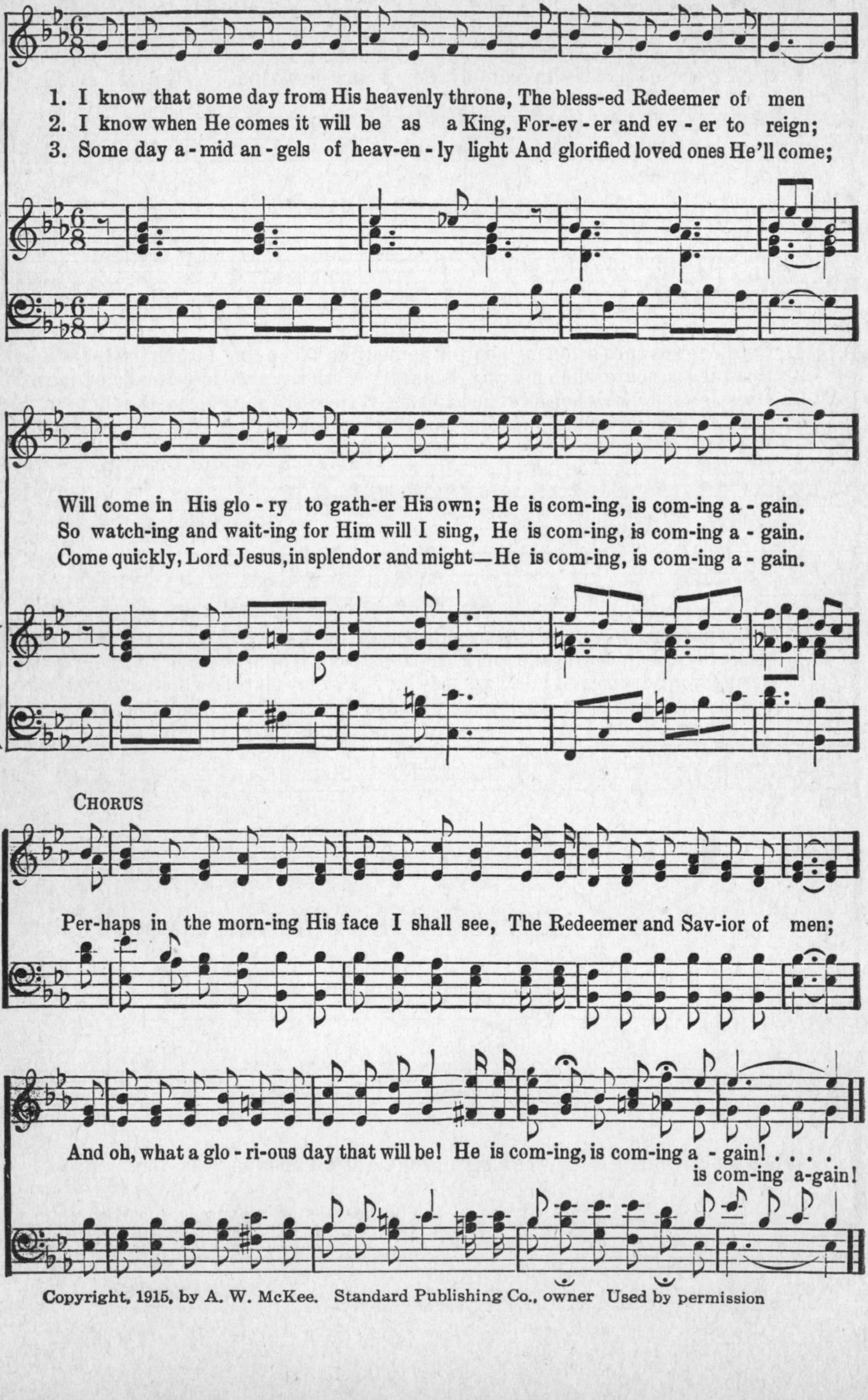

1. I know that some day from His heavenly throne, The bless-ed Redeemer of men
2. I know when He comes it will be as a King, For-ev - er and ev - er to reign;
3. Some day a - mid an - gels of heav-en - ly light And glorified loved ones He'll come;

Will come in His glo - ry to gath-er His own; He is com-ing, is com-ing a - gain.
So watch-ing and wait-ing for Him will I sing, He is com-ing, is com-ing a - gain.
Come quickly, Lord Jesus, in splendor and might—He is com-ing, is com-ing a - gain.

Chorus

Per-haps in the morn-ing His face I shall see, The Redeemer and Sav-ior of men;
And oh, what a glo - ri-ous day that will be! He is com-ing, is com-ing a - gain! . . . .
is com-ing a-gain!

101 Lead Me to Calvary

Jennie Evelyn Hussey — Wm. J. Kirkpatrick

1. King of my life, I crown Thee now, Thine shall the glo - ry be;
Lest I for - get Thy thorn-crowned brow, Lead me to Cal - va - ry.

2. Show me the tomb where Thou wast laid, Ten-der-ly mourned and wept;
An - gels in robes of light ar - rayed Guarded Thee whilst Thou slept.

3. Let me like Ma - ry, thro' the gloom, Come with a gift to Thee;
Show to me now the emp - ty tomb, Lead me to Cal - va - ry.

4. May I be will - ing, Lord, to bear Dai - ly my cross for Thee;
E - ven Thy cup of grief to share, Thou hast borne all for me.

CHORUS

Lest I for - get Geth-sem - a - ne; Lest I for - get Thine ag - o - ny;
Lest I for - get Thy love for me, Lead me to Cal - va - ry.

102 When the Roll is Called Up Yonder

J. M. B. — J. M. Black

1. When the trumpet of the Lord shall sound, and time shall be no more, And the morning breaks, e-ter-nal, bright and fair; When the saved of earth shall gather o - ver on the oth-er shore, And the roll is called up yon-der, I'll be there.
2. On that bright and cloudless morning when the dead in Christ shall rise, And the glo - ry of His res - ur-rec-tion share; When His cho-sen ones shall gather to their home beyond the skies, And the roll is called up yon-der, I'll be there.
3. Let us la - bor for the Mas - ter from the dawn till set - ting sun, Let us talk of all His wondrous love and care; Then when all of life is o - ver, and our work on earth is done, And the roll is called up yon-der, I'll be there.
Chorus.
When the roll . . . . . . is called up yon - - - - der, When the
When the roll is called up yon - der, I'll be there,
roll . . . . is called up yon - - der, When the roll . . . . is called up
When the roll is called up yon-der, I'll be there, When the roll is called up

When the Roll is Called Up Yonder

yon - der, When the roll is called up yon - der, I'll be there.
103 Leaning On the Everlasting Arms
E. A. Hoffman
A. J. Showalter
1. What a fel-low-ship, what a joy di-vine, Leaning on the ev-er-last-ing arms;
2. Oh, how sweet to walk in this pilgrim way, Leaning on the ev-er-last-ing arms;
3. What have I to dread, what have I to fear, Leaning on the ev-er-last-ing arms?
What a bless-ed-ness, what a peace is mine, Leaning on the ev-er-last-ing arms.
Oh, how bright the path grows from day to day, Leaning on the ev-er-last-ing arms.
I have bless-ed peace with my Lord so near, Leaning on the ev-er-last-ing arms.
Refrain
Lean - ing, lean - ing, Safe and se-cure from all a-larms;
Lean-ing on Je - sus, lean-ing on Je - sus,
Lean - ing, lean - ing, Lean-ing on the ev-er-last-ing arms.
Lean-ing on Je - sus, lean-ing on Je - sus,

By permission of A. J. Showalter

104 The Banner of the Cross

D. W. WHITTLE JAMES McGRANAHAN

1. There's a roy - al ban - ner giv - en for dis-play To the sol - diers
2. Though the foe may rage and gath - er as the flood, Let the stand-ard
3. O - ver land and sea, wher-ev - er man may dwell, Make the glo - rious
4. When the glo - ry dawns—'tis draw-ing ver - y near—It is has-t'ning
of the King; As an en - sign fair we lift it up to - day,
be dis - played; And be-neath its folds, as sol - diers of the Lord,
ti - dings known; Of the crim - son ban - ner now the sto - ry tell,
day by day— Then be - fore our King the foe shall dis - ap-pear,
While as ran-somed ones we sing.
For the truth be not dis - mayed!
While the Lord shall claim His own!
And the cross the world shall sway!
CHORUS
March-ing on, . . . march-ing on, on,
on, . . For Christ count ev - 'ry-thing but loss! . . . . And to
on, on, ev - 'ry-thing, ev - 'ry - thing but loss!
crown Him King, toil and sing 'Neath the ban - ner of the cross!
we'll Be - neath

105 I Will Sing the Wondrous Story

F. H. ROWLEY
PETER P. BILHORN
1. I will sing the won-drous sto - ry Of the Christ who died for me,
2. I was lost, but Je - sus found me, Found the sheep that went a - stray,
3. I was bruised, but Je - sus healed me; Faint was I from many a fall;
4. Days of dark-ness still come o'er me, Sor - row's paths I oft - en tread,
5. He will keep me till the riv - er Rolls its wa - ters at my feet;
How He left His home in glo - ry For the cross of Cal - va - ry.
Threw His lov - ing arms a-round me, Drew me back in - to His way.
Sight was gone, and fears possessed me, But He freed me from them all.
But the Sav - ior still is with me; By His hand I'm safe - ly led.
Then He'll bear me safe - ly o - ver, Where the loved ones I shall meet.
CHORUS
Yes, I'll sing . . . . . the won-drous sto - - - ry Of the
Yes, I'll sing
the won-drous sto - ry
Christ . . . . who died for me, ... Sing it with . . . . the saints in
Of the Christ
who died for me,
Sing it with
glo - - ry, Gath-ered by . . . . . . the crys-tal sea. . . . .
the saints in glo - ry,
Gath-ered by
the crys-tal sea.

106 I've Found a Friend

J. G. Small | Geo. C. Stebbins

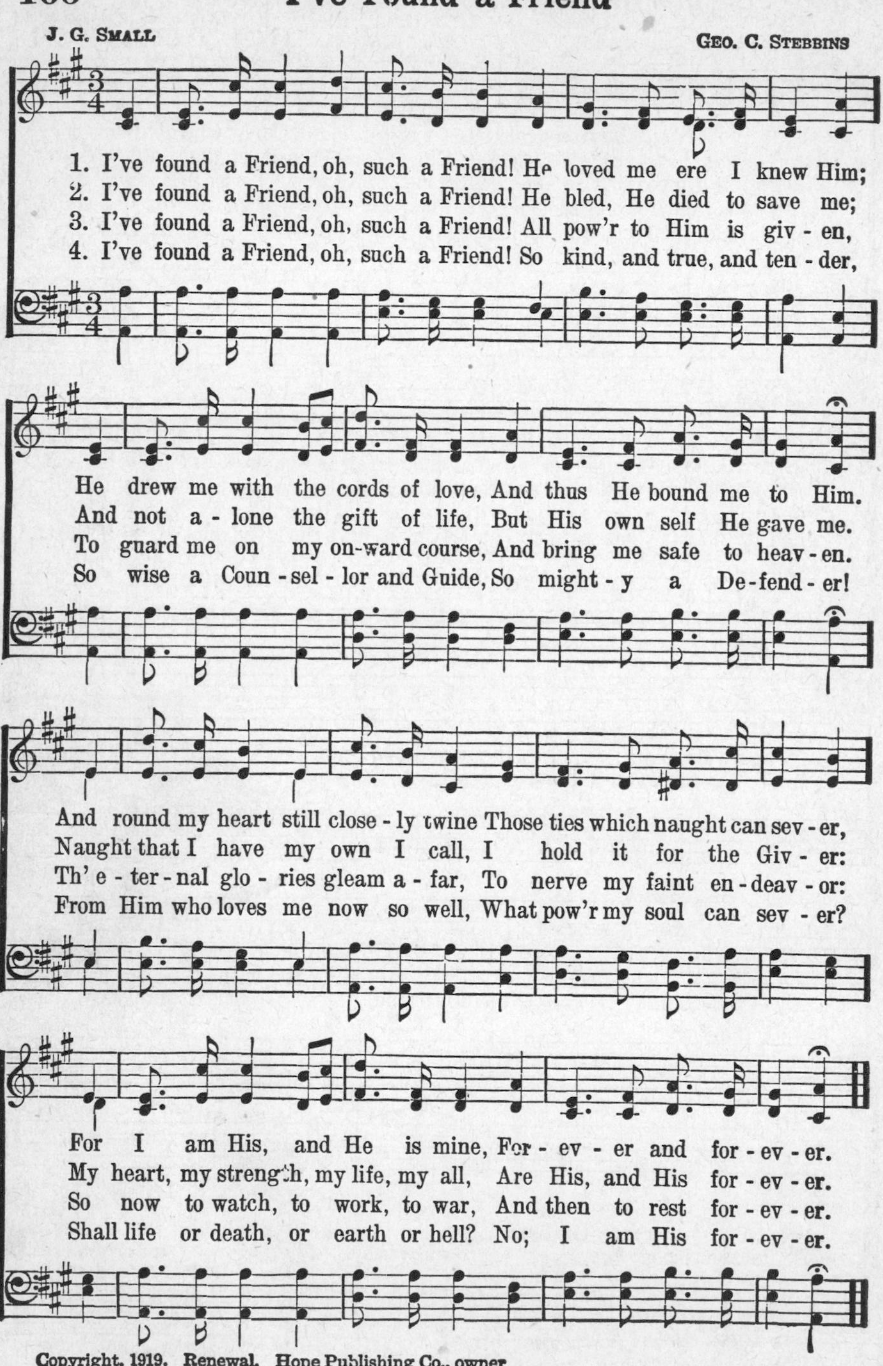
1. I've found a Friend, oh, such a Friend! He loved me ere I knew Him;
2. I've found a Friend, oh, such a Friend! He bled, He died to save me;
3. I've found a Friend, oh, such a Friend! All pow'r to Him is giv - en,
4. I've found a Friend, oh, such a Friend! So kind, and true, and ten - der,
He drew me with the cords of love, And thus He bound me to Him.
And not a - lone the gift of life, But His own self He gave me.
To guard me on my on-ward course, And bring me safe to heav - en.
So wise a Coun - sel - lor and Guide, So might - y a De-fend - er!
And round my heart still close - ly twine Those ties which naught can sev - er,
Naught that I have my own I call, I hold it for the Giv - er:
Th' e - ter - nal glo - ries gleam a - far, To nerve my faint en - deav - or:
From Him who loves me now so well, What pow'r my soul can sev - er?
For I am His, and He is mine, For - ev - er and for - ev - er.
My heart, my strength, my life, my all, Are His, and His for - ev - er.
So now to watch, to work, to war, And then to rest for - ev - er.
Shall life or death, or earth or hell? No; I am His for - ev - er.

107 Ivory Palaces

H. B. HENRY BARRACLOUGH

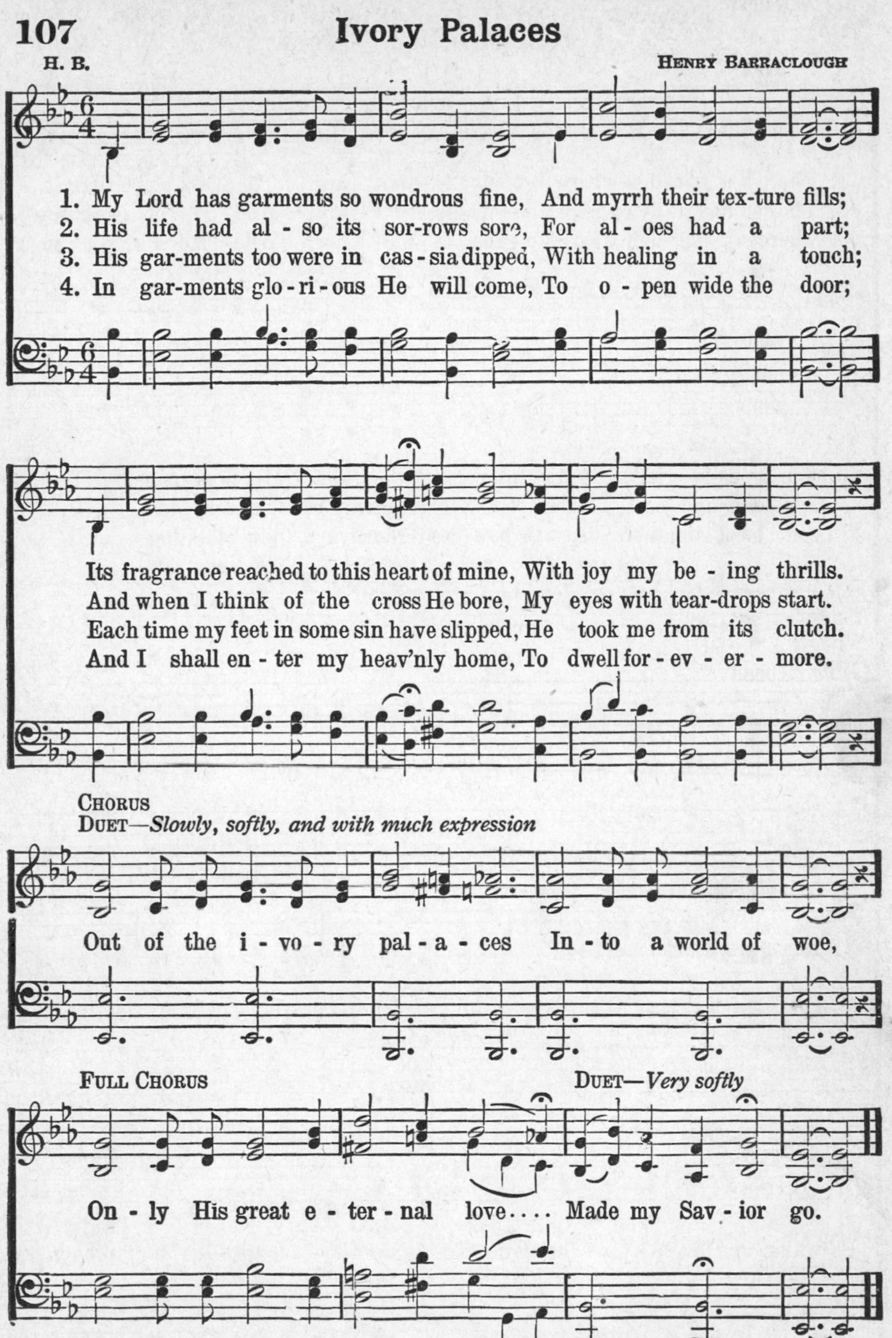
1. My Lord has garments so wondrous fine, And myrrh their tex-ture fills;
2. His life had al - so its sor-rows sore, For al - oes had a part;
3. His gar-ments too were in cas - sia dipped, With healing in a touch;
4. In gar-ments glo - ri - ous He will come, To o - pen wide the door;
Its fragrance reached to this heart of mine, With joy my be - ing thrills.
And when I think of the cross He bore, My eyes with tear-drops start.
Each time my feet in some sin have slipped, He took me from its clutch.
And I shall en - ter my heav'nly home, To dwell for - ev - er - more.
CHORUS
DUET—Slowly, softly, and with much expression
Out of the i - vo - ry pal - a - ces In - to a world of woe,
FULL CHORUS
DUET—Very softly
On - ly His great e - ter - nal love.... Made my Sav - ior go.

108 The Beautiful Garden of Prayer

Eleanor Allen Schroll — J. H. Fillmore

1. There's a gar-den where Je-sus is wait-ing, There's a place that is wondrous-ly fair; For it glows with the light of His pres-ence, 'Tis the beau-ti-ful gar-den of prayer.
2. There's a gar-den where Je-sus is wait-ing, And I go with my bur-den and care, Just to learn from His lips words of com-fort In the beau-ti-ful gar-den of prayer.
3. There's a gar-den where Je-sus is wait-ing, And He bids you to come meet Him there; Just to bow, and re-ceive a new bless-ing, In the beau-ti-ful gar-den of prayer.
Refrain
O the beau-ti-ful gar-den, the gar-den of prayer, O the beau-ti-ful gar-den of prayer; There my Sav-ior a-waits, and He o-pens the gates To the beau-ti-ful gar-den of prayer.

109 Get God's Sunshine

R. H. ROBERT HARKNESS

CHORUS
1. Trust - ing Je - sus, won - der - ful Guide, In His keep - ing safe - ly a - bide; Joys e - ter - nal He will im - part,
2. Won - drous prom - ise He will ful - fill, Glad - ly do - ing His ho - ly will; Peace un - end - ing He will im - part,
3. Friend of sin - ners, ev - er the same, Will - ing Sav - ior, praise His dear name, Full for - give - ness He will im - part,
Get God's sun-shine in - to your heart.
Get God's sun-shine in - to your heart.
Get God's sun-shine in - to your heart.
Get God's sunshine in - to your heart,
Get God's sun-shine in - to your heart; It will cheer you all the day, Drive the
gloom of life a - way, If you get God's sun-shine in - to your heart.

110 Bring Your Vessels, Not a Few

Mrs. C. H. M. — Mrs. C. H. Morris

1. Are you look - ing for the full - ness of the bless-ing of the Lord
2. Bring your emp-ty earth - en ves - sels, clean thro' Je-sus' pre-cious blood,
3. Like the cruse of oil un-fail - ing is His grace for - ev - er-more,
In your heart and life to - day? Claim the prom-ise of your Fa - ther,
Come, ye need - y, one and all; And in hu-man con - se - cra-tion
And His love un-chang-ing still; And ac-cord - ing to His prom-ise
come ac - cord - ing to His word, In the bless - ed old-time way.
wait be - fore the throne of God, Till the Ho - ly Ghost shall fall.
with the Ho - ly Ghost and pow'r, He will ev - 'ry ves - sel fill.
Chorus
He will fill your heart to-day to o - ver - flow - - - ing, As the
He will fill your heart to o - ver-flow-ing,
Lord commandeth you, "Bring your vessels, not a few;" He will fill your heart to-
He will fill

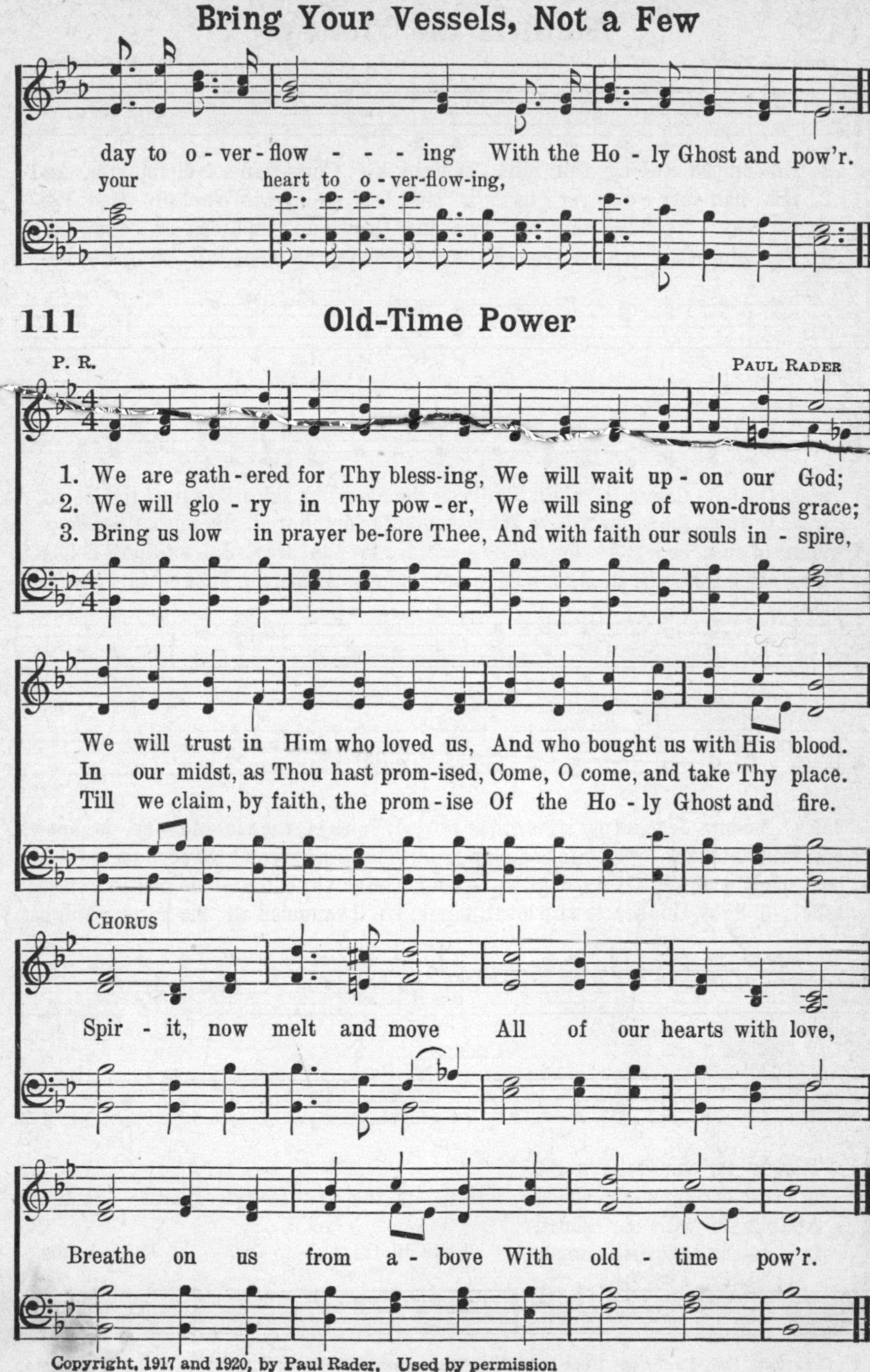
Bring Your Vessels, Not a Few
day to o-ver-flow - - - - ing With the Ho-ly Ghost and pow'r.
your heart to o-ver-flow-ing,
111
Old-Time Power
P. R.
Paul Rader
1. We are gath-ered for Thy bless-ing, We will wait up-on our God;
2. We will glo-ry in Thy pow-er, We will sing of won-drous grace;
3. Bring us low in prayer be-fore Thee, And with faith our souls in-spire,
We will trust in Him who loved us, And who bought us with His blood.
In our midst, as Thou hast prom-ised, Come, O come, and take Thy place.
Till we claim, by faith, the prom-ise Of the Ho-ly Ghost and fire.
Chorus
Spir-it, now melt and move All of our hearts with love,
Breathe on us from a-bove With old-time pow'r.

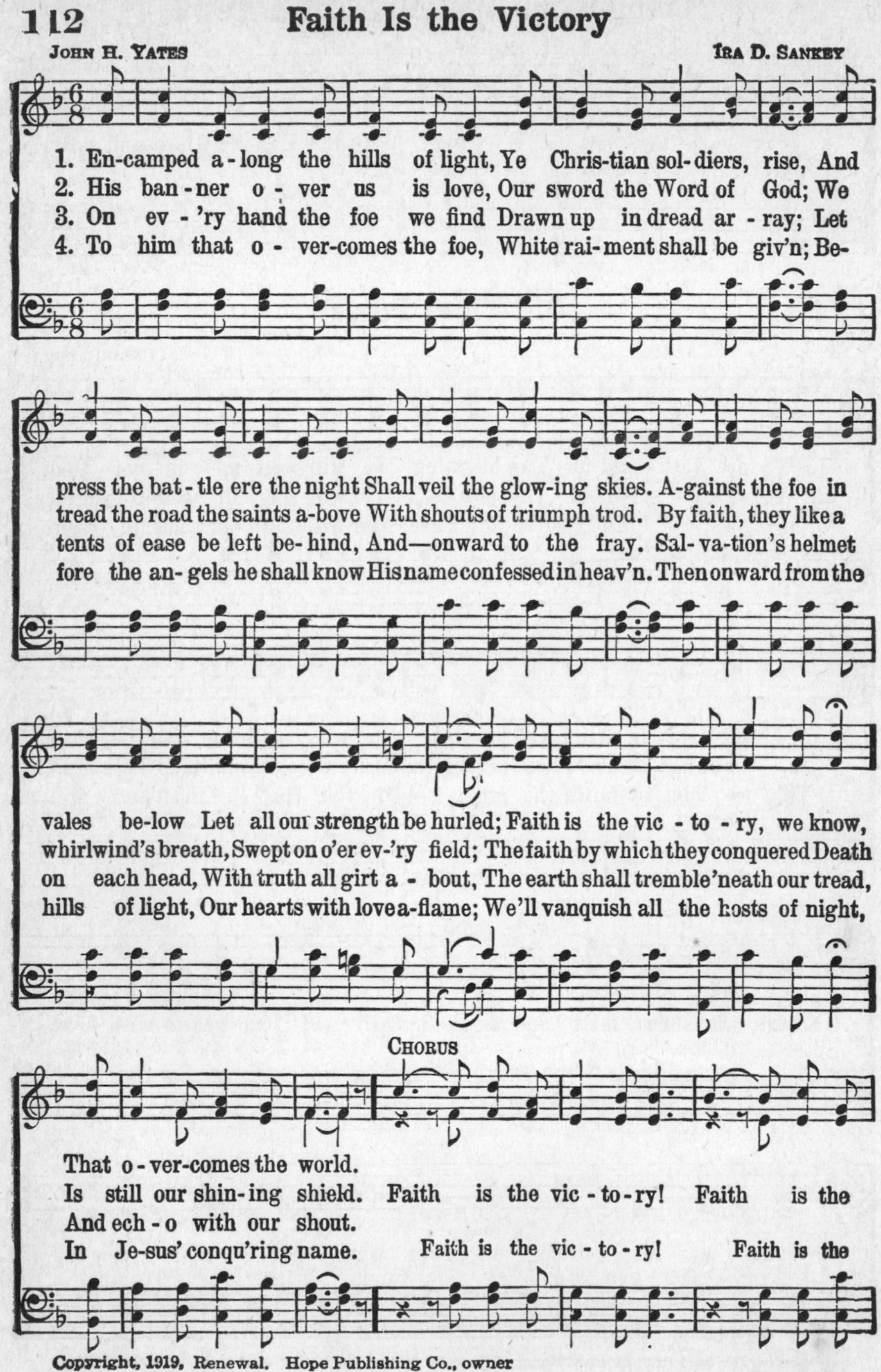
112 Faith Is the Victory
John H. Yates
Ira D. Sankey
1. En-camped a-long the hills of light, Ye Chris-tian sol-diers, rise, And
2. His ban-ner o-ver us is love, Our sword the Word of God; We
3. On ev-'ry hand the foe we find Drawn up in dread ar-ray; Let
4. To him that o-ver-comes the foe, White rai-ment shall be giv'n; Be-
press the bat-tle ere the night Shall veil the glow-ing skies. A-gainst the foe in
tread the road the saints a-bove With shouts of triumph trod. By faith, they like a
tents of ease be left be-hind, And—onward to the fray. Sal-va-tion's helmet
fore the an-gels he shall know His name confessed in heav'n. Then onward from the
vales be-low Let all our strength be hurled; Faith is the vic-to-ry, we know,
whirlwind's breath, Swept on o'er ev-'ry field; The faith by which they conquered Death
on each head, With truth all girt a-bout, The earth shall tremble 'neath our tread,
hills of light, Our hearts with love a-flame; We'll vanquish all the hosts of night,
Chorus
That o-ver-comes the world.
Is still our shin-ing shield. Faith is the vic-to-ry! Faith is the
And ech-o with our shout.
In Je-sus' conqu'ring name. Faith is the vic-to-ry! Faith is the

Faith Is the Victory

vic - to-ry! Oh, glo-ri-ous vic - to-ry, That o-ver-comes the world.
vic - to-ry!

113 Hiding In Thee

Wm O. Cushing — Ira D. Sankey

1. O safe to the Rock that is high-er than I, My soul in its con-flicts and sor-rows would fly; So sin-ful, so wea-ry, Thine, Thine would I be; Thou blest "Rock of A-ges," I'm hid-ing in Thee.
2. In the calm of the noon-tide, in sor-row's lone hour, In times when temp-ta-tion casts o'er me its pow'r; In the tem-pests of life, on its wide, heaving sea, Thou blest "Rock of A-ges," I'm hid-ing in Thee.
3. How oft in the con-flict, when pressed by the foe, I have fled to my Ref-uge and breathed out my woe; How oft-en, when tri-als like sea-bil-lows roll, Have I hid-den in Thee, O Thou Rock of my soul.
CHORUS
Hid-ing in Thee, Hiding in Thee, Thou blest "Rock of Ages," I'm hid-ing in Thee.

114 The Best Friend is Jesus

P. P. B. P. P. BILHORN

DUET
1. Oh, the best friend to have is Je - sus, When the cares of life up-on you roll; He will heal the wound-ed heart, He will strength and grace impart;
2. What a friend I have found in Je - sus! Peace and com-fort to my soul He brings; Lean-ing on His might-y arm, I will fear no ill nor harm;
3. Tho' I pass thro' the night of sor - row, And the chill-y waves of Jor-dan roll, Nev-er need I shrink nor fear, For my Sav-ior is so near;
4. When at last to our home we gath - er, With the loved ones who have gone be-fore, We will sing up - on the shore, Prais-ing Him for - ev - er-more;
Oh, the best friend to have is Je - sus.
CHORUS Spirited
The best friend to have is Je - - - sus, The best friend to have is Je - - - sus;
Je-sus ev-'ry day, Je-sus all the way;
He will help you when you fall, He will hear you when you call, Oh, the best friend to have is Je-sus.
3
3

115 Let Us Crown Him

E. PERRONET — JAMES McGRANAHAN

Allegro

1. All hail the pow'r of Je - sus' name! Let an - gels pros - trate fall;
2. Let ev - 'ry kin - dred, ev - 'ry tribe, On this ter - res - trial ball,
3. O that with yon - der sa - cred throng We at His feet may fall!

Bring forth the roy - al di - a - dem, And crown Him Lord of all.
To Him all maj - es - ty as - cribe, And crown Him Lord of all.
We'll join the ev - er - last - ing song, And crown Him Lord of all.

CHORUS

Let us crown Him, . . . Let us crown Him, . . . Let us
Him Lord of all, Him Lord of all,
crown the great Re - deem - er Lord of all; . . . . Let us crown Him, ...
Him Lord of all,
Let us crown Him, . . . Let us crown Him Lord of all.
Him Lord of all, the great Re - deem - er Lord of all.

116 Tell Me the Old, Old Story

KATE HANKEY W. H. DOANE

1. Tell me the old, old sto - ry, Of un-seen things a - bove, Of Je - sus
2. Tell me the sto - ry slow - ly, That I may take it in— That won - der -
3. Tell me the sto - ry soft - ly, With ear - nest tones and grave; Re - mem - ber
4. Tell me the same old sto - ry, When you have cause to fear That this world's
and His glo - ry, Of Je - sus and His love; Tell me the sto - ry
ful re - demp - tion, God's rem - e - dy for sin; Tell me the sto - ry
I'm the sin - ner Whom Je - sus came to save; Tell me the sto - ry
emp - ty glo - ry Is cost - ing me too dear; Yes, and when that world's
sim - ply, As to a lit - tle child, For I am weak and wea - ry,
oft - en, For I for - get so soon, The "ear - ly dew" of morn - ing
al - ways, If you would real - ly be, In an - y time of troub - le,
glo - ry is dawn - ing on my soul, Tell me the old, old sto - ry:
And help - less and de - filed.
Has passed a - way at noon.
A com - fort - er to me.
"Christ Je - sus makes thee whole."
CHORUS
Tell me the old, old sto - ry, Tell me the old, old sto - ry, Tell me the old, old sto - ry, Of Je - sus and His love.

117 Believe On the Lord Jesus Christ

Avis B. Christiansen Harry D. Clarke

1. "What must I do?" the trem-bling jail - or cried, When dazed by
2. What must I do! O wea - ry, trem-bling soul, Just turn to-
3. His blood is all thy plea for sav - ing grace, The pre - cious
fear and won - der; "Be - lieve on Christ!" was all that Paul re - plied,
day to Je - sus; He will re - ceive, for-give and make thee whole—
fount of cleans-ing! O come, ac - cept His love, be - hold His face,
"And thou shalt be saved from sin."
Christ a - lone can set thee free.
And be saved for - ev - er - more.
Chorus
Be - lieve on the
Be - lieve
Lord Je - sus Christ, Be - lieve on the Lord Je - sus Christ, Be-
Be - lieve
lieve on the Lord Je - sus Christ, And thou shalt be saved!
Be - lieve

118 My Savior First of All

Fanny J. Crosby — Jno. R. Sweney

1. When my life-work is ended, and I cross the swelling tide, When the bright and glorious morning I shall see; I shall know my Redeemer when I reach the other side, And His smile will be the first to welcome me.

2. Oh, the soul-thrilling rapture when I view His blessed face, And the luster of His kindly beaming eye; How my full heart will praise Him for the mercy, love, and grace, That prepare for me a mansion in the sky.

3. Oh, the dear ones in glory, how they beckon me to come, And our parting at the river I recall; To the sweet vales of Eden they will sing my welcome home; But I long to meet my Savior first of all.

4. Thro' the gates to the city in a robe of spotless white, He will lead me where no tears will ever fall; In the glad song of ages I shall mingle with delight; But I long to meet my Savior first of all.

Chorus

I shall know . . Him, I shall know Him, And redeemed by His side I shall stand,
I shall know Him,
I shall know . . Him, I shall know Him By the print of the nails in His hand.
I shall know Him,

119 **To Eternity**

PAUL RADER — ARTHUR W. MCKEE

1. The riv-er of Thy grace is flow-ing free, We launch up-on its depths to sail to Thee; In the o-cean of Thy love we soon shall be, We are sail-ing to e-ter-ni-ty.
2. The breez-es of Thy love are blow-ing free, They tell Thy love to all hu-man-i-ty; They are sing-ing of the blood of Cal-va-ry, Mak-ing white thro' all e-ter-ni-ty.
3. Thy Spir-it calls to all, "Come home to-day;" Come back and find the Sav-ior while you may; Find that Je-sus is the Life, the Truth, the Way, Lead-ing, guid-ing, to e-ter-ni-ty.
CHORUS
Earth-ly joys can-not com-pare with all the glo-ry, When our longing eyes shall see Thy face; We shall have Thy fel-low-ship for-ev-er, In the splendor of the throne of grace.

120 A Shelter in the Time of Storm

Words arranged — IRA D. SANKEY

1. The Lord's our Rock, in Him we hide, A shel-ter in the time of storm;
2. A shade by day, de-fense by night, A shel-ter in the time of storm;
3. The rag-ing storms may round us beat, A shel-ter in the time of storm;
4. O Rock di-vine, O Ref-uge dear, A shel-ter in the time of storm;
Se-cure what-ev-er ill be-tide, A shel-ter in the time of storm.
No fears a-larm, no foes af-fright, A shel-ter in the time of storm.
We'll nev-er leave our safe re-treat, A shel-ter in the time of storm.
Be Thou our help-er ev-er near, A shel-ter in the time of storm.
CHORUS
Oh, Je-sus is a Rock in a wea-ry land, A wea-ry land, a wea-ry land;
Oh, Je-sus is a Rock in a wea-ry land, A shel-ter in the time of storm.

121 The Broken Heart

T. D. T. DENNIS

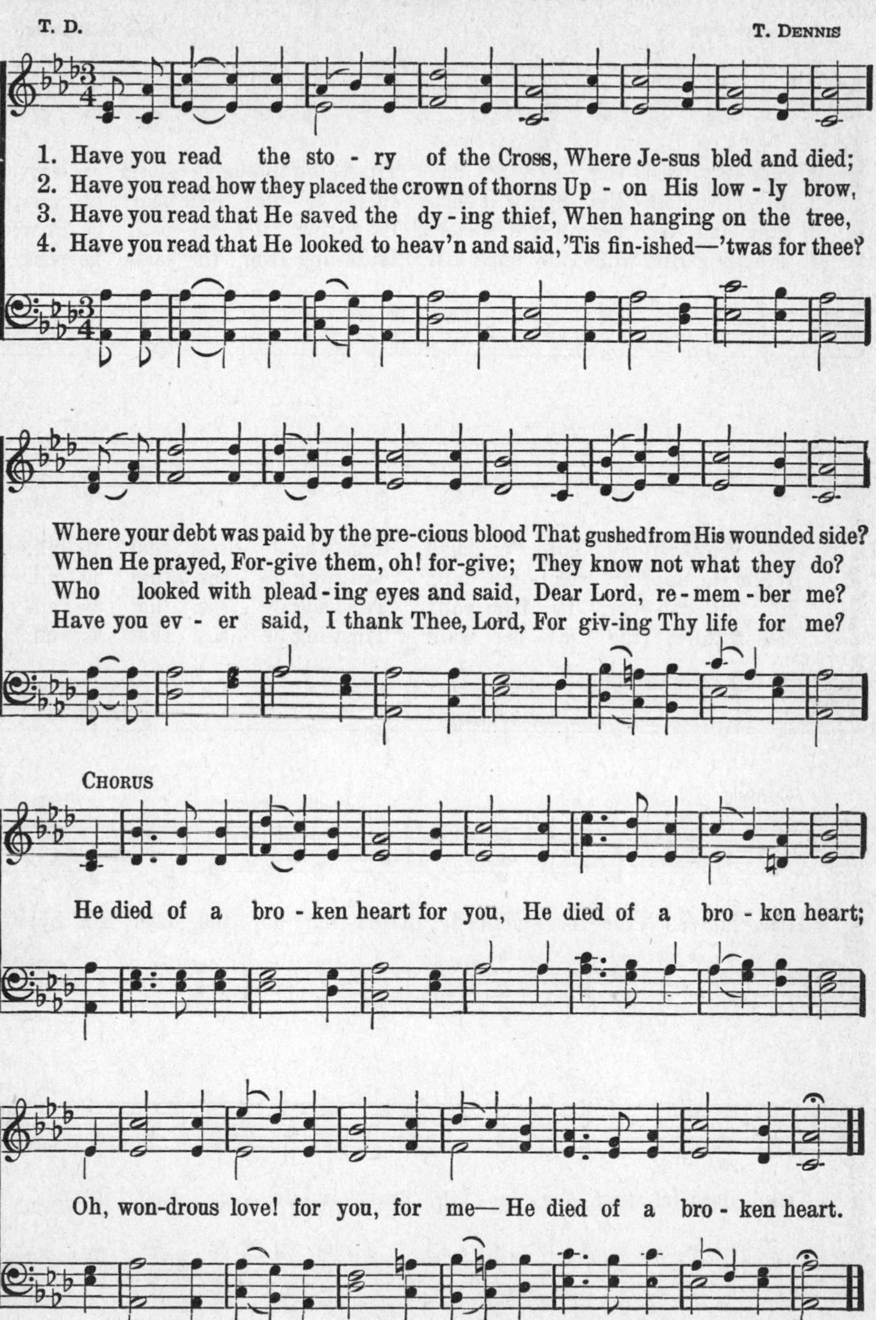
1. Have you read the sto - ry of the Cross, Where Je-sus bled and died;
2. Have you read how they placed the crown of thorns Up - on His low - ly brow,
3. Have you read that He saved the dy - ing thief, When hanging on the tree,
4. Have you read that He looked to heav'n and said, 'Tis fin-ished—'twas for thee?
Where your debt was paid by the pre-cious blood That gushed from His wounded side?
When He prayed, For-give them, oh! for-give; They know not what they do?
Who looked with plead - ing eyes and said, Dear Lord, re - mem - ber me?
Have you ev - er said, I thank Thee, Lord, For giv-ing Thy life for me?
CHORUS
He died of a bro - ken heart for you, He died of a bro - ken heart;
Oh, won-drous love! for you, for me— He died of a bro - ken heart.

122 Trusting Jesus

E. Page — Ira D. Sankey

1. Sim-ply trust-ing ev-'ry day, Trust-ing through a storm-y way;
2. Bright-ly doth His Spir-it shine In-to this poor heart of mine;
3. Sing-ing if my way is clear; Pray-ing if the path be drear;
4. Trust-ing Him while life shall last, Trust-ing Him till earth be past;
E-ven when my faith is small, Trust-ing Je-sus, that is all.
While He leads I can-not fall; Trust-ing Je-sus, that is all.
If in dan-ger, for Him call; Trust-ing Je-sus, that is all.
Till with-in the jas-per wall: Trust-ing Je-sus, that is all.
Chorus
Trust-ing as the mo-ments fly, Trust-ing as the days go by;
Trust-ing Him what-e'er be-fall, Trust-ing Je-sus, that is all.

Jesus Saves

PRISCILLA J. OWENS WM. J. KIRKPATRICK

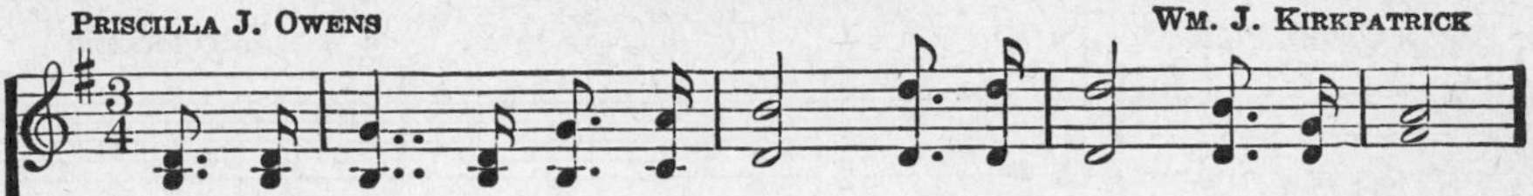

1. We have heard the joy - ful sound: Je - sus saves! Je - sus saves!
2. Waft it on the roll - ing tide; Je - sus saves! Je - sus saves!
3. Sing a - bove the bat - tle strife, Je - sus saves! Je - sus saves!
4. Give the winds a might - y voice, Je - sus saves! Je - sus saves!

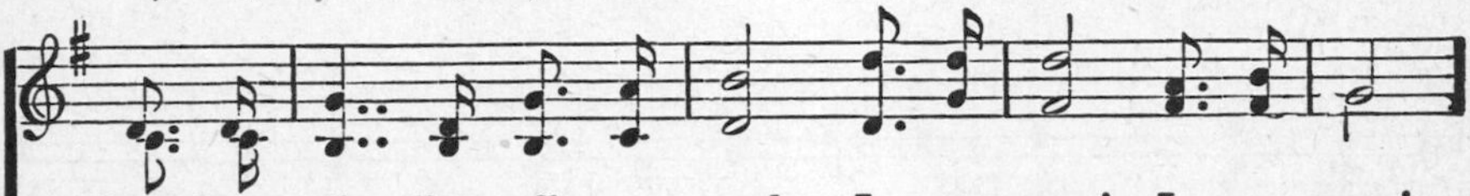

Spread the ti - dings all a - round: Je - sus saves! Je - sus saves!
Tell to sin - ners far and wide: Je - sus saves! Je - sus saves!
By His death and end - less life, Je - sus saves! Je - sus saves!
Let the na - tions now re - joice,— Je - sus saves! Je - sus saves!

Bear the news to ev - 'ry land, Climb the steeps and cross the waves;
Sing, ye is - lands of the sea; Ech - o back, ye o - cean caves;
Sing it soft - ly thro' the gloom, When the heart for mer - cy craves;
Shout sal - va - tion full and free; High - est hills and deep - est caves;

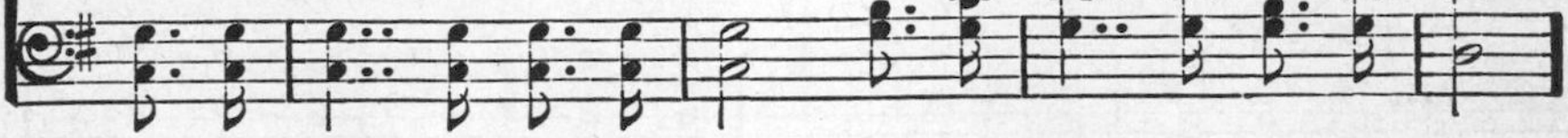

On - ward!—'tis our Lord's com - mand; Je - sus saves! Je - sus saves!
Earth shall keep her ju - bi - lee: Je - sus saves! Je - sus saves!
Sing in tri - umph o'er the tomb,— Je - sus saves! Je - sus saves!
This our song of vic - to - ry,— Je - sus saves! Je - sus saves!

Jesus, I Am Resting

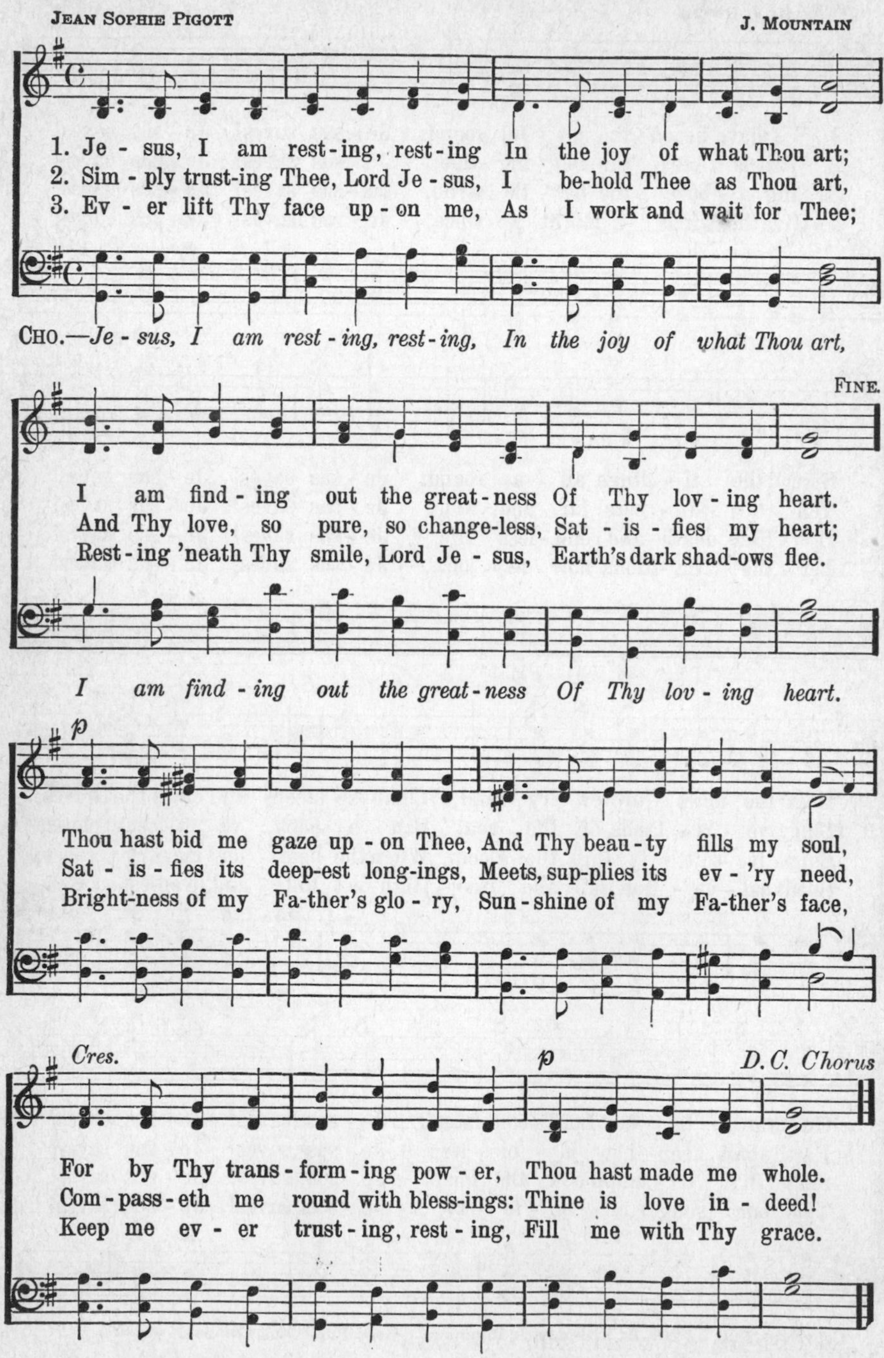
Jean Sophie Pigott
J. Mountain
1. Je - sus, I am rest - ing, rest - ing In the joy of what Thou art;
2. Sim - ply trust - ing Thee, Lord Je - sus, I be - hold Thee as Thou art,
3. Ev - er lift Thy face up - on me, As I work and wait for Thee;
Cho.—Je - sus, I am rest - ing, rest - ing, In the joy of what Thou art,
Fine.
I am find - ing out the great - ness Of Thy lov - ing heart.
And Thy love, so pure, so change - less, Sat - is - fies my heart;
Rest - ing 'neath Thy smile, Lord Je - sus, Earth's dark shad - ows flee.
I am find - ing out the great - ness Of Thy lov - ing heart.
p
Thou hast bid me gaze up - on Thee, And Thy beau - ty fills my soul,
Sat - is - fies its deep - est long - ings, Meets, sup - plies its ev - 'ry need,
Bright - ness of my Fa - ther's glo - ry, Sun - shine of my Fa - ther's face,
Cres.
p
D.C. Chorus
For by Thy trans - form - ing pow - er, Thou hast made me whole.
Com - pass - eth me round with bless - ings: Thine is love in - deed!
Keep me ev - er trust - ing, rest - ing, Fill me with Thy grace.

125 The Sun Will Shine!

P. R. PAUL RADER

1. All things work to-geth-er for good To them that love the Lord.
2. All things work to-geth-er for good To them that love the Lord.
3. All things work to-geth-er for good To them that love the Lord.
4. All things work to-geth-er for good To them that love the Lord.
No - ah's ark the flood with-stood: Our God has kept His word.
Mo - ses walked when wa-ters stood: Our God has kept His word.
Christ did all He said He would: Our God has kept His word.
Christ can win; He said He could: Our God has kept His word.
CHORUS
The sun will shine! . . . . . . The sun will shine! . . . . . Soon God's
The sun will shine!
The sun will shine!
rain-bow will ap-pear, The sun will shine! The sun will shine! The sun will
rit.
shine! . . . Turn your dark clouds in - to back-ground for God's rain - bow.

126 Redeemed

FANNY J. CROSBY — WM. J. KIRKPATRICK

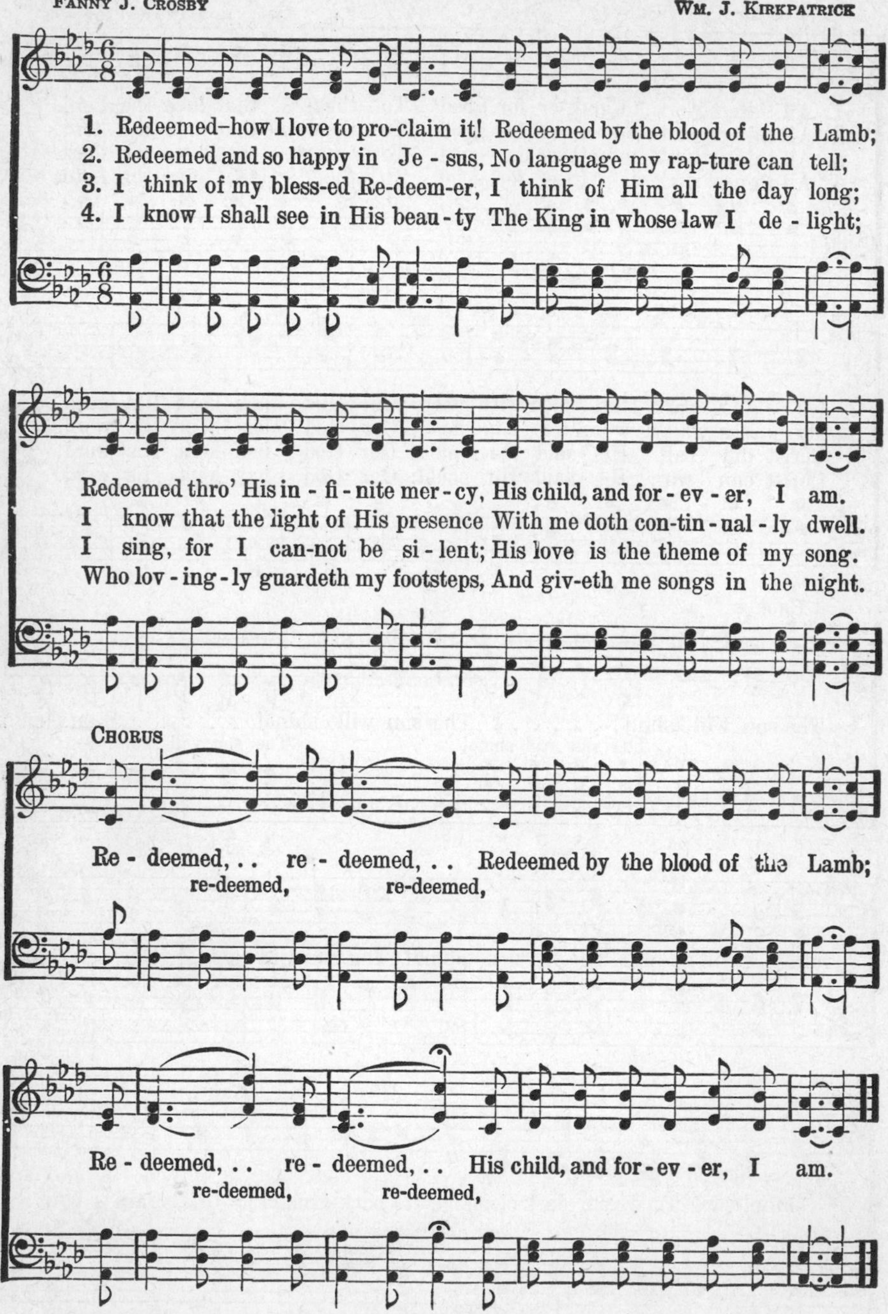

1. Redeemed—how I love to pro-claim it! Redeemed by the blood of the Lamb;
2. Redeemed and so happy in Je - sus, No language my rap-ture can tell;
3. I think of my bless-ed Re-deem-er, I think of Him all the day long;
4. I know I shall see in His beau - ty The King in whose law I de - light;
Redeemed thro' His in - fi - nite mer - cy, His child, and for - ev - er, I am.
I know that the light of His presence With me doth con-tin - ual - ly dwell.
I sing, for I can-not be si - lent; His love is the theme of my song.
Who lov - ing - ly guardeth my footsteps, And giv-eth me songs in the night.
CHORUS
Re - deemed, . . re - deemed, . . Redeemed by the blood of the Lamb;
re-deemed, re-deemed,
Re - deemed, . . re - deemed, . . His child, and for - ev - er, I am.
re-deemed, re-deemed,

127 I Believe It!

H. H. L. HELEN HOWARTH LEMMEL

Not too fast
1. I do not know how Ad-am's sin Lives on in you and me, Nor how it
2. I do not know how God could give Un - to a maid-en fair His Ho - ly
3. I do not know how God could lay My sins up - on His Son, Nor how, on
4. I do not know how God could call His Son from out the grave, Nor how that
5. I do not know how Je - sus' blood Can cleanse my heart from sin, Nor how, by
6. I do not know how one day He Can come to earth a - gain, Nor how like
caus-es all the wrong And sor-row that we see.
Son, in Bethl'hem born, His bed a man-ger bare.
Cal-v'ry's Cross, for me He per-fect par - don won.
way to me His ev - er - last-ing life He gave.
faith, in ev - 'ry fight The vic-t'ry I may win.
Him I shall be made, And ev - er with Him reign.
REFRAIN With decision
But I read it in God's
Word, and I be - lieve it—Yes, I be - lieve it, Ful - ly be - lieve it! I
Yes, I be - lieve it!
ff
read it in God's Word, and I be-lieve it— And that is all I need to do.
be - lieve it,

Softly and Tenderly

W. L. T. WILL L. THOMPSON

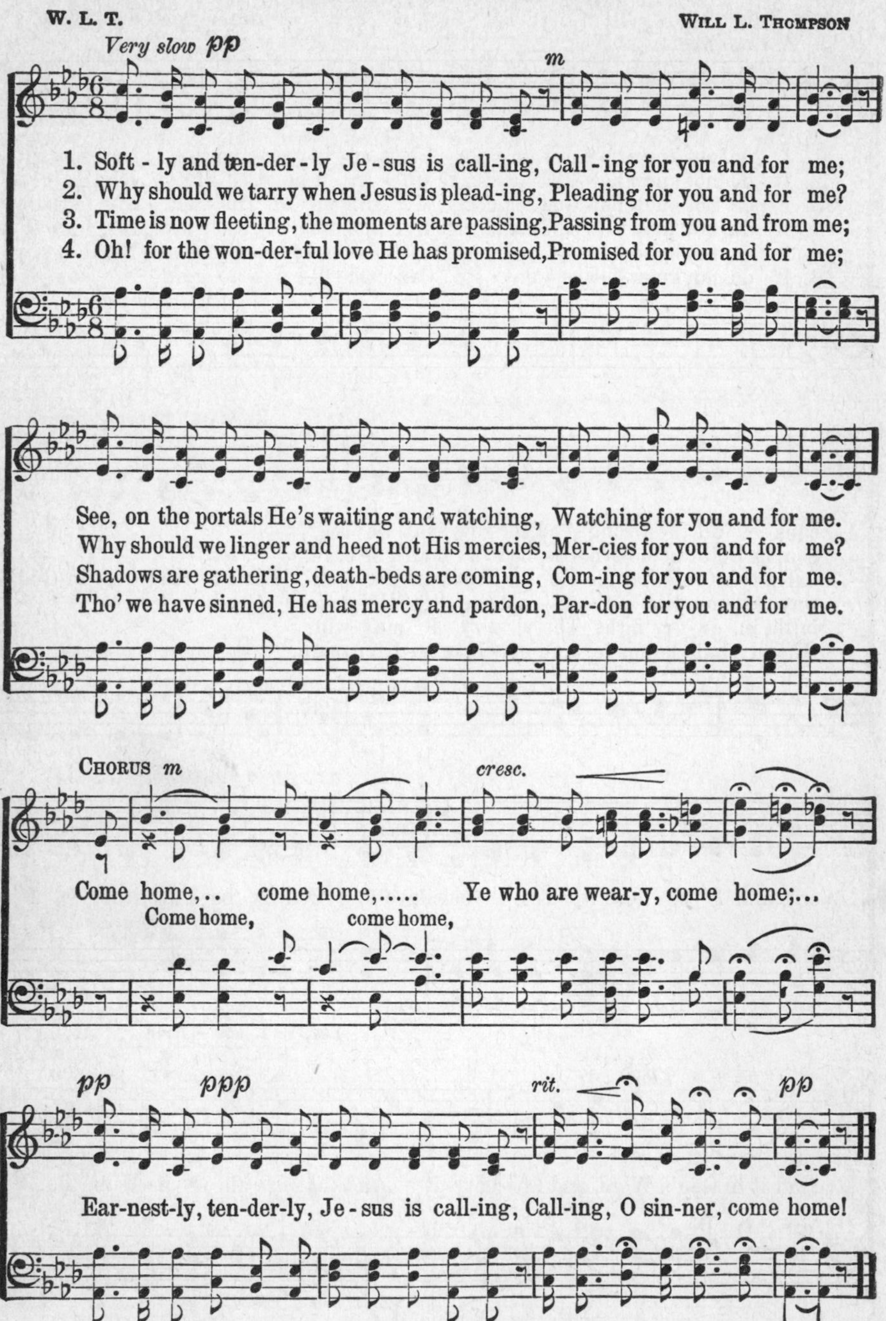
Very slow pp
m
1. Soft - ly and ten-der - ly Je - sus is call-ing, Call - ing for you and for me;
2. Why should we tarry when Jesus is plead-ing, Pleading for you and for me?
3. Time is now fleeting, the moments are passing, Passing from you and from me;
4. Oh! for the won-der-ful love He has promised, Promised for you and for me;
See, on the portals He's waiting and watching, Watching for you and for me.
Why should we linger and heed not His mercies, Mer-cies for you and for me?
Shadows are gathering, death-beds are coming, Com-ing for you and for me.
Tho' we have sinned, He has mercy and pardon, Par-don for you and for me.
CHORUS m
cresc.
Come home,.. come home,..... Ye who are wear-y, come home;...
Come home, come home,
pp ppp rit. pp
Ear-nest-ly, ten-der-ly, Je - sus is call-ing, Call-ing, O sin-ner, come home!

129 **Only a Sinner**

JAMES M. GRAY D. B. TOWNER

1. Naught have I got-ten but what I re-ceived; Grace hath be-stowed it since I have be-lieved; Boast-ing ex-clud-ed pride I a-base; I'm on-ly a
2. Once I was fool-ish, and sin ruled my heart, Caus-ing my foot-steps from God to de-part; Je-sus hath found me hap-py my case; I now am a
3. Tears un-a-vail-ing, no mer-it had I; Mer-cy had saved me, or else I must die; Sin had a-larmed me fear-ing God's face; But now I'm a
4. Suf-fer a sin-ner whose heart o-ver-flows, Lov-ing his Sav-ior to tell what he knows; Once more to tell it would I em-brace—I'm on-ly a
CHORUS
sin-ner saved by grace! On-ly a sin-ner saved by grace! On-ly a sin-ner saved by grace! This is my sto-ry, to God be the glo-ry,—I'm on-ly a sin-ner saved by grace!

130

In The Garden

C. A. M. C. Austin Miles

1. I come to the gar - den a - lone, While the dew is still on the
2. He speaks, and the sound of His voice Is so sweet the birds hush their
3. I'd stay in the gar - den with Him Tho' the night a - round me be
ros - es, And the voice I hear, Fall - ing on my ear, The
sing - ing, And the mel - o - dy That He gave to me, With-
fall - ing, But He bids me go; Thro' the voice of woe His
Son of God dis - clos - es.
in my heart is ring - ing.
voice to me is call - ing.
CHORUS
And He walks with me, and He
talks with me, And He tells me I am His own; And the
joy we share as we tar - ry there, None oth - er has ev - er known.

131 Tell It to Jesus

J. E. Rankin — E. S. Lorenz

1. Are you wea - ry, are you heav - y-heart - ed? Tell it to Je - sus,
2. Do the tears flow down your cheeks un-bid - den? Tell it to Je - sus,
3. Do you fear the gath-'ring clouds of sor - row? Tell it to Je - sus,
4. Are you troub - led at the thought of dy - ing? Tell it to Je - sus,
Tell it to Je - sus; Are you griev - ing o - ver joys de - part - ed?
Tell it to Je - sus; Have you sins that to men's eyes are hid - den?
Tell it to Je - sus; Are you anx - ious what shall be to - mor-row?
Tell it to Je - sus; For Christ's com-ing King-dom are you sigh-ing?
Chorus
Tell it to Je - sus a - lone. Tell it to Je - sus, tell it to Je - sus,
He is a friend that's well known; You've no oth - er
such a friend or broth - er, Tell it to Je - sus a - lone.

Sound the Battle Cry

W. F. S. — Wm. F. Sherwin

1. Sound the bat-tle cry! See, the foe is nigh; Raise the standard high For the Lord; Gird your ar-mor on, Stand firm, ev-'ry one; Rest your cause up-on His ho-ly Word.
2. Strong to meet the foe, Marching on we go, While our cause we know, Must pre-vail; Shield and banner bright, Gleam-ing in the light; Bat-tling for the right We ne'er can fail.
3. O Thou God of all, Hear us when we call, Help us one and all By Thy grace; When the bat-tle's done, And the vic-t'ry's won, May we wear the crown Be-fore Thy face.
CHORUS ff
Rouse, then, sol-diers, ral-ly round the ban-ner, Read-y, stead-y, pass the word a-long; On-ward, for-ward, shout a-loud Ho-san-na! Christ is Cap-tain of the might-y throng.

133 When the Shadows Flee Away

R. H. ROBERT HARKNESS

DUET

1. Some day I shall hear God's call of love, ... Call-ing to the land of end-less day; . . . . I shall then be with my Lord a - bove. . . .
2. Soon that dawn e - ter - nal shall ap - pear, ... When shall come the end of life's dark way; . . . . . . I shall be with loved ones I hold dear. . . .
3. Some day toil and care of life shall cease, ... In that land my Lord shall have full sway; . . . . Naught can mar its wondrous joy and peace. . . .
4. Tears and sighs for-ev - er o - ver - past, ... In that land il-lumined by His ray; . . . . Cloud of sin can nev-er o - ver - cast. . . .

Harmony

Some day! Some day! When the shadows flee a - way.

CHORUS

Some day when the shadows flee a - way, Sor-row shall be o'er, Care be known no more; Some day when the shadows flee away! Some day! Some day! When the shadows flee a-way.

134 The Child of a King

Hattie E. Buell | John B. Sumner

1. My Fa - ther is rich in hous - es and lands, He hold - eth the
2. My Fa - ther's own Son, the Sav - ior of men, Once wan-dered o'er
3. I once was an out - cast stran - ger on earth, A sin - ner by
4. A tent or a cot - tage, why should I care? They're build-ing a
wealth of the world in His hands! Of ru - bies and diamonds, of
earth as the poor - est of them; But now He is reign-ing for-
choice, and an al - ien by birth! But I've been a - dopt - ed, my
pal - ace for me o - ver there! Tho' ex - iled from home, yet
sil - ver and gold, His cof - fers are full,— He has rich-es un - told.
ev - er on high, And will give me a home in heav'n by and by.
name's written down,–An heir to a man - sion, a robe, and a crown.
still I may sing: All glo - ry to God, I'm the child of a King!
Chorus
I'm the child of a King, The child of a King!
ad lib.
With Je - sus, my Sav - ior, I'm the child of a King.

135 The Old Rugged Cross

G. B. — Geo. Bennard

1. On a hill far a-way stood an old rug-ged cross, The em-blem of
2. Oh, that old rug-ged cross so de-spised by the world, Has a wondrous at-
3. In the old rug-ged cross, stained with blood so di-vine, A won-drous
4. To the old rug-ged cross I will ev-er be true, Its shame and re-
suf-f'ring and shame; And I love that old cross where the dear-est and best
trac-tion for me; For the dear Lamb of God left His glo-ry a-bove,
beau-ty I see; For 'twas on that old cross Je-sus suf-fered and died,
proach gladly bear; Then He'll call me some day to my home far a-way,
For a world of lost sin-ners was slain.
To bear it to dark Cal-va-ry.
To par-don and sanc-ti-fy me.
Where His glo-ry for-ev-er I'll share.
CHORUS
So I'll cher-ish the old rug-ged
cross, the
cross, ... Till my tro-phies at last I lay down; I will cling to the
old rugged cross,
old rug-ged cross, ... And ex-change it some day for a crown.
cross, the old rug-ged cross,

136 I Am Praying for You

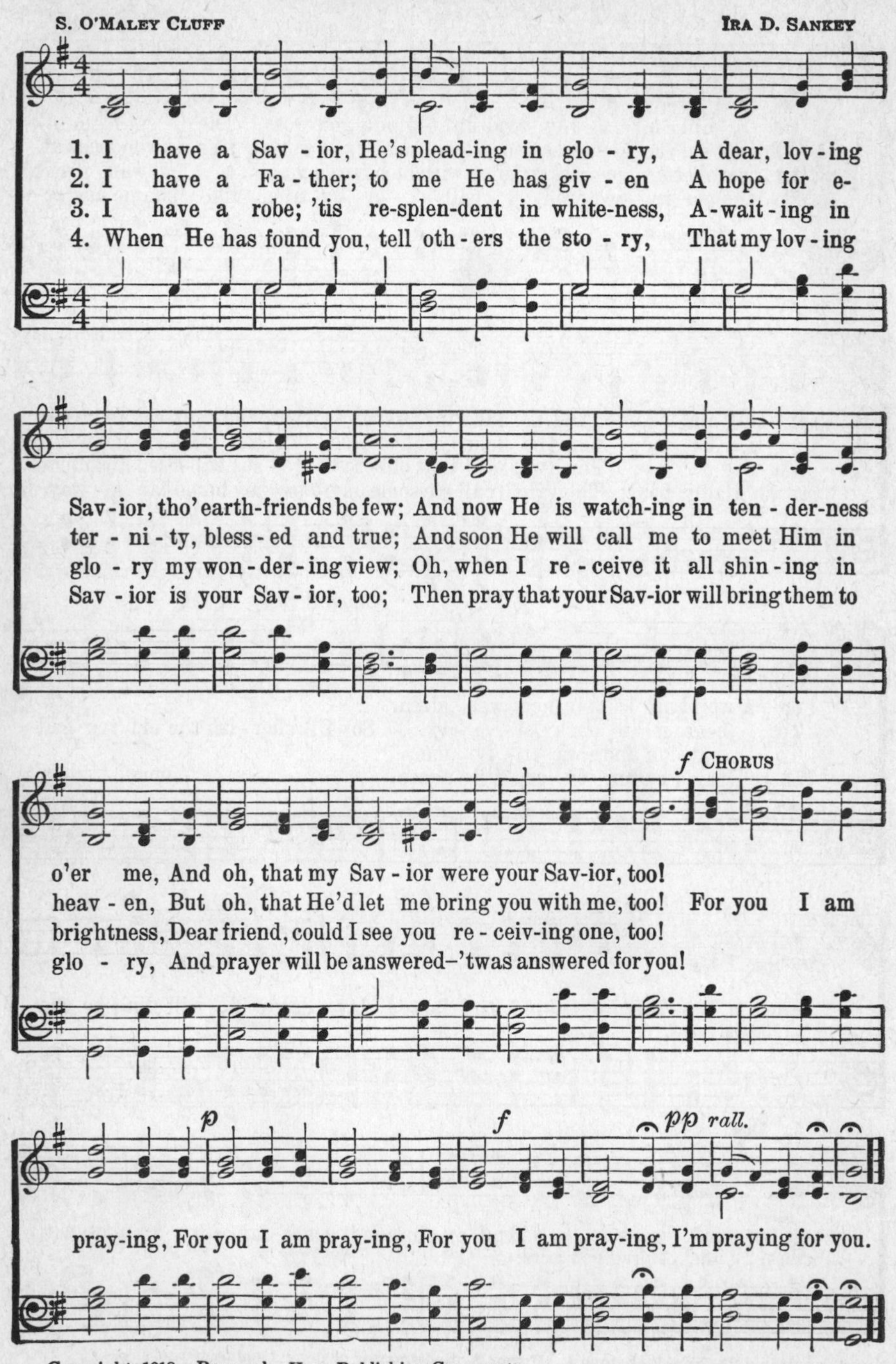
S. O'Maley Cluff
Ira D. Sankey
1. I have a Sav - ior, He's plead-ing in glo - ry, A dear, lov-ing
2. I have a Fa - ther; to me He has giv - en A hope for e-
3. I have a robe; 'tis re-splen-dent in white-ness, A-wait-ing in
4. When He has found you, tell oth - ers the sto - ry, That my lov-ing
Sav-ior, tho' earth-friends be few; And now He is watch-ing in ten - der-ness
ter - ni - ty, bless - ed and true; And soon He will call me to meet Him in
glo - ry my won - der - ing view; Oh, when I re - ceive it all shin - ing in
Sav - ior is your Sav - ior, too; Then pray that your Sav-ior will bring them to
f Chorus
o'er me, And oh, that my Sav - ior were your Sav-ior, too!
heav - en, But oh, that He'd let me bring you with me, too! For you I am
brightness, Dear friend, could I see you re - ceiv-ing one, too!
glo - ry, And prayer will be answered–'twas answered for you!
p
f
pp rall.
pray-ing, For you I am pray-ing, For you I am pray-ing, I'm praying for you.

137 Once for All

P. P. B. P. P. Bliss

1. Free from the law, O hap-py con-di-tion, Je-sus hath
2. Now are we free—there's no con-dem-na-tion, Je-sus pro-
3. "Chil-dren of God," O glo-ri-ous call-ing, Sure-ly His
bled, and there is re-mis-sion; Cursed by the law and bruised by the
vides a per-fect sal-va-tion; "Come un-to Me," O hear His sweet
grace will keep us from fall-ing; Pass-ing from death to life at His
fall, Grace hath redeemed us once for all.
call, Come, and He saves us once for all.
call, Bless-ed sal-va-tion once for all.
CHORUS
Once for all, O sin-ner, re-
ceive it, Once for all, O broth-er, be-lieve it; Cling to the
Cross, the bur-den will fall, Christ hath re-deemed us once for all.

138 One Day!

J. WILBUR CHAPMAN — CHAS. H. MARSH

1. One day when heav - en was filled with His prais - es, One day when sin was as black as could be,... Je - sus came forth to be born of a vir - gin—Dwelt amongst men, my ex - am - ple is He!...
2. One day they led Him up Cal - va - ry's moun - tain, One day they nailed Him to die on the tree;.. Suf - fer - ing an - guish, de - spised and re - ject - ed: Bear - ing our sins, my Re - deem - er is He!...
3. One day they left Him a - lone in the gar - den, One day He rest - ed, from suf - fer - ing free;.. An - gels came down o'er His tomb to keep vig - il; Hope of the hope - less, my Sav - ior is He!...
4. One day the grave could con - ceal Him no lon - ger, One day the stone rolled a - way from the door;. Then He a - rose, o - ver death He had con - quered; Now is as - cend - ed, my Lord ev - er - more!.
5. One day the trump - et will sound for His com - ing, One day the skies with His glo - ries will shine; Won - der - ful day, my be - lov - ed ones bring - ing; Glo - ri - ous Sav - ior, this Je - sus is mine!.

CHORUS

Liv - ing, He loved me; dy - ing, He saved me; Bur - ied, He car - ried my sins far a - way;.. Ris - ing, He jus - ti - fied

One Day!
cres.
rit.
free-ly for-ev-er: One day He's com-ing—oh, glo-ri-ous day!
139
What a Friend
Joseph Scriven
Charles C. Converse
1. What a Friend we have in Je-sus, All our sins and griefs to bear!
2. Have we tri-als and temp-ta-tions? Is there troub-le an-y-where?
3. Are we weak and heav-y-la-den, Cumbered with a load of care?—
What a priv-i-lege to car-ry Ev-'ry-thing to God in prayer!
We should nev-er be dis-cour-aged, Take it to the Lord in prayer.
Pre-cious Sav-ior, still our ref-uge,—Take it to the Lord in prayer.
O what peace we oft-en for-feit, O what need-less pain we bear,
Can we find a friend so faith-ful Who will all our sor-rows share?
Do thy friends despise, for-sake thee? Take it to the Lord in prayer;
All be-cause we do not car-ry Ev-'ry-thing to God in prayer!
Je-sus knows our ev-'ry weak-ness, Take it to the Lord in prayer.
In His arms He'll take and shield thee, Thou wilt find a sol-ace there.

140 I Would Be Like Jesus

James Rowe B. D. Ackley

1. Earth-ly pleas-ures vain-ly call me, I would be like Je - sus;
2. He has bro-ken ev - 'ry fet-ter, I would be like Je - sus;
3. All the way from earth to Glo-ry, I would be like Je - sus;
4. That in Heav-en He may meet me, I would be like Je - sus;
would be like Je-sus;
Noth-ing world-ly shall en-thrall me, I would be like Je - sus.
That my soul may serve Him bet-ter, I would be like Je - sus.
Tell-ing o'er and o'er the sto-ry, I would be like Je - sus.
That His words "Well done" may greet me, I would be like Je - sus.
would be like Je-sus.
Chorus.
Be like Je-sus, this my song, In the home and in the throng;
Be like Je-sus, all day long! I would be like Je-sus.

141 Oh, It Is Wonderful!

C. H. G.
Chas. H. Gabriel
1. I stand all amazed at the love Jesus offers me, Confused at the grace that so fully He proffers me; I tremble to know that for me He was crucified—That for me, a sinner, He suffered, He bled, and died.
2. I marvel that He would descend from His throne divine, To rescue a soul so rebellious and proud as mine; That He should extend His great love unto such as I; Sufficient to own, to redeem, and to justify.
3. I think of His hands pierced and bleeding to pay the debt! Such mercy, such love and devotion can I forget? No, no! I will praise and adore at the mercy-seat, Until at the glorified throne I kneel at His feet.
rit.
Chorus
rit.
Oh, it is wonderful that He should care for me, Enough to die for me! Oh, it is wonderful, wonderful to me!
wonderful!
a tempo
wonderful!

142 I Love to Tell the Story

CATHERINE HANKEY WILLIAM G. FISCHER

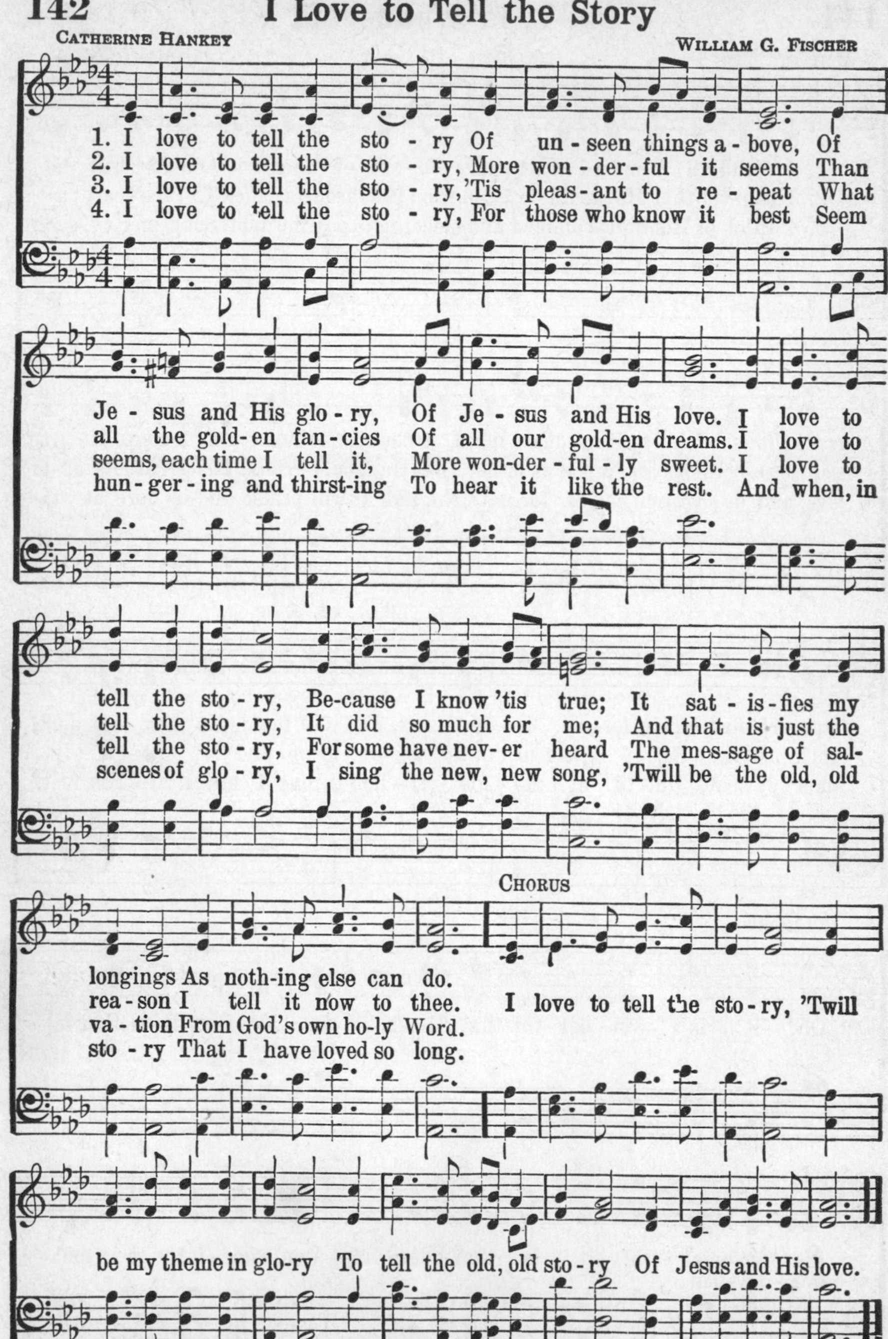
1. I love to tell the sto - ry Of un - seen things a - bove, Of
2. I love to tell the sto - ry, More won - der - ful it seems Than
3. I love to tell the sto - ry, 'Tis pleas - ant to re - peat What
4. I love to tell the sto - ry, For those who know it best Seem
Je - sus and His glo - ry, Of Je - sus and His love. I love to
all the gold - en fan - cies Of all our gold - en dreams. I love to
seems, each time I tell it, More won - der - ful - ly sweet. I love to
hun - ger - ing and thirst - ing To hear it like the rest. And when, in
tell the sto - ry, Be - cause I know 'tis true; It sat - is - fies my
tell the sto - ry, It did so much for me; And that is just the
tell the sto - ry, For some have nev - er heard The mes - sage of sal -
scenes of glo - ry, I sing the new, new song, 'Twill be the old, old
CHORUS
longings As noth - ing else can do.
rea - son I tell it now to thee. I love to tell the sto - ry, 'Twill
va - tion From God's own ho - ly Word.
sto - ry That I have loved so long.
be my theme in glo - ry To tell the old, old sto - ry Of Jesus and His love.

Used by permission of W. G. Fischer

143 The Haven of Rest

H. L. GILMOUR | GEO. D. MOORE

1. My soul in sad ex - ile was out on life's sea, So
2. I yield - ed my - self to His ten - der em - brace, And
3. The song of my soul, since the Lord made me whole, Has
4. How pre - cious the thought that we all may re - cline, Like
5. O come to the Sav - ior, He pa - tient - ly waits To
bur-dened with sin and dis - trest, Till I heard a sweet voice say-ing,
faith tak - ing hold of the Word, My fet - ters fell off, and I
been the old sto - ry so blest, Of Je - sus, who'll save who-so-
John the be - lov - ed and blest, On Je - sus' strong arm, where no
save by His pow - er di - vine; Come, an - chor your soul in the
D. S.—The tem - pest may sweep o'er the
FINE.
"Make me your choice;" And I en-tered the "Ha - ven of Rest!"
an - chored my soul; The "Ha-ven of Rest" is my Lord.
ev - er will have A home in the "Ha - ven of Rest!"
tem - pest can harm,— Se - cure in the "Ha - ven of Rest!"
"Ha - ven of Rest," And say, "My Be - lov - ed is mine."
wild, storm-y deep, In Je - sus I'm safe ev - er - more.
CHORUS
D. S.
I've anchored my soul in the "Ha-ven of Rest," I'll sail the wide seas no more;

144 What If It Were To-day?

Mrs. C. H. M. — Mrs. C. H. Morris

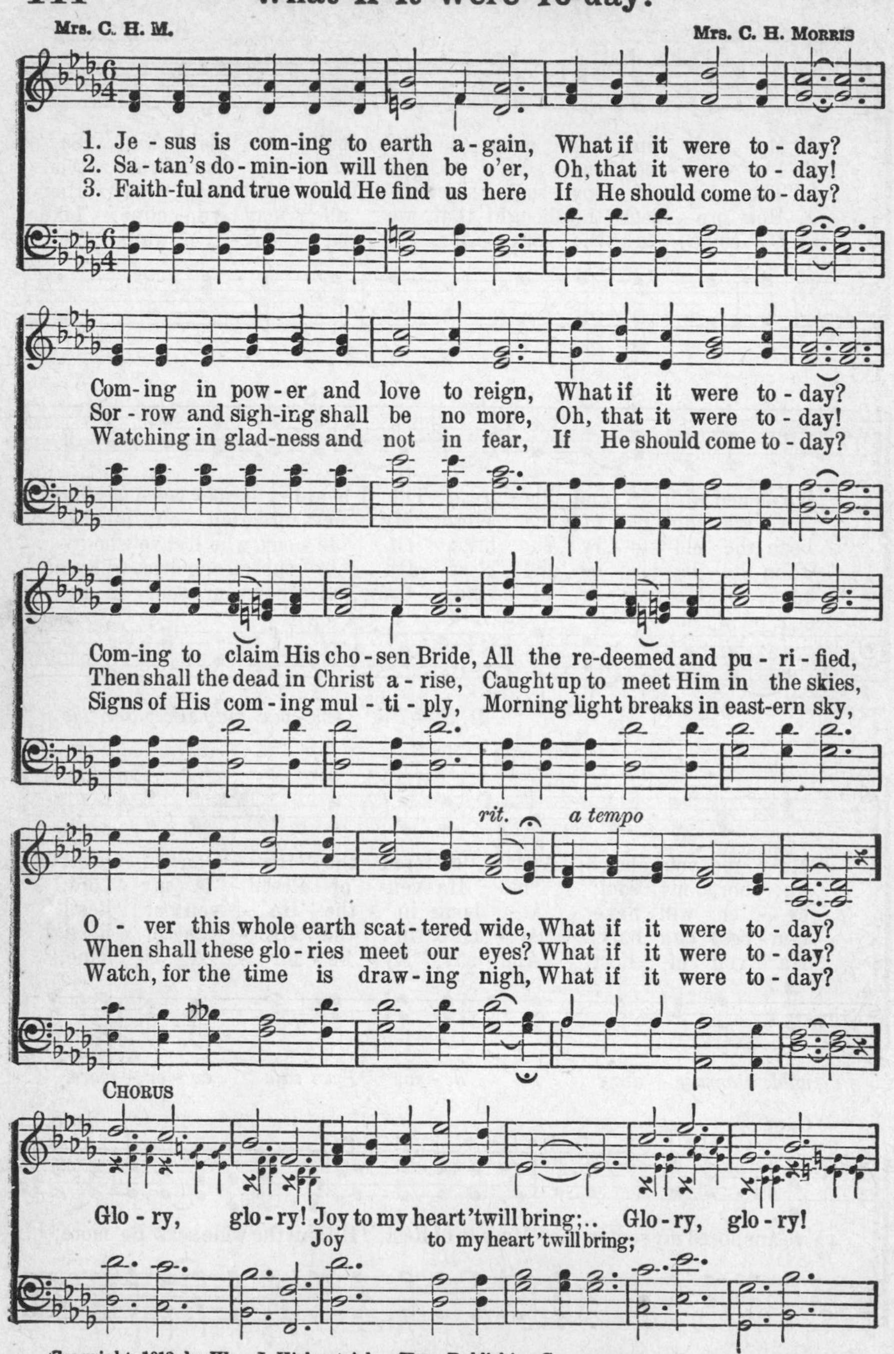
1. Je - sus is com-ing to earth a - gain, What if it were to - day?
2. Sa - tan's do - min-ion will then be o'er, Oh, that it were to - day!
3. Faith-ful and true would He find us here If He should come to - day?
Com-ing in pow-er and love to reign, What if it were to - day?
Sor - row and sigh-ing shall be no more, Oh, that it were to - day!
Watching in glad-ness and not in fear, If He should come to - day?
Com-ing to claim His cho - sen Bride, All the re-deemed and pu - ri - fied,
Then shall the dead in Christ a - rise, Caught up to meet Him in the skies,
Signs of His com - ing mul - ti - ply, Morning light breaks in east-ern sky,
rit.
a tempo
O - ver this whole earth scat - tered wide, What if it were to - day?
When shall these glo - ries meet our eyes? What if it were to - day?
Watch, for the time is draw - ing nigh, What if it were to - day?
Chorus
Glo - ry, glo - ry! Joy to my heart 'twill bring;.. Glo - ry, glo - ry!
Joy to my heart 'twill bring;

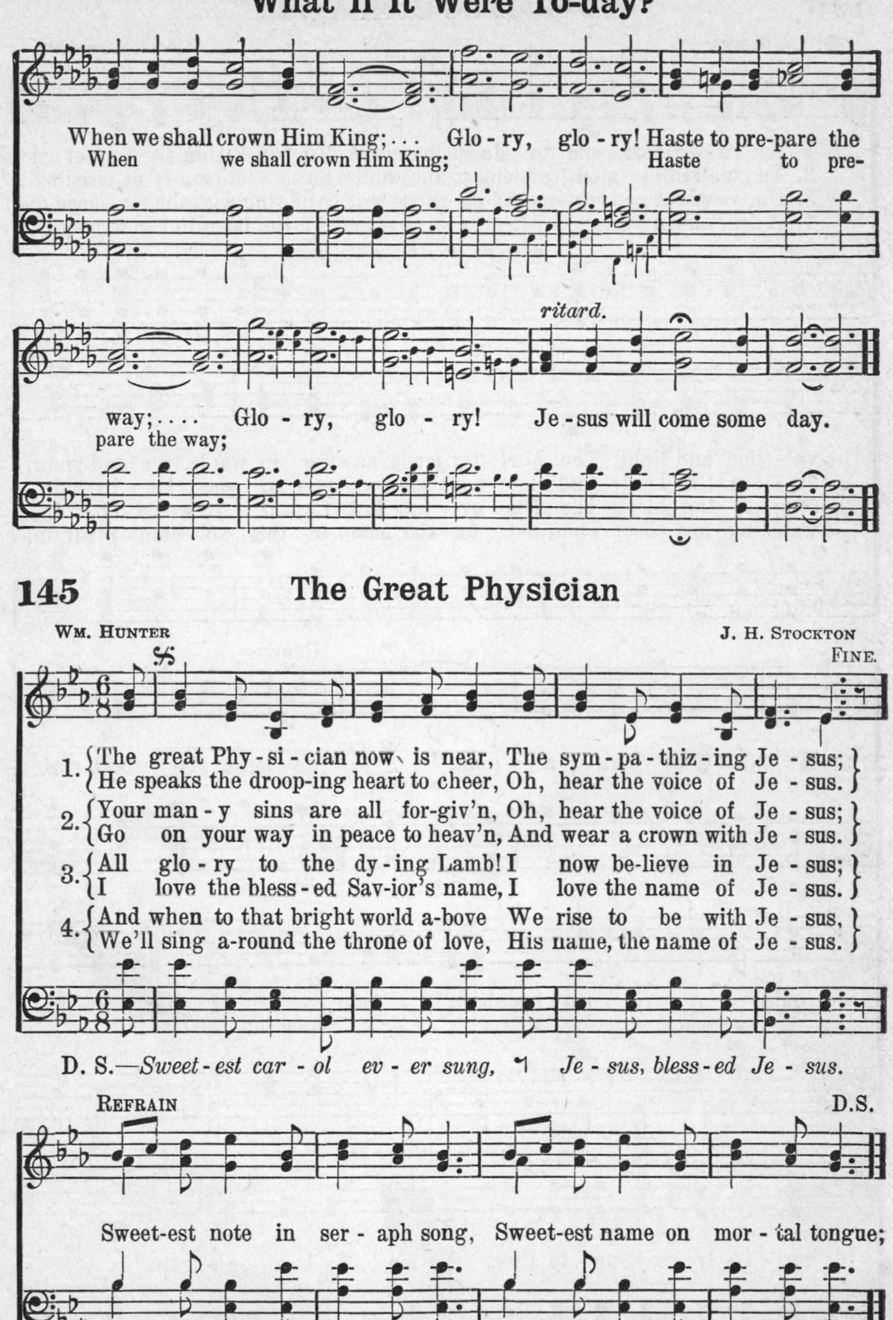

What If It Were To-day?
When we shall crown Him King; . . . Glo - ry, glo - ry! Haste to pre-pare the
When we shall crown Him King; Haste to pre-
ritard.
way; . . . . Glo - ry, glo - ry! Je - sus will come some day.
pare the way;
145 The Great Physician
Wm. Hunter
J. H. Stockton
Fine.
1. The great Phy - si - cian now is near, The sym - pa - thiz - ing Je - sus;
He speaks the droop-ing heart to cheer, Oh, hear the voice of Je - sus.
2. Your man - y sins are all for-giv'n, Oh, hear the voice of Je - sus;
Go on your way in peace to heav'n, And wear a crown with Je - sus.
3. All glo - ry to the dy - ing Lamb! I now be-lieve in Je - sus;
I love the bless - ed Sav-ior's name, I love the name of Je - sus.
4. And when to that bright world a-bove We rise to be with Je - sus,
We'll sing a-round the throne of love, His name, the name of Je - sus.
D. S.—Sweet - est car - ol ev - er sung, Je - sus, bless-ed Je - sus.
Refrain
D.S.
Sweet-est note in ser - aph song, Sweet-est name on mor - tal tongue;

146 Ye Must Be Born Again

W. T. SLEEPER GEO. C. STEBBINS

1 A ru - ler once came to Je - sus by night, To ask Him the way of sal
2. Ye children of men, at - tend to the word So sol - emn - ly ut - tered by
3. Oh, ye who would en - ter that glo - ri - ous rest, And sing with the ransomed the
4. A dear one in heaven thy heart yearns to see, At the beautiful gate may be
va - tion and light; The Mas - ter made an - swer in words true and plain,
Je - sus the Lord; And let not this mes - sage to you be in vain,
song of the blest; The life ev - er - last - ing if ye would ob - tain,
watching for thee; Then list to the note of this sol - emn re - frain,
CHORUS
"Ye must be born a - gain." . . "Ye must be born a-
a - gain.
gain, . . Ye must be born a - gain; . . I ver - i - ly,
a - gain,
a - gain;
ver - i - ly say un - to thee, Ye must be born a - gain." . . .
a - gain.

147 Saved By the Blood

S. J. HENDERSON — D. B. TOWNER

1. Saved by the blood of the Cru-ci-fied One! Now ran-somed from sin and a new work be-gun, Sing praise to the Fa-ther and praise to the Son, Saved by the blood of the Cru-ci-fied One!
2. Saved by the blood of the Cru-ci-fied One! The an-gels re-joic-ing be-cause it is done; A child of the Fa-ther, joint-heir with the Son, Saved by the blood of the Cru-ci-fied One!
3. Saved by the blood of the Cru-ci-fied One! The Fa-ther He spake, and His will it was done; Great price of my par-don, His own pre-cious Son; Saved by the blood of the Cru-ci-fied One!
4. Saved by the blood of the Cru-ci-fied One! All hail to the Fa-ther, all hail to the Son, All hail to the Spir-it, the great Three in One! Saved by the blood of the Cru-ci-fied One!
CHORUS
Saved! . . saved! . . My sins are all pardoned my guilt is all gone!
Glo-ry, I'm saved! glo-ry, I'm saved!
Saved! . . saved! . I am saved by the blood of the Cru-ci-fied One!
Glo-ry, I'm saved! glo-ry, I'm saved!

148 Wonderful Peace

H. L. | HALDOR LILLENAS

1. Com - ing to Je - sus, my Sav - ior, I found Won - der - ful peace, won - der - ful peace; Storms in their fu - ry may rage all a - round, I have peace, sweet peace.
2. Peace like a riv - er, so deep and so broad, Won - der - ful peace, won - der - ful peace; Rest - ing my soul on the bos - om of God, I have peace, sweet peace.
3. Peace like a ho - ly and in - fi - nite calm, Won - der - ful peace, won - der - ful peace; Like to the strains of an e - ven - ing psalm, I have peace, sweet peace.
4. Gone is the bat - tle that once raged with - in, Won - der - ful peace, won - der - ful peace; Je - sus has saved me and cleansed me from sin, I have peace, sweet peace.
REFRAIN
Peace, peace, won - der - ful peace,
Peace, peace, glo - ri - ous peace; Since my Re - deem - er has
ran - somed my soul, I have peace, sweet peace. . . . . . .
won - der - ful peace.

149 Wonderful Peace

W. D. Cornell. Alt. W. G. Cooper

1. Far a-way in the depths of my spir-it to-night Rolls a mel-o-dy sweet-er than psalm; In ce-les-tial-like strains it un-ceas-ing-ly falls O'er my soul like an in-fi-nite calm.
2. What a treas-ure I have in this won-der-ful peace, Bur-ied deep in the heart of my soul; So se-cure that no pow-er can mine it a-way, While the years of e-ter-ni-ty roll.
3. I am rest-ing to-night in this won-der-ful peace, Rest-ing sweet-ly in Je-sus' con-trol; For I'm kept from all dan-ger by night and by day, And His glo-ry is flood-ing my soul.
4. And me-thinks when I rise to that Cit-y of peace, Where the Au-thor of peace I shall see, That one strain of the song which the ran-somed will sing, In that heav-en-ly king-dom shall be:
5. Ah! soul, are you here with-out com-fort or rest, March-ing down the rough pathway of time? Make Je-sus your friend ere the shad-ows grow dark; Oh, ac-cept this sweet peace so sub-lime.

Chorus

Peace! peace! won-der-ful peace, Com-ing down from the Fa-ther a-bove; Sweep o-ver my spir-it for-ev-er, I pray, In fath-om-less bil-lows of love.

150 Jesus Leads

John R. Clements
Jno. R. Sweney
Andante
1. Like a shep-herd, ten-der, true, Je-sus leads,... Je-sus leads,...
2. All a-long life's rug-ged road Je-sus leads,... Je-sus leads,...
3. Thro' the sun-lit ways of life Je-sus leads,... Je-sus leads,...
Je-sus leads, Je-sus leads,
Dai-ly finds us pas-tures new, Je-sus leads,... Je-sus leads;
Till we reach yon blest a-bode, Je-sus leads,... Je-sus leads;
Thro' the warrings and the strife Je-sus leads,... Je-sus leads;
Je-sus leads, Je-sus leads;
If thick mists are o'er the way, Or the flock 'mid danger feeds,
All the way, be-fore, He's trod, And He now the flock precedes,
When we reach the Jordan's tide, Where life's bound'ry-line re-cedes,
If thick mists are o'er the way, Or the flock 'mid danger feeds,
rit.
He will watch them lest they stray, Je-sus leads,... Je-sus leads.
Safe in-to the fold of God, Je-sus leads,... Je-sus leads.
He will spread the waves a-side, Je-sus leads,... Je-sus leads.
Je-sus leads,

151 My Lord and I

Mrs. L. Shorey — Joseph D. Little

1. I have a Friend so pre - cious, So ver - y dear to me,
2. Some-times I'm faint and wea - ry, He knows that I am weak;
3. He knows how much I love Him, He knows I love Him well;
4. I tell Him all my sor - rows, I tell Him all my joys,
5. He knows how I am long - ing Some wea-ry soul to win,
He loves me with a ten - der love, He loves me faith - ful - ly;
And as He bids me lean on Him, His help I'll glad - ly seek;
But with what love He lov - eth me, My tongue can nev - er tell;
I tell Him all that pleas - es me, I tell Him what an - noys;
And so He bids me go and speak A lov - ing word for Him;
I could not live a - part from Him, I love to feel Him nigh;
He leads me in the path of light, Be-neath a sun - ny sky;
It is an ev - er - last - ing love In ev - er rich sup - ply;
He tells me what I ought to do, He tells me what to try;
He bids me tell His won-drous love, And why He came to die;
rit.
And so we dwell to - geth - er, My Lord and I.
And so we walk to - geth - er, My Lord and I.
And so we love to - geth - er, My Lord and I.
And so we talk to - geth - er, My Lord and I.
And so we work to - geth - er, My Lord and I.

152 You May Have the Joy-bells

J. Edw. Ruark — Wm. J. Kirkpatrick

1. You may have the joy-bells ring-ing in your heart, And a peace that from you nev-er will de-part; Walk the straight and nar-row way, Live for Je-sus ev-'ry day, He will keep the joy-bells ringing in your heart.
2. Love of Je-sus in its full-ness you may know, And this love to those a-round you sweet-ly show; Words of kind-ness al-ways say, Deeds of mer-cy do each day, Then He'll keep the joy-bells ringing in your heart.
3. You will meet with tri-als as you jour-ney home; Grace suf-fi-cient He will give to o-ver-come; Tho' un-seen by mor-tal eye, He is with you ev-er nigh, And He'll keep the joy-bells ringing in your heart.
4. Let your life speak well of Je-sus ev-'ry day; Own His right to ev-'ry serv-ice you can pay; Sin-ners you can help to win If your life is pure and clean, And you keep the joy-bells ringing in your heart.
FINE
Chorus
Joy - - - bells ring-ing in your heart, Joy - - - - bells
Ring-ing in your heart, You may have the joy-bells
ringing in your heart; Take the Sav-ior here below With you ev'rywhere you go;
D. S.—He will keep the joy-bells ring-ing in your heart.
D.S.

153 Moment By Moment

D. W. Whittle — May Whittle Moody

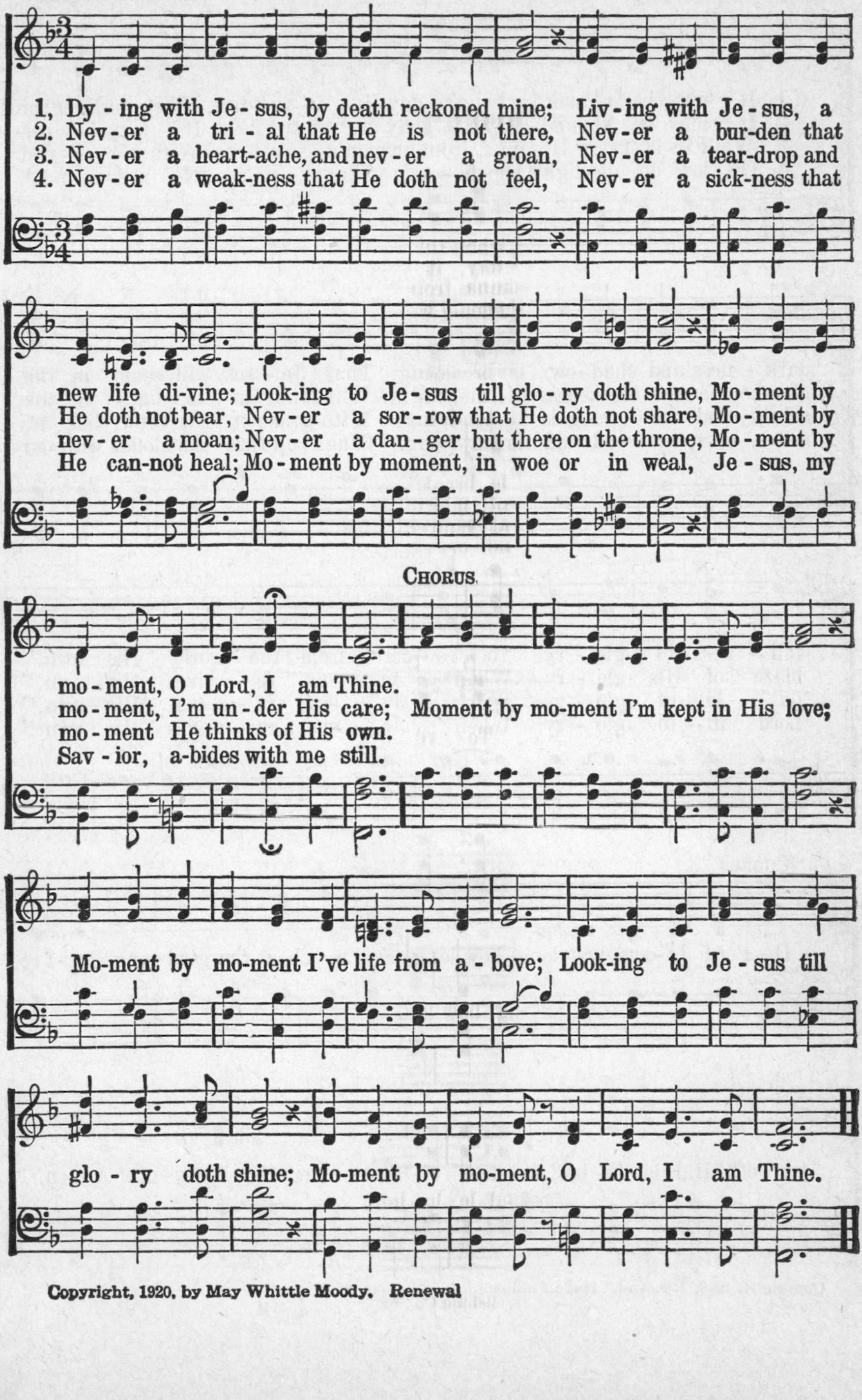

1, Dy - ing with Je - sus, by death reckoned mine; Liv - ing with Je - sus, a
2. Nev - er a tri - al that He is not there, Nev - er a bur-den that
3. Nev - er a heart-ache, and nev - er a groan, Nev - er a tear-drop and
4. Nev - er a weak-ness that He doth not feel, Nev - er a sick-ness that

new life di-vine; Look-ing to Je - sus till glo - ry doth shine, Mo - ment by
He doth not bear, Nev - er a sor - row that He doth not share, Mo - ment by
nev - er a moan; Nev - er a dan - ger but there on the throne, Mo - ment by
He can-not heal; Mo - ment by moment, in woe or in weal, Je - sus, my

CHORUS.

mo - ment, O Lord, I am Thine.
mo - ment, I'm un - der His care; Moment by mo-ment I'm kept in His love;
mo - ment He thinks of His own.
Sav - ior, a-bides with me still.

Mo-ment by mo-ment I've life from a - bove; Look-ing to Je - sus till

glo - ry doth shine; Mo-ment by mo-ment, O Lord, I am Thine.

154 Christ Returneth

H. L. TURNER

JAMES MCGRANAHAN

1. It may be at morn, when the day is a - wak-ing, When sunlight thro'
2. It may be at mid - day, it may be at twi-light, It may be, per-
3. While its hosts cry Hosanna, from heaven de-scend-ing, With glo - ri - fied
4. Oh, joy! oh, de - light! should we go with-out dy - ing, No sick-ness, no
dark - ness and shad - ow is break-ing, That Je - sus will come in the
chance, that the black-ness of mid-night Will burst in - to light in the
saints and the an - gels at - tend-ing, With grace on His brow, like a
sad - ness, no dread and no cry - ing, Caught up thro' the clouds with our
full - ness of glo - ry, To re - ceive from the world "His own."
blaze of His glo - ry, When Je - sus re - ceives "His own."
ha - lo of glo - ry, Will Je - sus re - ceive "His own."
Lord in - to glo - ry, When Je - sus re - ceives "His own."
CHORUS
O Lord Je - sus, how long, how long Ere we shout the glad song, Christ re-
rit.
turn-eth! Hal - le - lu - jah! hal - le - lu - jah! A - men, Hal - le - lu - jah! A-men.

155 I Love My Savior Dear

J. N. JAMES NEILSON

1. Je - sus, the name high o - ver all, Name that I love so
2. Fair-er than lil - ies of the field, Bright-er than morn - ing

well, ... He saved my soul and He made me whole, And with Him I'll
star, ... He sent His light to make my path bright, When I came to

ev - er dwell. . . . .
Him from a - far. . . . . .

CHORUS

I love my Sav - ior dear, . . .

I love my Sav - ior dear, ... When I think of the love that

brought Him from a - bove, I love Him, my Sav - ior dear. . . . .

156 My Savior's Love

C. H. G. — Chas. H Gabriel

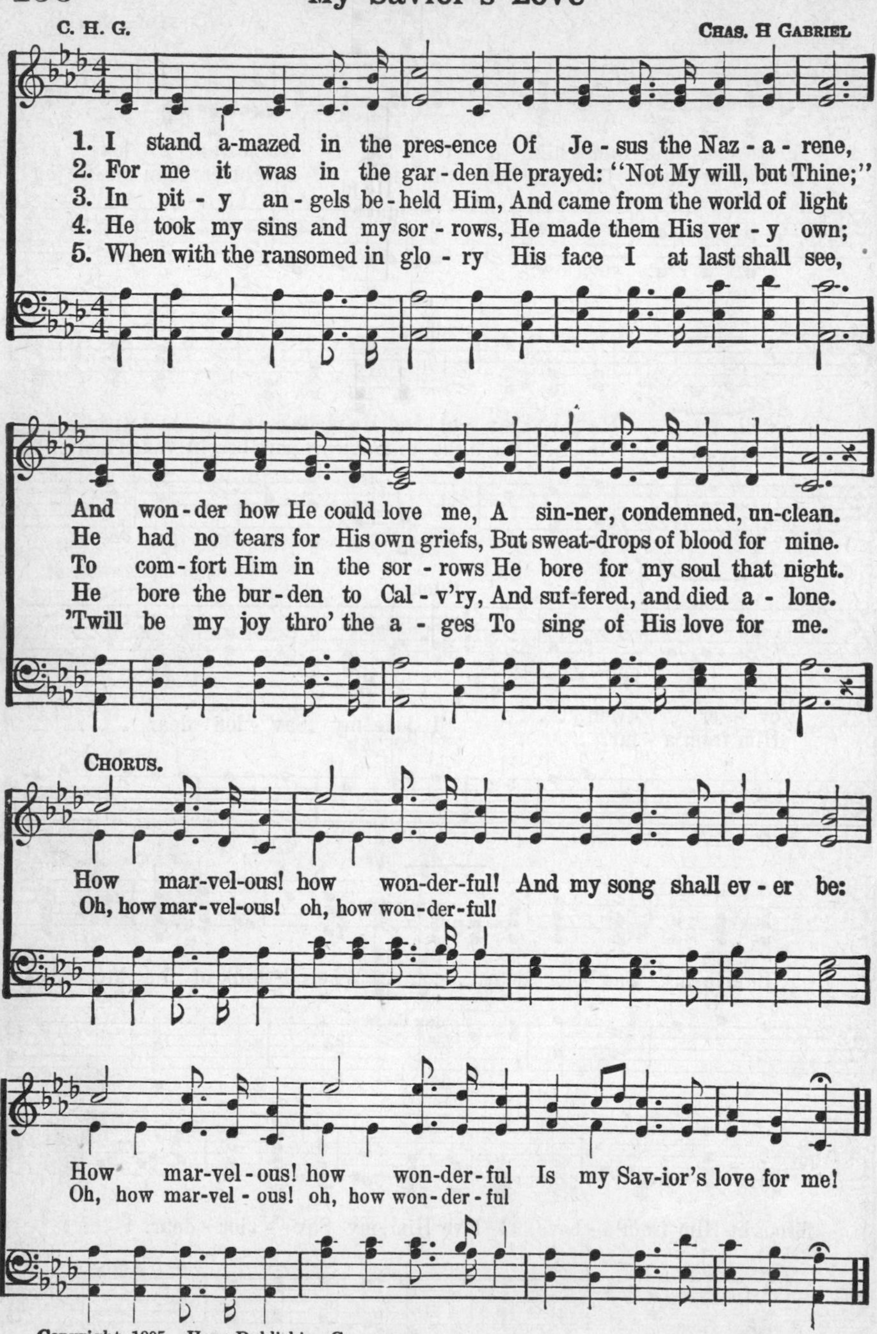
1. I stand a-mazed in the pres-ence Of Je-sus the Naz-a-rene,
2. For me it was in the gar-den He prayed: "Not My will, but Thine;"
3. In pit-y an-gels be-held Him, And came from the world of light
4. He took my sins and my sor-rows, He made them His ver-y own;
5. When with the ransomed in glo-ry His face I at last shall see,
And won-der how He could love me, A sin-ner, condemned, un-clean.
He had no tears for His own griefs, But sweat-drops of blood for mine.
To com-fort Him in the sor-rows He bore for my soul that night.
He bore the bur-den to Cal-v'ry, And suf-fered, and died a-lone.
'Twill be my joy thro' the a-ges To sing of His love for me.
Chorus.
How mar-vel-ous! how won-der-ful! And my song shall ev-er be:
Oh, how mar-vel-ous! oh, how won-der-ful!
How mar-vel-ous! how won-der-ful Is my Sav-ior's love for me!
Oh, how mar-vel-ous! oh, how won-der-ful

157 Give Me Jesus

FANNY J. CROSBY | JNO. R. SWENEY

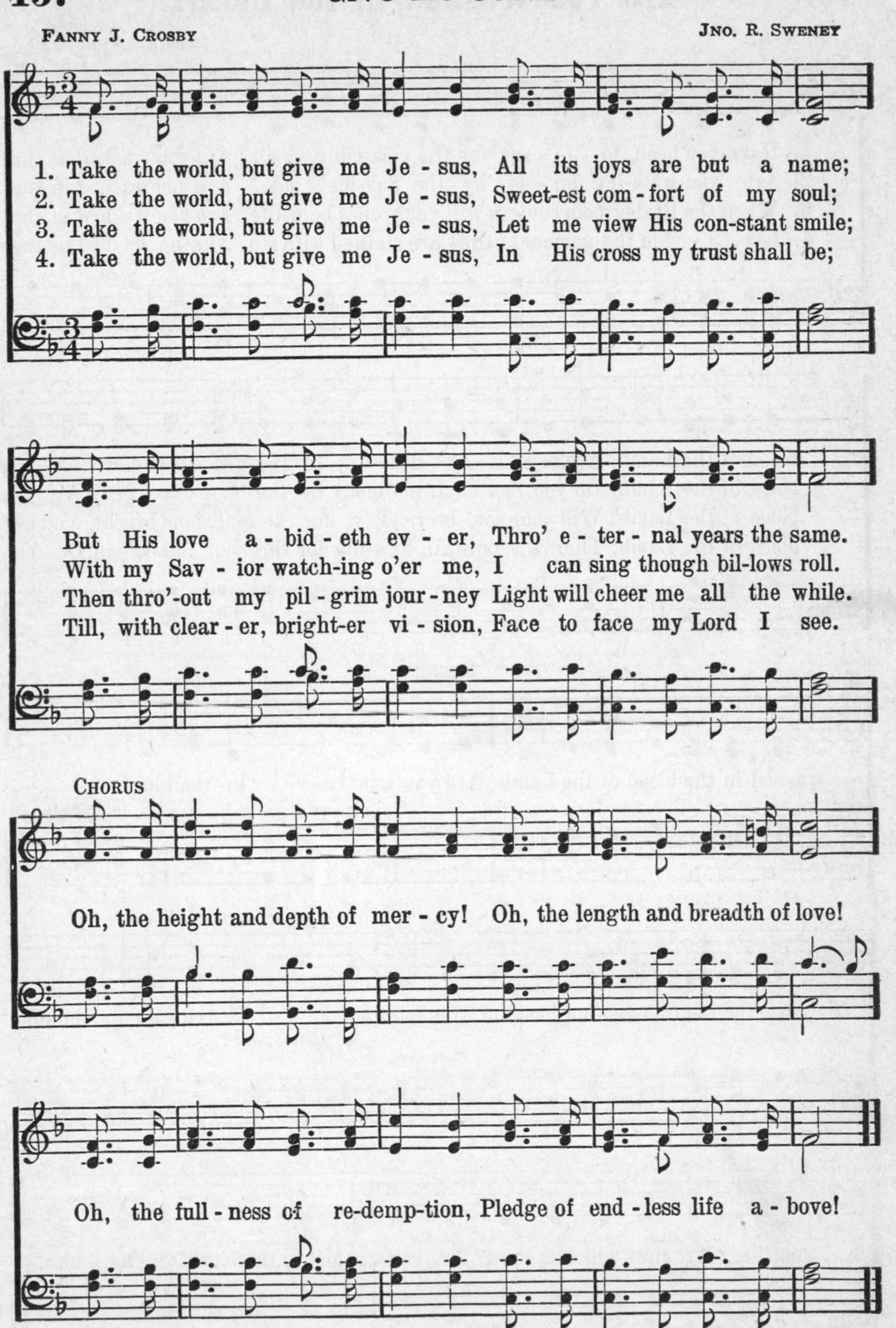
1. Take the world, but give me Je - sus, All its joys are but a name;
2. Take the world, but give me Je - sus, Sweet-est com - fort of my soul;
3. Take the world, but give me Je - sus, Let me view His con-stant smile;
4. Take the world, but give me Je - sus, In His cross my trust shall be;
But His love a - bid - eth ev - er, Thro' e - ter - nal years the same.
With my Sav - ior watch-ing o'er me, I can sing though bil-lows roll.
Then thro'-out my pil - grim jour - ney Light will cheer me all the while.
Till, with clear - er, bright-er vi - sion, Face to face my Lord I see.
CHORUS
Oh, the height and depth of mer - cy! Oh, the length and breadth of love!
Oh, the full - ness of re-demp-tion, Pledge of end - less life a - bove!

158 Are You Washed In the Blood?

E. A. H. — Elisha A. Hoffman

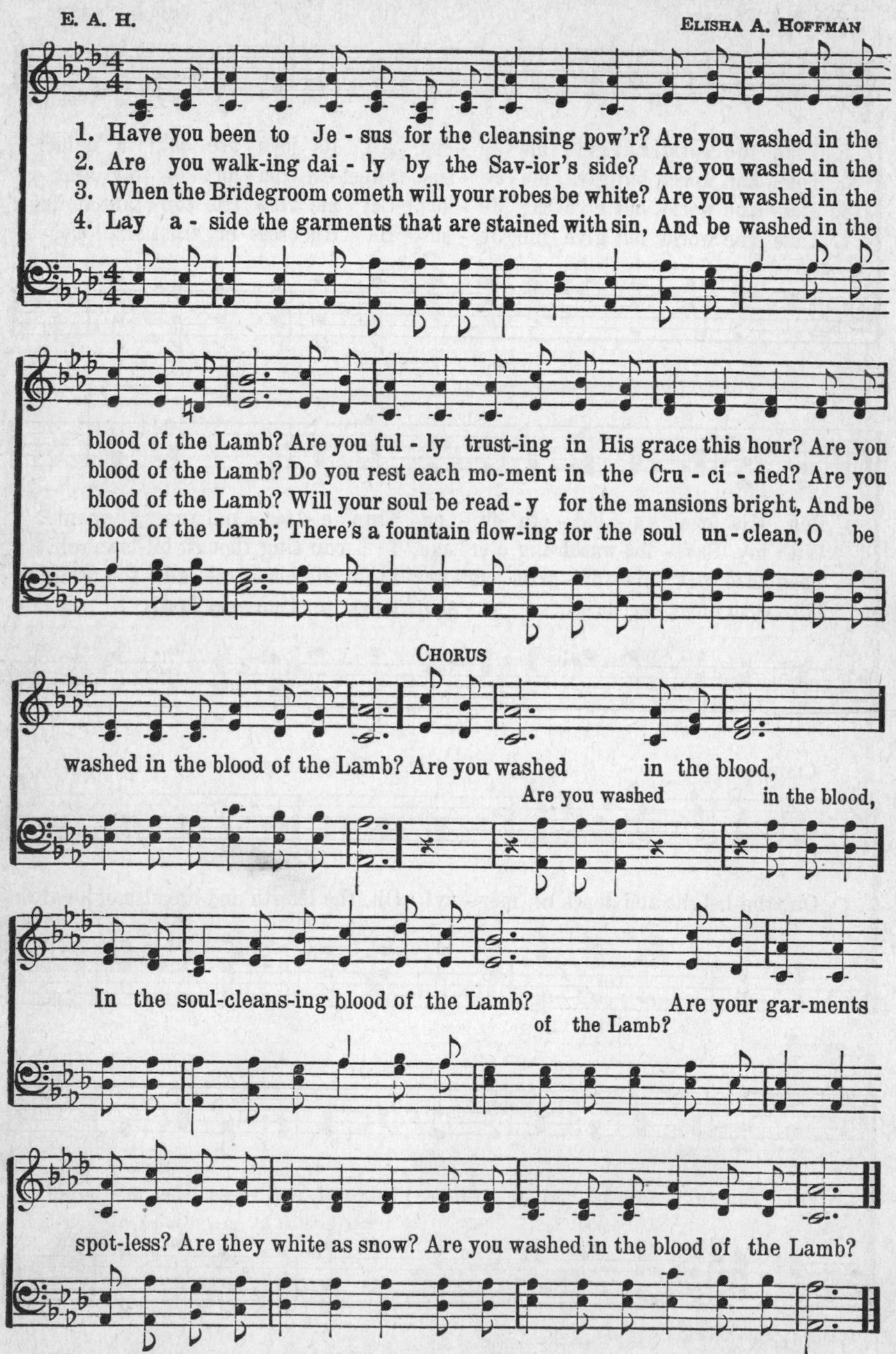
1. Have you been to Je - sus for the cleansing pow'r? Are you washed in the blood of the Lamb? Are you ful - ly trust-ing in His grace this hour? Are you washed in the blood of the Lamb?
2. Are you walk-ing dai - ly by the Sav-ior's side? Are you washed in the blood of the Lamb? Do you rest each mo-ment in the Cru - ci - fied? Are you
3. When the Bridegroom cometh will your robes be white? Are you washed in the blood of the Lamb? Will your soul be read - y for the mansions bright, And be
4. Lay a - side the garments that are stained with sin, And be washed in the blood of the Lamb; There's a fountain flow-ing for the soul un - clean, O be
Chorus
Are you washed in the blood,
Are you washed in the blood,
In the soul-cleans-ing blood of the Lamb?
of the Lamb?
Are your gar-ments spot-less? Are they white as snow? Are you washed in the blood of the Lamb?

159 Verily, Verily

G. M. J.
JAMES McGRANAHAN
1. Oh, what a Sav - ior, that He died for me! From con - dem-
2. All my in - iq - ui - ties on Him were laid, All my in-
3. Though poor and need - y I can trust my Lord, Though weak and
4. Though all un - wor - thy, yet I will not doubt, For him that
na - tion He hath made me free; "He that be - liev - eth on the
debt - ed - ness by Him was paid; All who be-lieve on Him, the
sin - ful I be - lieve His Word; Oh, glad mes-sage! ev - 'ry
com - eth, He will not cast out; "He that be - liev-eth," oh, the
Son," saith He, "Hath ev - er - last - ing life."
Lord hath said, "Hath ev - er - last - ing life."
child of God "Hath ev - er - last - ing life."
good news shout, "Hath ev - er - last - ing life!"
CHORUS
"Ver - i - ly, ver - i - ly,
I say un - to you," "Ver - i - ly, ver - i - ly," mes-sage ev - er new;
"He that be - liev-eth on the Son," 'tis true, "Hath ev - er - last - ing life"

Stepping In the Light

E. E. HEWITT WM. J. KIRKPATRICK

1. Try-ing to walk in the steps of the Sav-ior, Try-ing to fol-low our
2. Press-ing more close-ly to Him who is lead-ing, When we are tempted to
3. Walk-ing in foot-steps of gen-tle for-bear-ance, Foot-steps of faith-ful-ness,
4. Try-ing to walk in the steps of the Sav-ior, Up-ward, still upward we'll
Sav-ior and King; Shap-ing our lives by His bless-ed ex-am-ple,
turn from the way; Trust-ing the arm that is strong to de-fend us,
mer-cy and love, Look-ing to Him for the grace free-ly prom-ised,
fol-low our Guide; When we shall see Him, "the King in His beau-ty,"
Hap-py, how hap-py, the songs that we bring.
Hap-py, how hap-py, our prais-es each day.
Hap-py, how hap-py, our jour-ney a-bove.
Hap-py, how hap-py, our place at His side.
CHORUS
How beau-ti-ful to walk in the steps of the Sav-ior, Stepping in the light, Step-ping in the light; How beau-ti-ful to walk in the steps of the Sav-ior, Led in paths of light.

161 When Jesus the Savior Comes In

E. J. SHEETS

W. R. COLE

1. Do you need one to help you to bat-tle with sin? Do you seek for a vic-t'ry o'er doubts from within? Do you know that new life in your soul will be-gin, When Je-sus the Sav-ior comes in.
2. Do you need a com-pan-ion to walk by your side, Thro' the world and its e-vils your footsteps to guide? There's a Friend and a Brother, who e'er will abide
3. Do you want to be use-ful to God ev-'ry day? Do you want to win those who have gone far astray? Let His love be your mo-tive, His will be your way,
CHORUS
When Je-sus the Sav-ior comes in, . . . comes in, When Je-sus the Sav-ior comes in, From your sins you are free, a new crea-ture to be, When Je-sus the Sav-ior comes in.
rit.

162 No Night There

JOHN R. CLEMENTS | H. P. DANKS

1. In the land of fade-less day Lies the "cit-y four-square,"
2. All the gates of pearl are made, In the "cit-y four-square,"
3. And the gates shall nev-er close To the "cit-y four-square,"
4. There they need no sun-shine bright, In that "cit-y four-square,"
It shall nev-er pass a-way, And there is "no night there."
All the streets with gold are laid, And there is "no night there."
There life's crys-tal riv-er flows, And there is "no night there."
For the Lamb is all the light, And there is "no night there."
CHORUS
mf
God shall "wipe a-way all tears;" There's no death, no pain, nor fears;
God shall "wipe a - way all tears;" There's no death, no pain, nor fears;
f
dim.
mf
And they count not time by years, For there is "no night there."
And they count not time by years, by years, For there is "no night..... there."

163 Jesus is All the World to Me

W. L. T. WILL L. THOMPSON

1. Je - sus is all the world to me, My life, my joy, my all;
2. Je - sus is all the world to me, My Friend in tri - als sore;
3. Je - sus is all the world to me, And true to Him I'll be;
4. Je - sus is all the world to me, I want no bet - ter friend;
He is my strength from day to day, With - out Him I would fall.
I go to Him for bless-ings, and He gives them o'er and o'er.
Oh, how could I this Friend de - ny, When He's so true to me?
I trust Him now, I'll trust Him when Life's fleet - ing days shall end.
When I am sad, to Him I go, No oth - er one can
He sends the sun - shine and the rain, He sends the har - vest's
Fol - low - ing Him I know I'm right, He watch - es o'er me
Beau - ti - ful life with such a Friend; Beau - ti - ful life that
cheer me so; When I am sad He makes me glad, He's my Friend.
gold - en grain; Sun-shine and rain, har - vest of grain, He's my Friend.
day and night; Fol - low - ing Him, by day and night, He's my Friend.
has no end; E - ter - nal life, e - ter - nal joy, He's my Friend.
f
pp

164 Standing On the Promises

R. K. C. R. Kelso Carter

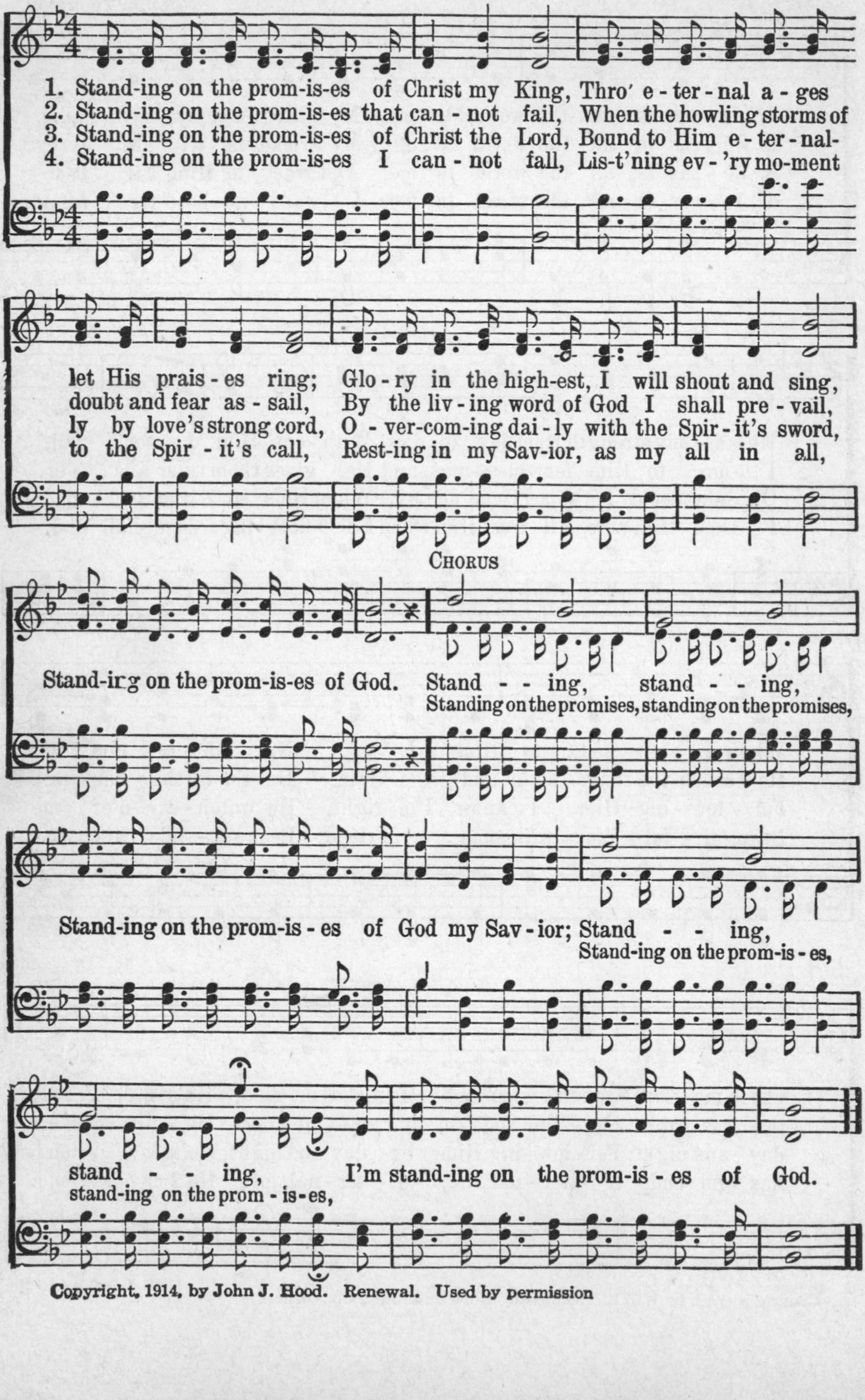

1. Stand-ing on the prom-is-es of Christ my King, Thro' e-ter-nal a-ges
2. Stand-ing on the prom-is-es that can-not fail, When the howling storms of
3. Stand-ing on the prom-is-es of Christ the Lord, Bound to Him e-ter-nal-
4. Stand-ing on the prom-is-es I can-not fall, Lis-t'ning ev-'ry mo-ment

let His prais-es ring; Glo-ry in the high-est, I will shout and sing,
doubt and fear as-sail, By the liv-ing word of God I shall pre-vail,
ly by love's strong cord, O-ver-com-ing dai-ly with the Spir-it's sword,
to the Spir-it's call, Rest-ing in my Sav-ior, as my all in all,

Stand-ing on the prom-is-es of God.

CHORUS

Stand-ing, stand-ing,
Standing on the promises, standing on the promises,

Stand-ing on the prom-is-es of God my Sav-ior; Stand-ing,
Stand-ing on the prom-is-es,

stand-ing, I'm stand-ing on the prom-is-es of God.
stand-ing on the prom-is-es,

165 No Longer Lonely

R. H. ROBERT HARKNESS

1. On life's pathway I am nev-er lone-ly, My Lord is with me, my Lord di-vine; Ev-er pre-sent Guide, I trust Him on-ly, No lon-ger lone-ly, for He is mine. .
2. I shall not be lone-ly in my sor-row, He will sus-tain me un-til the end; Dark-est night He turns to brightest mor-row, No lon-ger lone-ly! He is my Friend.
3. I shall not be lone-ly in the val-ley, Tho' shadows gath-er, I will not fear; He has prom-ised ev-er to up-hold me, No lon-ger lone-ly! He will be near. .

CHORUS

No longer lone-ly, No longer lone-ly, For Je-sus is the Friend of friends to me; . . . No lon-ger lone-ly, No lon-ger lone-ly, For Je-sus is the Friend of friends to me.

to me;

of friends to me.

166 Rescue the Perishing

Fanny J. Crosby — William H. Doane

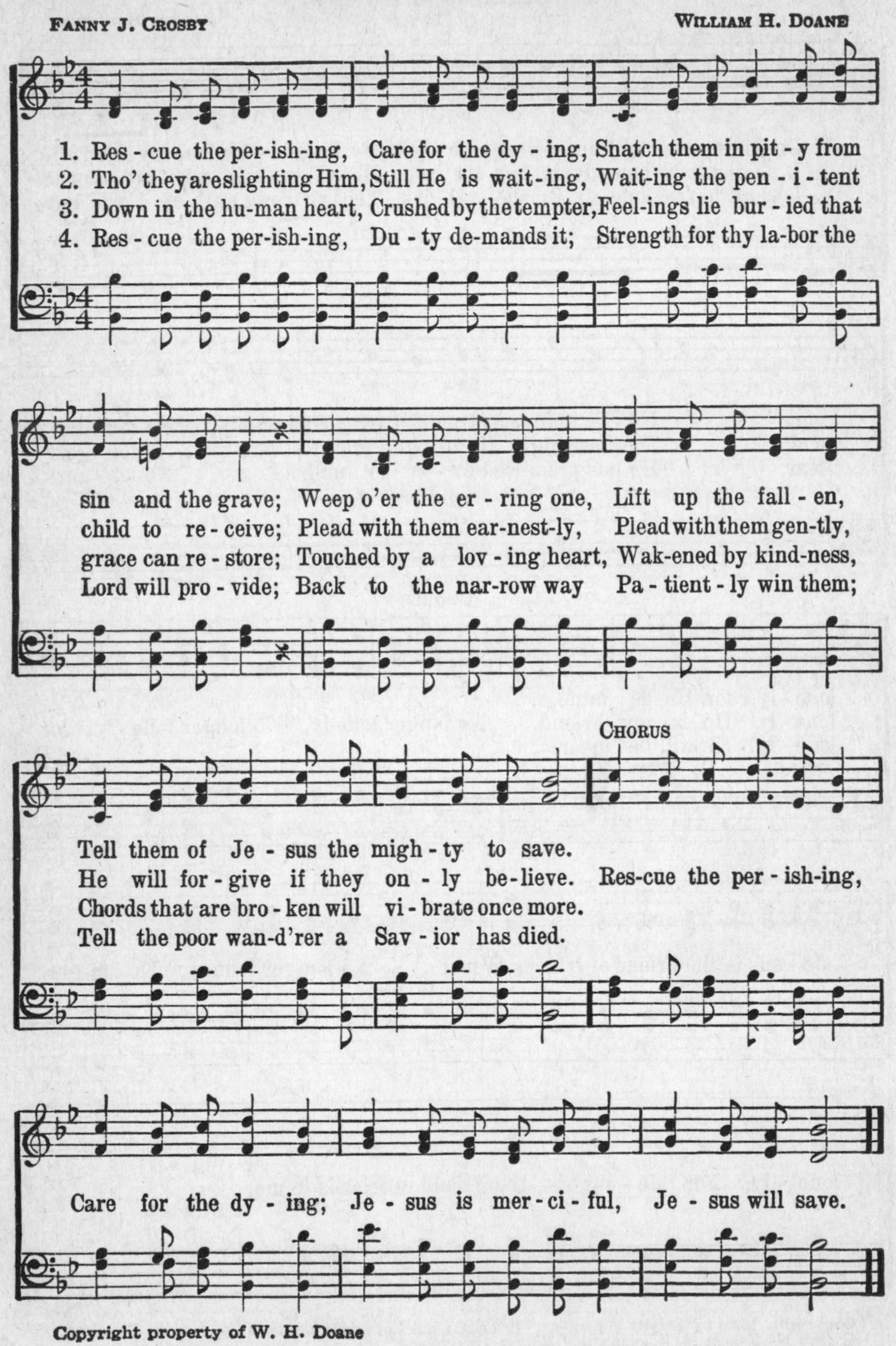
1. Res - cue the per-ish-ing, Care for the dy - ing, Snatch them in pit - y from
2. Tho' they are slighting Him, Still He is wait-ing, Wait-ing the pen - i - tent
3. Down in the hu-man heart, Crushed by the tempter, Feel-ings lie bur - ied that
4. Res - cue the per-ish-ing, Du - ty de-mands it; Strength for thy la-bor the
sin and the grave; Weep o'er the er - ring one, Lift up the fall - en,
child to re - ceive; Plead with them ear-nest-ly, Plead with them gen-tly,
grace can re - store; Touched by a lov - ing heart, Wak-ened by kind-ness,
Lord will pro - vide; Back to the nar-row way Pa - tient - ly win them;
Chorus
Tell them of Je - sus the migh - ty to save.
He will for - give if they on - ly be-lieve. Res-cue the per - ish-ing,
Chords that are bro - ken will vi - brate once more.
Tell the poor wan-d'rer a Sav - ior has died.
Care for the dy - ing; Je - sus is mer - ci - ful, Je - sus will save.

167 Blessed Calvary

Christian B. Anson
Lance B. Latham
1. I look at the cross up - on Cal - va - ry, And oh, what a won - der di - vine, . . . To think of the wealth it holds for me—The rich - es of heav - en are mine.
2. I find at the cross bless - ed vic - to - ry, And grace for each step of my way. . . . The fount of God's love is flow - ing free, And sweet - er it grows day by day.
3. The cross is my hope for e - ter - ni - ty, No mer - it have I of my own; . . . The shed blood of Christ my on - ly plea—My trust is in Je - sus a - lone.
Chorus
Bless-ed Cal - va - ry! Pre - cious Cal - va - ry! 'Neath thy shad-ow I'll ev - er a - bide. . . . Bless-ed Cal - va - ry! Pre-cious Cal - va - ry! 'Twas there Jesus suf-fered and died.

Whiter Than Snow

JAMES NICHOLSON | WM. G. FISCHER

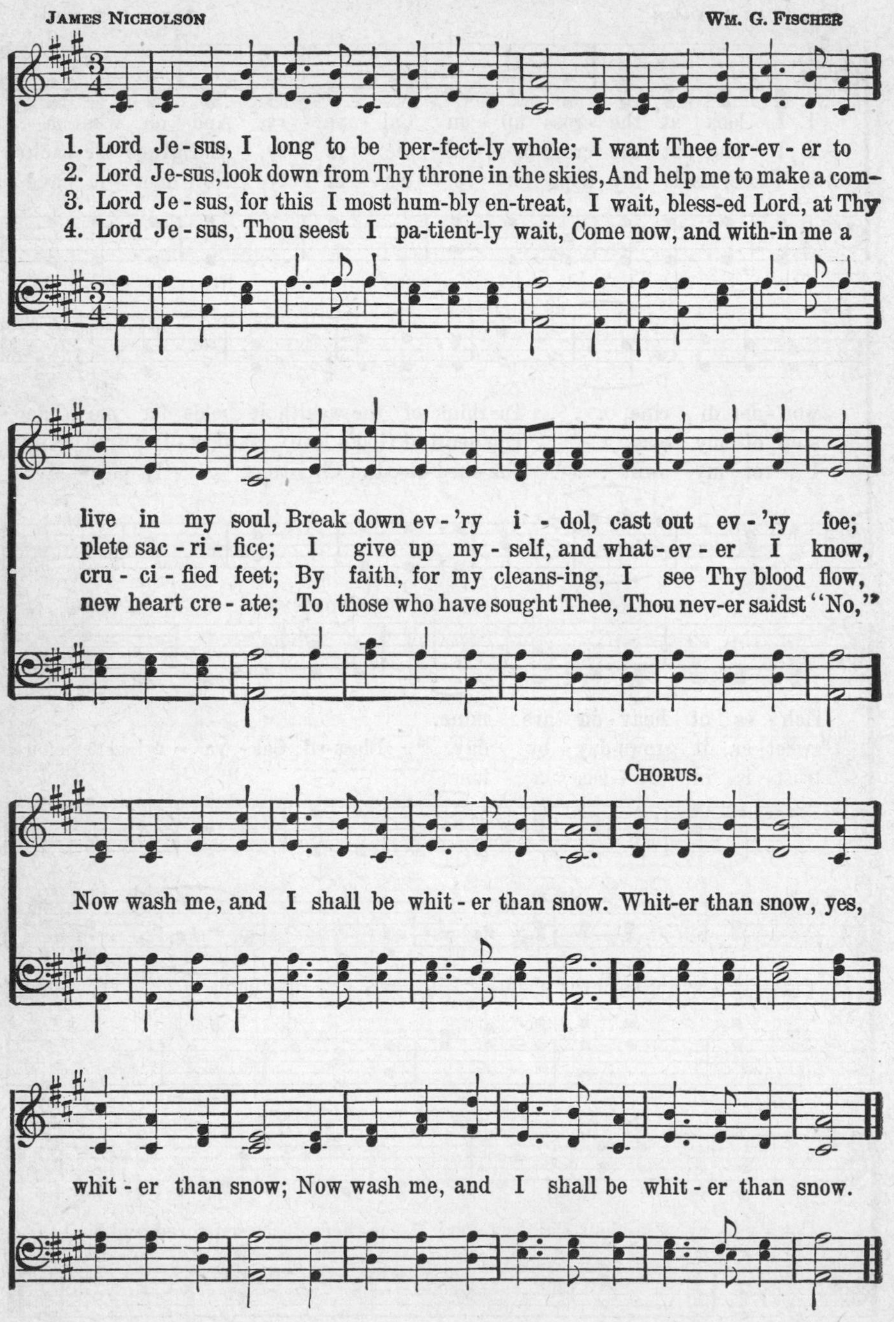
1. Lord Je-sus, I long to be per-fect-ly whole; I want Thee for-ev - er to
2. Lord Je-sus, look down from Thy throne in the skies, And help me to make a com-
3. Lord Je-sus, for this I most hum-bly en-treat, I wait, bless-ed Lord, at Thy
4. Lord Je-sus, Thou seest I pa-tient-ly wait, Come now, and with-in me a
live in my soul, Break down ev - 'ry i - dol, cast out ev - 'ry foe;
plete sac - ri - fice; I give up my - self, and what - ev - er I know,
cru - ci - fied feet; By faith, for my cleans-ing, I see Thy blood flow,
new heart cre - ate; To those who have sought Thee, Thou nev-er saidst "No,"
CHORUS.
Now wash me, and I shall be whit - er than snow. Whit-er than snow, yes,
whit - er than snow; Now wash me, and I shall be whit - er than snow.

169 Blessed Quietness

Manie Payne Ferguson

W. S. Marshall
Adapted by James M. Kirk

1. Joys are flow-ing like a riv - er, Since the Com - fort-er has come;
2. Bring-ing life, and health and glad-ness, All a - round this heav'nly Guest,
3. Like the rain that falls from heav - en, Like the sun-light from the sky,
4. See, a fruit-ful field is grow-ing, Bless-ed fruit of right-eous-ness;
5. What a won-der-ful sal-va - tion, Where we al-ways see His face!
He a - bides with us for - ev - er, Makes the trust - ing heart His home.
Ban-ished un - be - lief and sad-ness, Changed our wea - ri - ness to rest.
So the Ho - ly Ghost is giv - en, Com - ing on us from on high.
And the streams of life are flow-ing In the lone - ly wil-der-ness.
What a per-fect hab - i - ta - tion, What a qui - et rest-ing place!
Refrain
Bless-ed qui - et - ness, ho - ly qui - et - ness, What as-sur - ance in my soul!
rit.
On the storm-y sea, He speaks peace to me, How the bil-lows cease to roll!

170 'Tis Jesus

J. WILBUR CHAPMAN — ROBERT HARKNESS

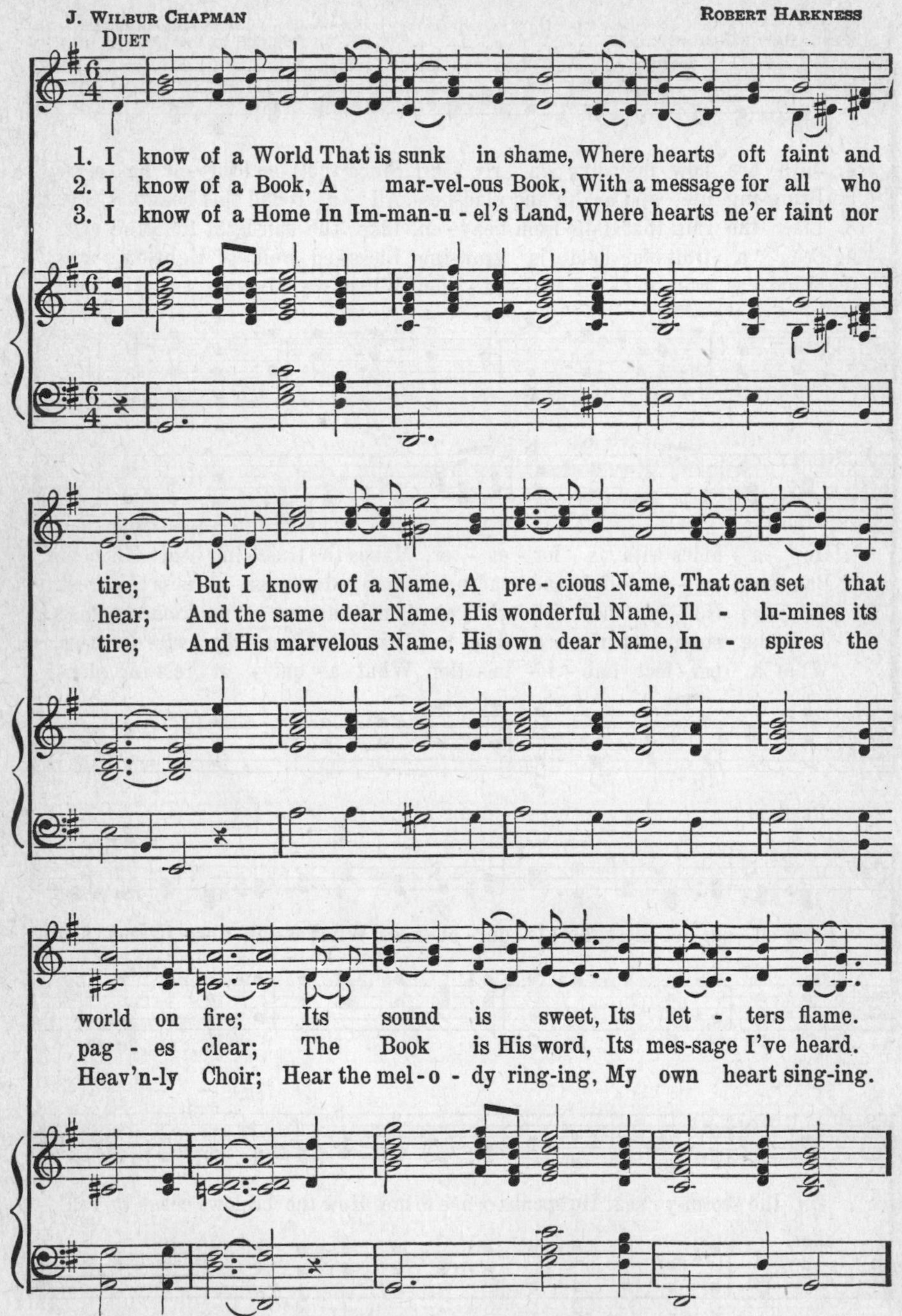
DUET
1. I know of a World That is sunk in shame, Where hearts oft faint and tire; But I know of a Name, A pre - cious Name, That can set that world on fire; Its sound is sweet, Its let - ters flame.
2. I know of a Book, A mar-vel-ous Book, With a message for all who hear; And the same dear Name, His wonderful Name, Il - lu-mines its pag - es clear; The Book is His word, Its mes-sage I've heard.
3. I know of a Home In Im-man-u - el's Land, Where hearts ne'er faint nor tire; And His marvelous Name, His own dear Name, In - spires the Heav'n-ly Choir; Hear the mel-o - dy ring-ing, My own heart sing-ing.

'Tis Jesus

Refrain
I know of a Name, a pre-cious Name, 'Tis Je - - - - sus.
'Tis Je - - sus.

171
On the Mountain Top
C. W. J.
Clarence W. Jones
1. On the moun-tain top a-bove the world be - low, . . .
2. I have left the val-ley low-lands long a - go, . . .
Where the fruits of vic-t'ry in a-bun - dance grow, . . .
On my path-way bright-ly beams a heav'n - ly glow; . . .
There the streams of bless-ings flow from foun-tains of His grace, . .
Lift - ed in His arms to heights I tho't could ne'er be mine, . . .
I've been on the moun-tain top, and seen His face! . . .
I've been on the moun-tain top by grace di - - vine! . . .

172 Nor Silver Nor Gold

James M. Gray — D. B. Towner

1. Nor sil - ver nor gold hath ob-tained my re-demp-tion, Nor rich - es of
2. Nor sil - ver nor gold hath ob-tained my re-demp-tion, The guilt on my
3. Nor sil - ver nor gold hath ob-tained my re-demp-tion, The ho - ly com-
4. Nor sil - ver nor gold hath ob-tained my re-demp-tion, The way in - to
earth could have saved my poor soul; The blood of the cross is my
con-science too heav - y had grown; The blood of the cross is my
mand-ment for - bade me draw near; The blood of the cross is my
heav - en could not thus be bought; The blood of the cross is my
on - ly foun - da-tion, The death of my Sav - ior now mak - eth me whole.
on - ly foun - da-tion, The death of my Sav - ior could on - ly a - tone.
on - ly foun - da-tion, The death of my Sav - ior re - mov - eth my fear.
on - ly foun - da-tion, The death of my Sav - ior re-demp-tion hath wrought
Chorus
I am re - deemed, ... but not with sil - ver;
I am re-deemed, I am re-deemed, but not with sil - ver;
I am bought, . but not with gold; Bought with a
I am bought, I am bought, but not with gold;

Nor Silver Nor Gold

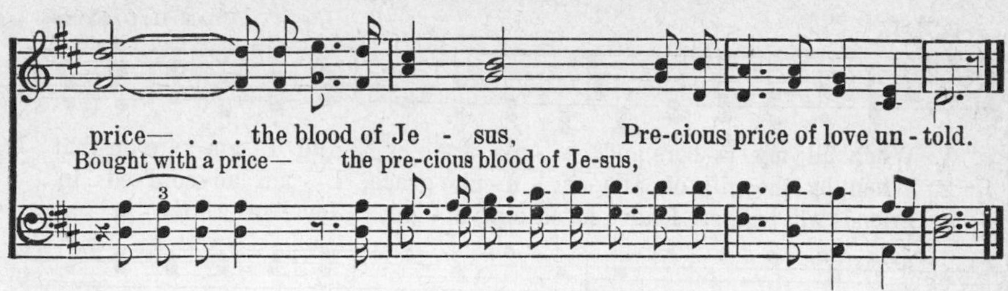
price— . . . the blood of Je - sus, Pre-cious price of love un - told.
Bought with a price— the pre-cious blood of Je-sus,
3

173 Christ Liveth in Me

Maj. D. W. WHITTLE (El Nathan) — JAMES MCGRANAHAN

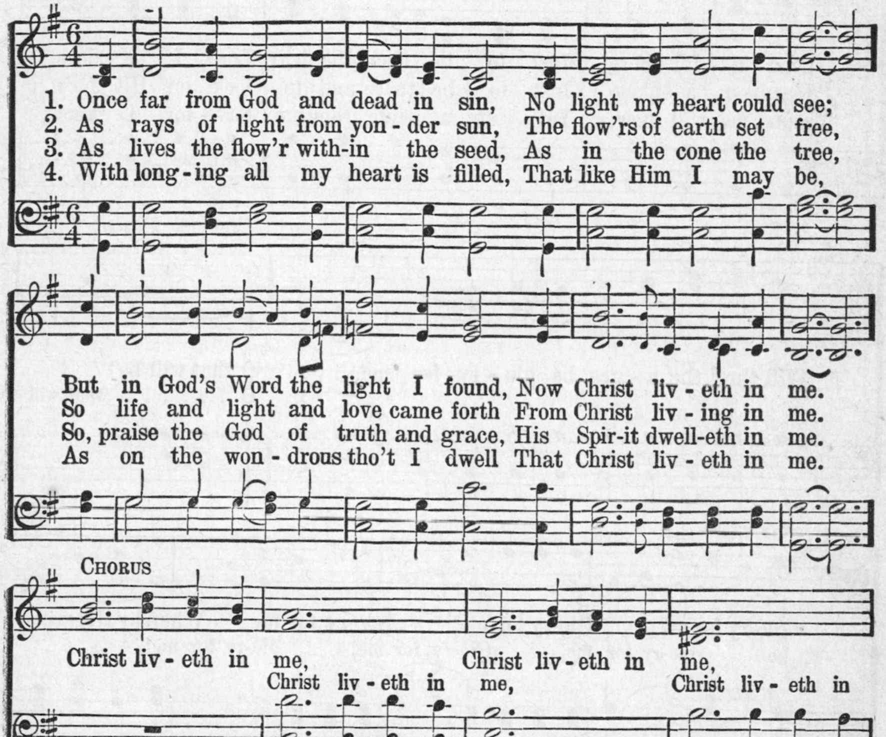

1. Once far from God and dead in sin, No light my heart could see;
But in God's Word the light I found, Now Christ liv-eth in me.

2. As rays of light from yon-der sun, The flow'rs of earth set free,
So life and light and love came forth From Christ liv-ing in me.

3. As lives the flow'r with-in the seed, As in the cone the tree,
So, praise the God of truth and grace, His Spir-it dwell-eth in me.

4. With long-ing all my heart is filled, That like Him I may be,
As on the won-drous tho't I dwell That Christ liv-eth in me.

CHORUS

Christ liv-eth in me, Christ liv-eth in me,
Christ liv-eth in me, Christ liv-eth in me, Oh!
Oh! what a sal-va-tion this, That Christ liv-eth in me.

O That Will Be Glory

C. H. G. Chas. H. Gabriel

1. When all my labors and trials are o'er, And I am safe on that beautiful shore, Just to be near the dear Lord I adore, Will thro' the ages be glory for me. . . .
2. When, by the gift of His infinite grace, I am accorded in Heaven a place, Just to be there and to look on His face,
3. Friends will be there I have loved long ago; Joy like a river around me will flow; Yet, just a smile from my Savior, I know,
rit.
Chorus. Faster
O that will be glory for me, Glory for me, glory for me; When by His grace I shall look on His face, That will be glory, be glory for me.
O . . . . . . that will be glory for me, Glory for me, glory for me;. . . . .
rit.

175 Jesus Has Lifted Me

Avis B. Christiansen
Haldor Lillenas
1. Out of the depths to the glo - ry a - bove, I have been
2. Out of the world in - to heav - en - ly rest, In - to the
3. Out of my - self in - to Him I a - dore, There to a-
lift - ed in won - der - ful love; From ev - 'ry fet - ter my
land of the ran-somed and blest; There in the glo - ry with
bide in His love ev - er - more; Thro' end - less a - ges His
spir - it is free— For Je - sus has lift - ed me! . . . .
Him I shall be— For Je - sus has lift - ed me! . . . .
glo - ry to see— My Je - sus has lift - ed me! . . . .
lift - ed me!
Chorus
Je - sus has lift - ed me! . . . Je - sus has lift - ed me! . . .
lift - ed me!
lift - ed me!
Out of the night in - to glo - ri - ous light, Yes, Je - sus has lift - ed me! . . .
lift - ed me!

176 Saved By Grace

FANNY J. CROSBY GEO. C. STEBBINS

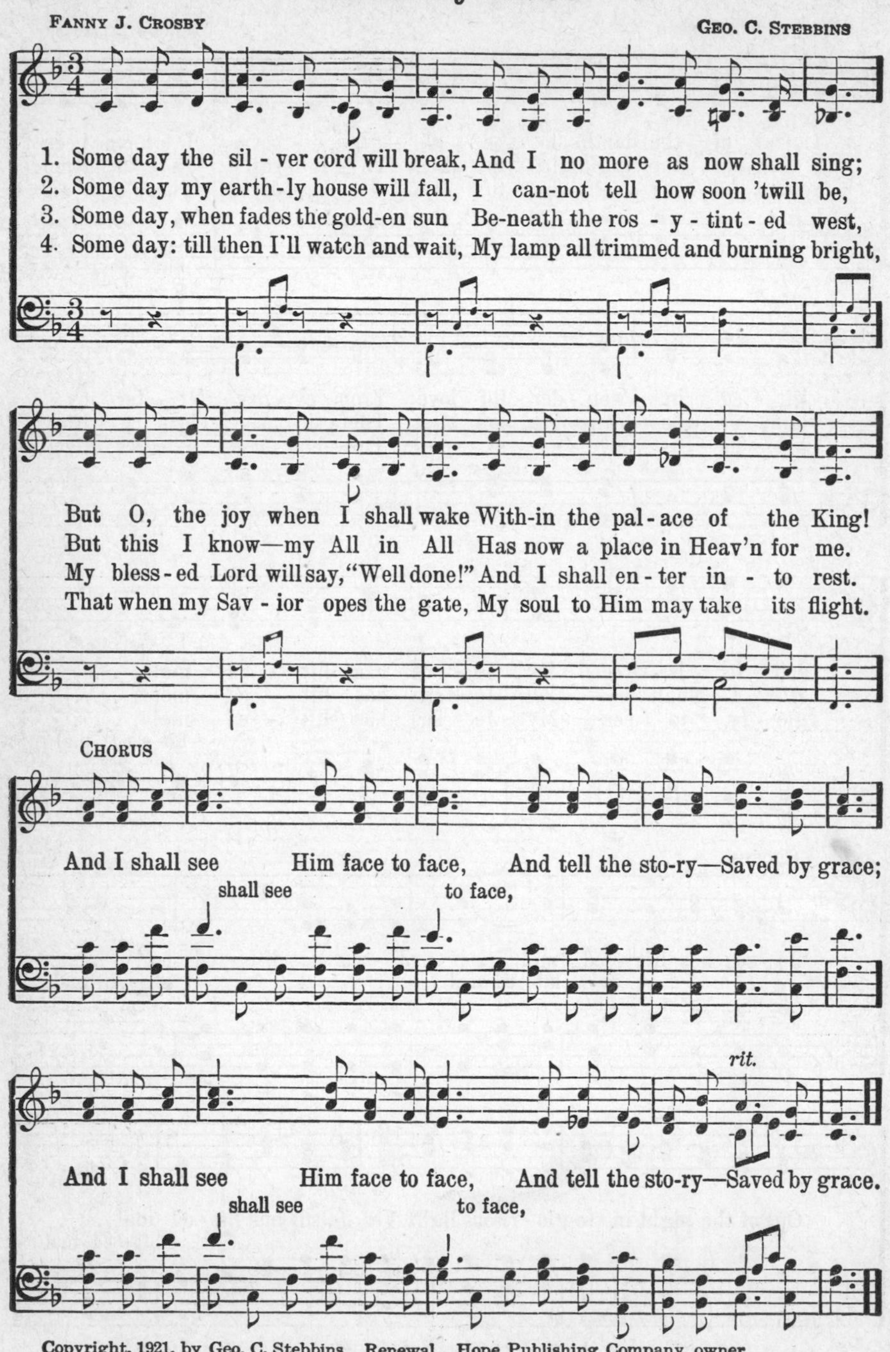
1. Some day the sil - ver cord will break, And I no more as now shall sing;
2. Some day my earth - ly house will fall, I can-not tell how soon 'twill be,
3. Some day, when fades the gold-en sun Be-neath the ros - y - tint - ed west,
4. Some day: till then I'll watch and wait, My lamp all trimmed and burning bright,
But O, the joy when I shall wake With-in the pal - ace of the King!
But this I know—my All in All Has now a place in Heav'n for me.
My bless - ed Lord will say, "Well done!" And I shall en - ter in - to rest.
That when my Sav - ior opes the gate, My soul to Him may take its flight.
CHORUS
And I shall see Him face to face, And tell the sto-ry—Saved by grace;
shall see
to face,
And I shall see Him face to face, And tell the sto-ry—Saved by grace.
shall see
to face,
rit.

177 He Will Hold Me Fast

Ada R. Habershon — Robert Harkness

1. When I fear my faith will fail, Christ will hold me fast;
2. I could nev - er keep my hold, He must hold me fast;
3. I am pre - cious in His sight, He will hold me fast;
4. He'll not let my soul be lost, Christ will hold me fast;
rall.
When the tempt - er would pre - vail, He can hold me fast. . .
For my love is oft - en cold, He must hold me fast. . .
Those He saves are His de - light, He will hold me fast. . .
Bought by Him at such a cost, He will hold me fast. . .
Refrain a tempo
He will hold me fast, He will hold me fast;
hold me fast, hold me fast;
rall.
For my Sav - ior loves me so, He will hold me fast.

He Gives the Power

R. M. H.
Roger M. Hickman
1. Je - sus came to earth by a low - ly birth, Gave Him-self as an of-
2. Grace and par-don free, all for you and me, Ev - 'ry one who re-ceives
3. Not by works we come as the Fa-ther's son, To re-ceive as a wel-
f'ring of matchless worth; To His own He came in His Father's name, But they
Him a son may be; For His blood He spilt to re-move our guilt, When He
come the words "well done;" Lest we fain would boast as a might - y host, Knowing
Chorus
scorned to re-ceive Him their King.
of - fered Him-self once for all. But as man - y as received Him to
not 'tis the free gift of God.
them He gave the pow'r, The pow-er to be-come the sons of God; But as
man - y as received Him to them He gave the pow'r to become the sons of God.
Copyright. 1915, by J. R. Hemminger. Used by permission

179 Jesus Is Calling

FANNY J. CROSBY GEO. C. STEBBINS

1. Je - sus is ten - der - ly call - ing thee home—Call - ing to - day,
2. Je - sus is call - ing the wea - ry to rest— Call - ing to - day,
3. Je - sus is wait-ing; O come to Him now— Wait-ing to - day,
4. Je - sus is plead-ing; O list to His voice: Hear Him to - day,
call - ing to - day; Why from the sun - shine of love wilt thou roam
call - ing to - day; Bring Him thy bur - den and thou shalt be blest:
wait - ing to - day; Come with thy sins; at His feet low - ly bow;
hear Him to - day; They who be - lieve on His name shall re - joice;
Far-ther and far-ther a - way?
He will not turn thee a - way.
Come, and no lon-ger de - lay.
Quick-ly a - rise and a - way.
REFRAIN
Call - - ing to - day, ...
Call - ing, call - ing to - day, to - day,
Call - - ing to - day, ... Je - - - - sus is
Call - ing, call - ing to - day, to - day, Je - sus is ten - der - ly
call - - - ing, is ten - der - ly call - ing to - day.
call - ing to - day,

180 Saved!

OSWALD J. SMITH ROGER M. HICKMAN

1. Saved! saved! saved! my sins are all for-giv'n; Christ is
2. Saved! saved! saved! by grace and grace a-lone; Oh, what
3. Saved! saved! saved! oh, joy be-yond com-pare! Christ my

mine! I'm on my way to heav'n; Once a guilt--y
won-drous love to me was shown, In my stead Christ
life, and I His con-stant care; Yield-ing all and

sin-ner, lost, un-done, Now a child of God, saved thro' His Son.
Je-sus bled and died, Bore my sins, for me was cru-ci-fied.
trust-ing Him a-lone, Liv-ing now each moment as His own.

CHORUS

Saved! I'm saved thro' Christ, my all in all; . . . . Saved! I'm saved, what-
my all in all;

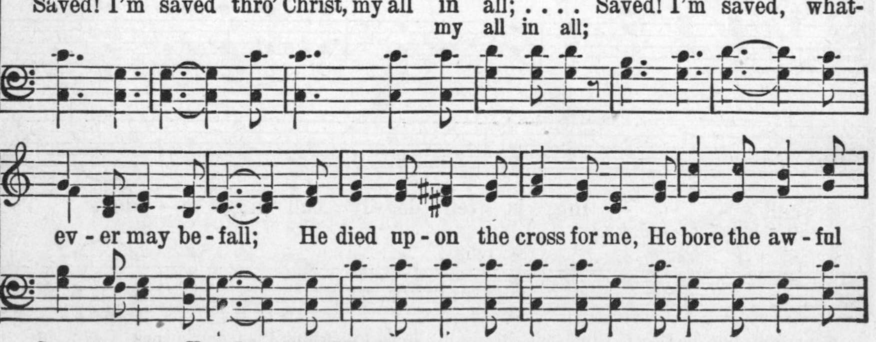
ev-er may be-fall; He died up-on the cross for me, He bore the aw-ful

Saved!

rit.
pen-al-ty; And now I'm saved e-ter-nal-ly—I'm saved! saved! saved!
181 Shall We Gather At the River?
R. L.
Robert Lowry
1. Shall we gath-er at the riv-er, Where bright an-gel feet have trod;
2. On the bos-om of the riv-er, Where the Sav-ior-King we own,
3. Ere we reach the shin-ing riv-er, Lay we ev-'ry bur-den down;
4. Soon we'll reach the shining riv-er, Soon our pil-grim-age will cease;
With its crys-tal tide for-ev-er Flow-ing by the throne of God?
We shall meet, and sor-row nev-er, 'Neath the glo-ry of the throne.
Grace our spir-its will de-liv-er, And pro-vide a robe and crown.
Soon our hap-py hearts will qui-ver With the mel-o-dy of peace.
Chorus
p
Yes, we'll gather at the riv-er, The beau-ti-ful, the beau-ti-ful riv-er,
Gath-er with the saints at the riv-er That flows by the throne of God.

182 Beulah Land

EDGAR PAGE — JNO. R. SWENEY

1. I've reached the land of corn and wine, And all its rich-es free-ly mine;
2. My Sav-ior comes and walks with me, And sweet com-mun-ion here have we;
3. A sweet per-fume up-on the breeze Is borne from ev-er-ver-nal trees,
4. The zeph-yrs seem to float to me, Sweet sounds of Heaven's mel-o-dy,
Here shines undimmed one bliss-ful day, For all my night has passed a-way.
He gen-tly leads me by His hand, For this is Heav-en's bor-der-land.
And flow'rs, that nev-er-fad-ing grow, Where streams of life for-ev-er flow.
As an-gels with the white-robed throng Join in the sweet Re-demp-tion song.
CHORUS
O Beu-lah Land, sweet Beu-lah Land, As on thy high-est mount I stand,
I look a-way a-cross the sea, Where mansions are pre-pared for me, And
view the shin-ing glo-ry-shore,—My Heav'n, my home for-ev-er-more!

183 Is It the Crowning Day?

George Walker Whitcomb — Charles H. Marsh

1. Je - sus may come to - day, Glad day! Glad day! And I would see my Friend; Dan-gers and trou - bles would end If Je - sus should come to - day.
2. I may go home to - day, Glad day! Glad day! Seem-eth I hear their song; Hail to the ra - di - ant throng! If I should go home to - day.
3. Why should I anx-ious be? Glad day! Glad day! Lights ap - pear on the shore, Storms will af - fright nev - er - more, For He is "at hand" to - day.
4. Faithful I'll be to - day, Glad day! Glad day! And I will free - ly tell Why I should love Him so well, For He is my all to - day.
Chorus
Glad day! Glad day! Is it the crowning day? I'll live for to - day, nor anx - ious be, Je - sus, my Lord, I soon shall see; Glad day! Glad day! Is it the crown-ing day?
rit.

184 In the Service of the King

A. H. Ackley — Bentley D. Ackley

1. I am hap - py in the serv - ice of the King, I am hap - py, oh, so hap - py; I have peace and joy that noth - ing else can bring, In the serv - ice of the King.
2. I am hap - py in the serv - ice of the King, I am hap - py, oh, so hap - py; Thro' the sun - shine and the shad - ow I can sing, In the serv - ice of the King.
3. I am hap - py in the serv - ice of the King, I am hap - py, oh, so hap - py; To His guid - ing hand for - ev - er I will cling, In the serv - ice of the King.
4. I am hap - py in the serv - ice of the King, I am hap - py, oh, so hap - py; All that I pos - sess to Him I glad - ly bring, In the serv - ice of the King.
Chorus
In the serv - ice of the King, Ev - 'ry tal - ent I will bring; I have peace and joy and bless - ing In the serv - ice of the King.

185 I Know I'll See Jesus Some Day

Avis B. Christiansen | Scott Lawrence

1. Sweet is the hope that is thrill-ing my soul— I know I'll see Je-sus some day! Then what if the dark clouds of sin o'er me roll,
2. Though I must trav-el by faith, not by sight, I know I'll see Je-sus some day! No e-vil can harm me, no foe can af-fright—
3. Dark-ness is gath-'ring, but hope shines with-in, I know I'll see Je-sus some day! What joy when He comes to wipe out ev-'ry sin;
Chorus
I know I'll see Je-sus some day! . . . I know I'll see Je-sus some day! . . .
some day!
I know I'll see Je-sus some day! . . . What a joy it will
some day!
be When His face I shall see, I know I'll see Je-sus some day!

186 Sweeter As the Years Go By

Mrs. C. H. M. Mrs. C. H. Morris

1. Of Je-sus' love that sought me, When I was lost in sin; Of wondrous grace that brought me Back to His fold a-gain; Of heights and depths of mer-cy, Far deep-er than the sea, And high-er than the heav-ens, My theme shall ev-er be.
2. He trod in old Ju-de-a Life's pathway long a-go; The peo-ple thronged a-bout Him, His sav-ing grace to know; He healed the bro-ken-heart-ed, And caused the blind to see; And still His great heart yearneth In love for e-ven me.
3. 'Twas wondrous love which led Him For us to suf-fer loss—To bear with-out a mur-mur, The an-guish of the cross; With saints redeemed in glo-ry, Let us our voi-ces raise, Till heav'n and earth re-ech-o With our Re-deem-er's praise.
CHORUS
Sweet-er as the years go by,..... Sweet-er as the years go by; Rich-er, full-er, deep-er,
Sweet-er as the years go by, 'Tis sweet-er as the years go by;

Sweeter As the Years Go By

rit.
Je - sus' love is sweet - er, Sweet - er as the years go by.

187 Have You Any Room For Jesus?

Arr. by W. W. D. from L. W. M. C. C. WILLIAMS

1. Have you an - y room for Je - sus, He who bore your load of sin?
2. Room for pleas-ure, room for busi - ness, But for Christ the Cru - ci - fied,
3. Have you an - y room for Je - sus, As in grace He calls a - gain?
4. Room and time now give to Je - sus, Soon will pass God's day of grace;
As He knocks and asks ad-mis - sion, Sin - ner, will you let Him in?
Not a place that He can en - ter, In the heart for which He died?
O to - day is time ac - cept - ed, To-mor - row you may call in vain.
Soon thy heart left cold and si - lent, And thy Sav-ior's pleading cease.
CHORUS
Room for Je - sus, King of glo - ry! Has - ten now His word o - bey;
Swing the heart's door wide-ly o - pen, Bid Him en - ter while you may.

188 Since Jesus Came Into My Heart

R. H. McDaniel — Chas. H. Gabriel

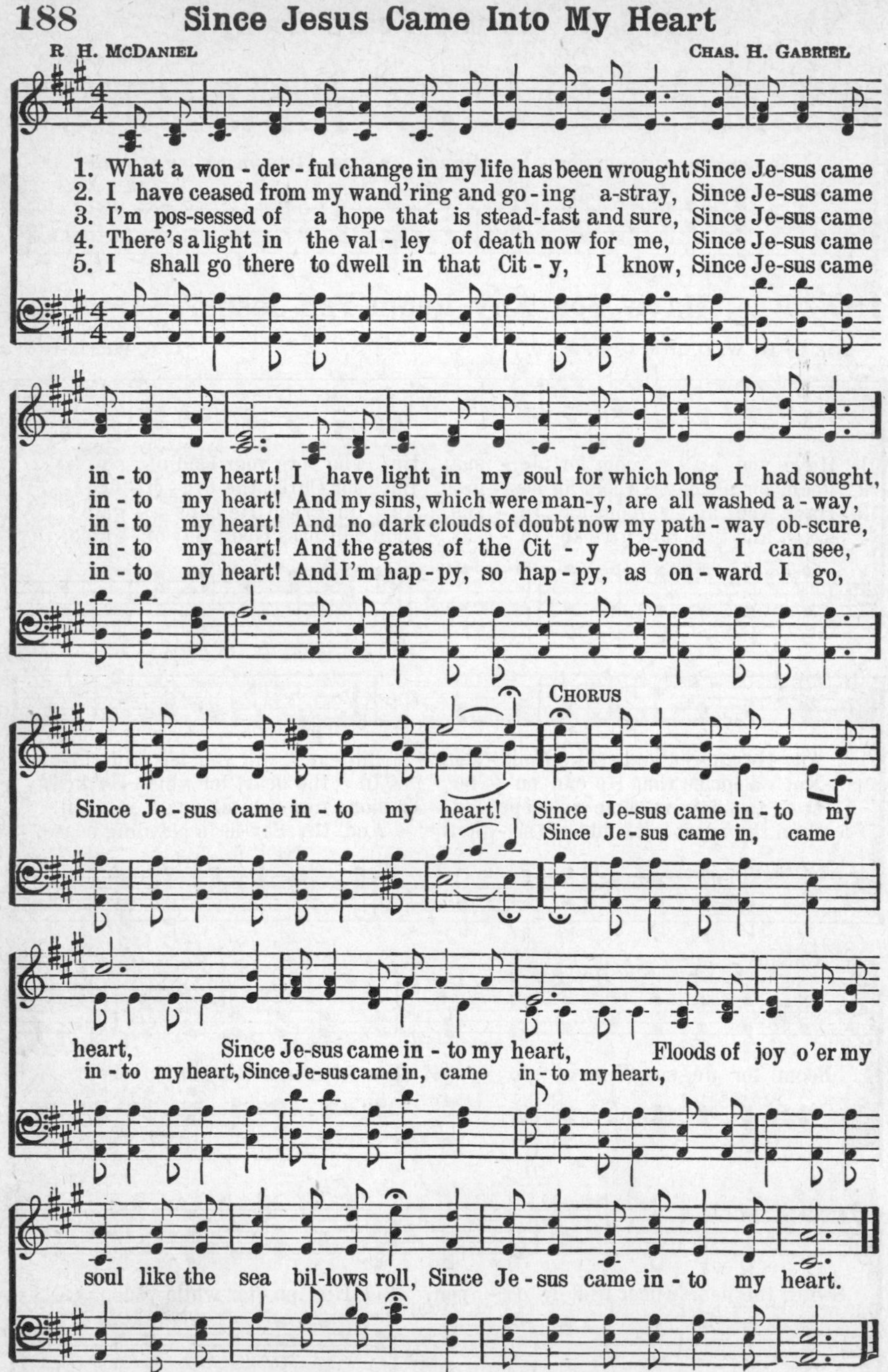
1. What a won - der - ful change in my life has been wrought Since Je-sus came in - to my heart! I have light in my soul for which long I had sought, Since Je-sus came in - to my heart!
2. I have ceased from my wand'ring and go - ing a-stray, Since Je-sus came in - to my heart! And my sins, which were man-y, are all washed a - way, Since Je-sus came in - to my heart!
3. I'm pos-sessed of a hope that is stead-fast and sure, Since Je-sus came in - to my heart! And no dark clouds of doubt now my path - way ob-scure, Since Je-sus came in - to my heart!
4. There's a light in the val - ley of death now for me, Since Je-sus came in - to my heart! And the gates of the Cit - y be-yond I can see, Since Je-sus came in - to my heart!
5. I shall go there to dwell in that Cit - y, I know, Since Je-sus came in - to my heart! And I'm hap - py, so hap - py, as on - ward I go, Since Je-sus came in - to my heart!
CHORUS
Since Je-sus came in - to my heart, Since Je-sus came in - to my heart,
Since Je-sus came in, came in - to my heart, Since Je-sus came in, came in - to my heart,
Floods of joy o'er my soul like the sea bil-lows roll, Since Je - sus came in - to my heart.

189 Jesus Satisfies

P. R. PAUL RADER

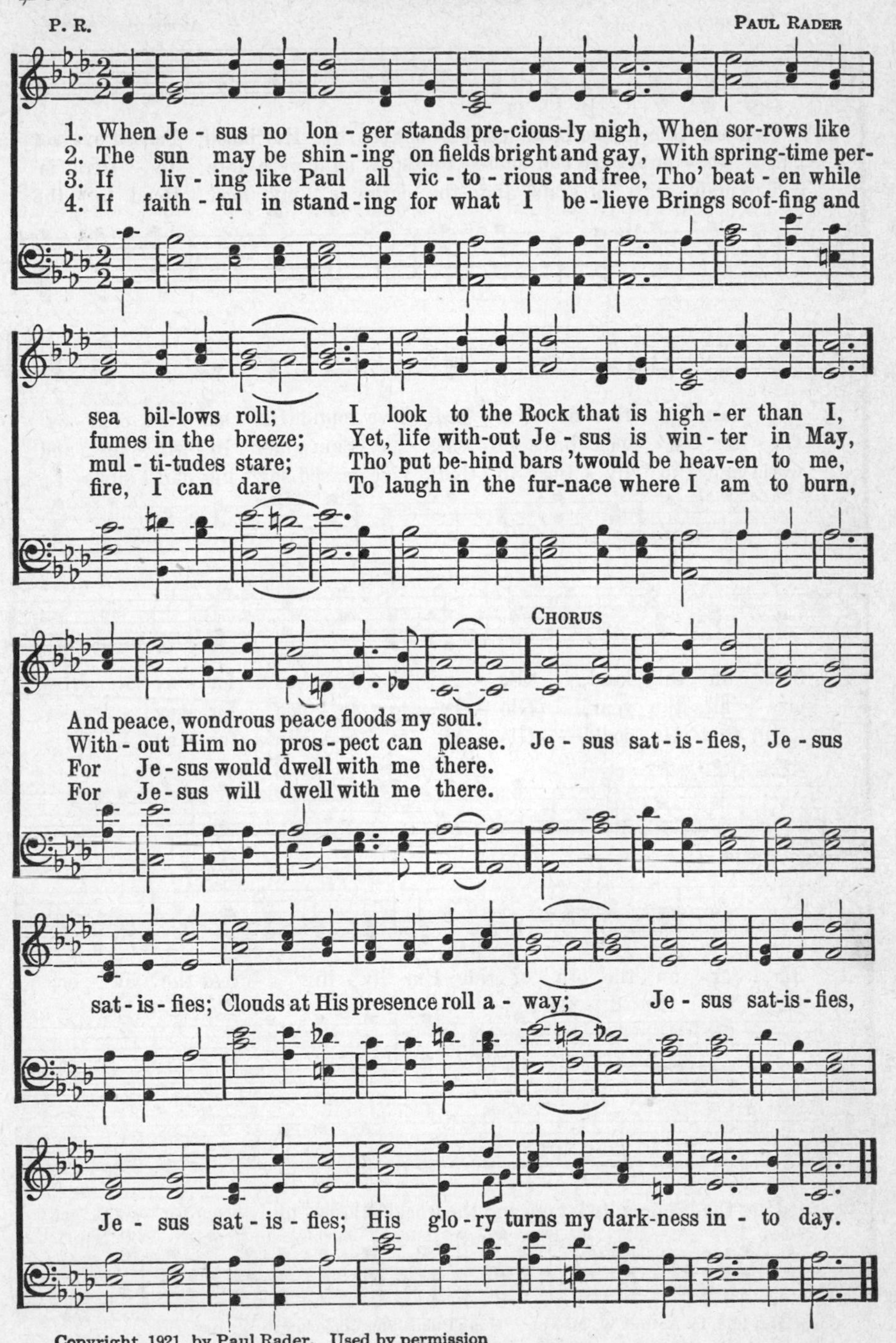
1. When Je - sus no lon - ger stands pre-cious-ly nigh, When sor-rows like
2. The sun may be shin - ing on fields bright and gay, With spring-time per-
3. If liv - ing like Paul all vic - to - rious and free, Tho' beat - en while
4. If faith - ful in stand - ing for what I be - lieve Brings scof-fing and
sea bil-lows roll; I look to the Rock that is high - er than I,
fumes in the breeze; Yet, life with-out Je - sus is win - ter in May,
mul - ti-tudes stare; Tho' put be-hind bars 'twould be heav-en to me,
fire, I can dare To laugh in the fur-nace where I am to burn,
CHORUS
And peace, wondrous peace floods my soul.
With - out Him no pros - pect can please. Je - sus sat - is - fies, Je - sus
For Je - sus would dwell with me there.
For Je - sus will dwell with me there.
sat - is - fies; Clouds at His presence roll a - way; Je - sus sat-is-fies,
Je - sus sat - is - fies; His glo - ry turns my dark-ness in - to day.

190 Far, Far On the Other Side

PAUL RADER

ARTHUR W. MCKEE

1. I've en - tered the land dear - ly bought by His blood, Passed o - ver Jor - dan, sur - ren - dered to God; I've found His suf - fi - cien - cy here in this land, Glo - ry to Je - sus for - ev - er!
2. The gi - ants are con - quered the spies said were here, Je - sus is vic - tor, I need have no fear; Sum - mer in win - ter and joy all the year, Glo - ry to Je - sus for - ev - er!
3. The man - na is gone and the corn is my food, Dead to the world and I'm liv - ing in God; I've ceased say - ing can't since I found that He could— Glo - ry to Je - sus for - ev - er!
CHORUS
Far, far on the oth - er side, I'm liv - ing a - cross the riv - er;
Burned are the bridges 'twixt me and the world, Glo - ry to Je - sus for - ev - er!

191 Sweet By and By

S. F. BENNETT — J. P. WEBSTER

1. There's a land that is fair - er than day, And by faith we can see it a - far; For the Fa - ther waits o - ver the way, To pre - pare us a dwell - ing-place there.
2. We shall sing on that beau - ti - ful shore The mel - o - di - ous songs of the blest, And our spir - its shall sor - row no more, Not a sigh for the bless - ing of rest.
3. To our boun - ti - ful Fa - ther a - bove, We will of - fer our trib - ute of praise, For the glo - ri - ous gift of His love, And the bless-ings that hal - low our days.
CHORUS
In the sweet by and by, We shall meet on that beau - ti - ful shore; In the sweet by and by, We shall meet on that beau - ti - ful shore.
In the sweet by and by, by and by, In the sweet by and by,

192 God Will Take Care of You

(Dedicated to my wife, Mrs. John A. Davis.)

C. D. Martin W. S. Martin

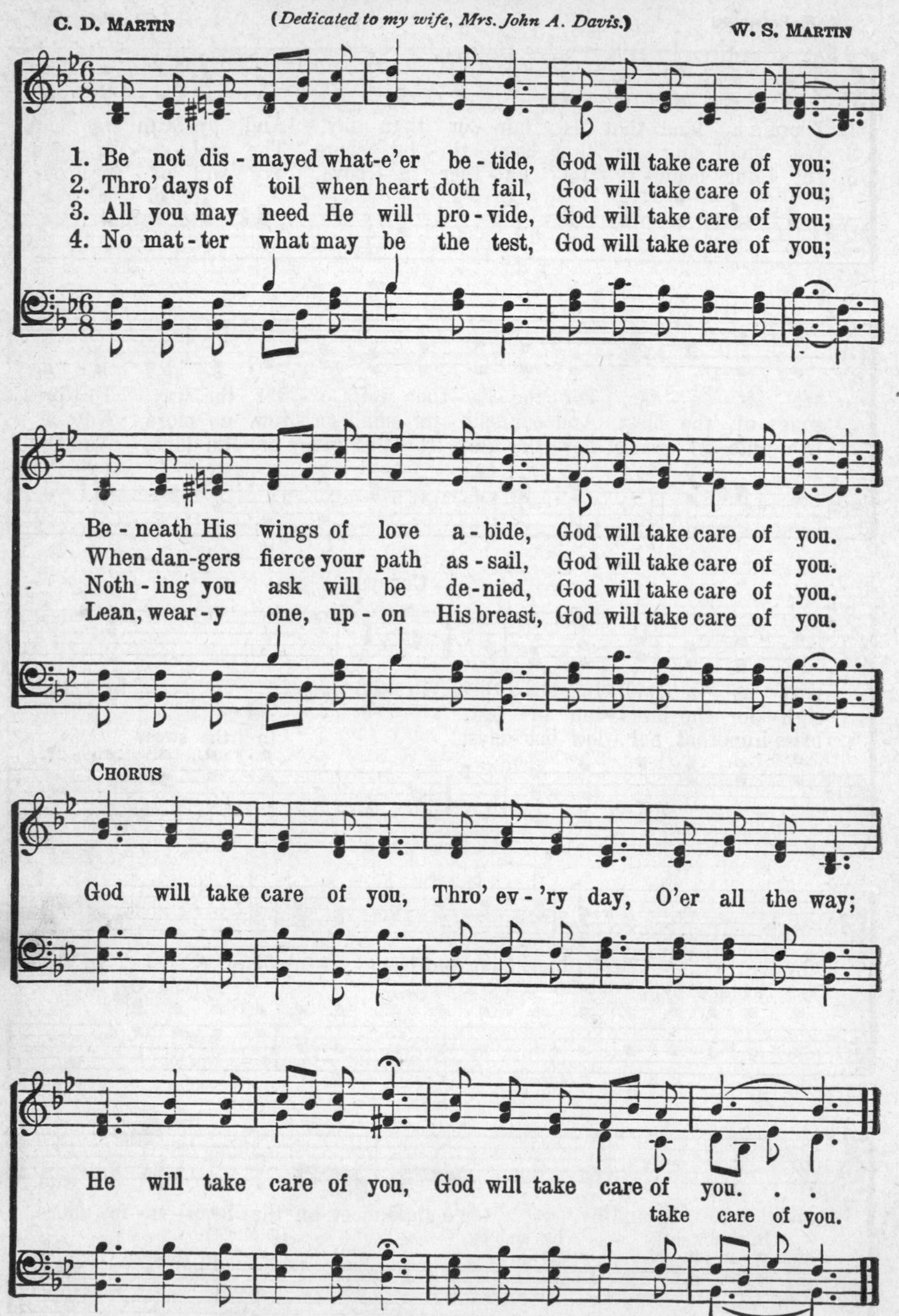

1. Be not dis-mayed what-e'er be-tide, God will take care of you;
2. Thro' days of toil when heart doth fail, God will take care of you;
3. All you may need He will pro-vide, God will take care of you;
4. No mat-ter what may be the test, God will take care of you;
Be-neath His wings of love a-bide, God will take care of you.
When dan-gers fierce your path as-sail, God will take care of you.
Noth-ing you ask will be de-nied, God will take care of you.
Lean, wear-y one, up-on His breast, God will take care of you.
Chorus
God will take care of you, Thro' ev-'ry day, O'er all the way;
He will take care of you, God will take care of you. . .
take care of you.

193 The Name of Jesus

W. C. Martin
E. S. Lorenz
1. The name of Je - sus is so sweet, I love its mu - sic to re - peat; It makes my joys full and com - plete, The pre - cious name of Je - sus.
2. I love the name of Him whose heart Knows all my griefs and bears a part; Who bids all anx - ious fears de - part— I love the name of Je - sus.
3. That name I fond - ly love to hear, It nev - er fails my heart to cheer, Its mu - sic dries the fall - ing tear; Ex - alt the name of Je - sus.
4. No word of man can ev - er tell How sweet the name I love so well; Oh, let its prais - es ev - er swell, Oh, praise the name of Je - sus.
The precious name
Chorus
"Je - sus," oh, how sweet the name! "Je - sus," ev - 'ry day the same; "Je - sus," let all saints pro - claim Its wor - thy praise for - ev - er.
Its wor - thy praise

194 Only Believe

P. R. PAUL RADER

1. Fear not, lit-tle flock, from the cross to the throne, From death in-to life He went for His own; All pow-er in earth, all pow-er a-bove, Is giv-en to Him for the flock of His love.
2. Fear not, lit-tle flock, He go-eth a-head, Your Shep-herd se-lect-eth the path you must tread; The wa-ters of Ma-rah He'll sweeten for thee, He drank all the bit-ter in Geth-sem-a-ne.
3. Fear not, lit-tle flock, what-ev-er your lot, He en-ters all rooms, "the doors be-ing shut;" He nev-er for-sakes, He nev-er is gone, So count on His pres-ence in dark-ness and dawn.
CHORUS
On-ly be-lieve, on-ly be-lieve; All things are pos-si-ble, on-ly be-lieve; On-ly be-lieve, on-ly be-lieve; All things are pos-si-ble, on-ly be-lieve.

195 Is My Name Written There?

M. A. K. FRANK M. DAVIS

1. Lord, I care not for rich-es, Nei-ther sil-ver nor gold; I would make sure of heav-en, I would en-ter the fold. In the book of Thy king-dom, With its pa-ges so fair, Tell me, Je-sus, my Sav-ior, Is my name writ-ten there?
2. Lord, my sins they are man-y, Like the sands of the sea, But Thy blood, O my Sav-ior, Is suf-fi-cient for me; For Thy prom-ise is writ-ten, In bright letters that glow, "Tho' your sins be as scar-let, I will make them like snow."
3. Oh! that beau-ti-ful cit-y, With its man-sions of light, With its glo-ri-fied be-ings, In pure gar-ments of white; Where no e-vil thing com-eth To de-spoil what is fair; Where the an-gels are watching, Yes, my name's written there. Yes, my name's, etc.
REFRAIN.
Is my name writ-ten there, On the page white and fair?
In the book of Thy king-dom, Is my name writ-ten there?
Yes, my name's writ-ten there.

196 "Whosoever Will"

P. P. B. P. P. Bliss

1. "Who-so-ev-er hear - eth," shout, shout the sound! Spread the bless-ed ti-dings
2. Who-so-ev-er com - eth, need not de - lay, Now the door is o - pen,
3. "Who-so-ev-er will," the prom-ise is se - cure; "Who-so-ev - er will," for-
all the world a-round; Tell the joy-ful news wher - ev - er man is found,
en - ter while you may; Je - sus is the true, the on - ly Liv - ing Way:
ev - er must en-dure; "Who-so - ev - er will," 'tis life for - ev - er - more;
Chorus
"Who-so-ev - er will may come." "Who-so-ev - er will, who - so-ev - er will!"
Send the proc - la - ma - tion o - ver vale and hill; 'Tis a lov - ing
Fa - ther calls the wan-d'rer home: "Who - so - ev - er will may come."

197 Tell Me the Story of Jesus

FANNY J. CROSBY — JNO. R. SWENEY

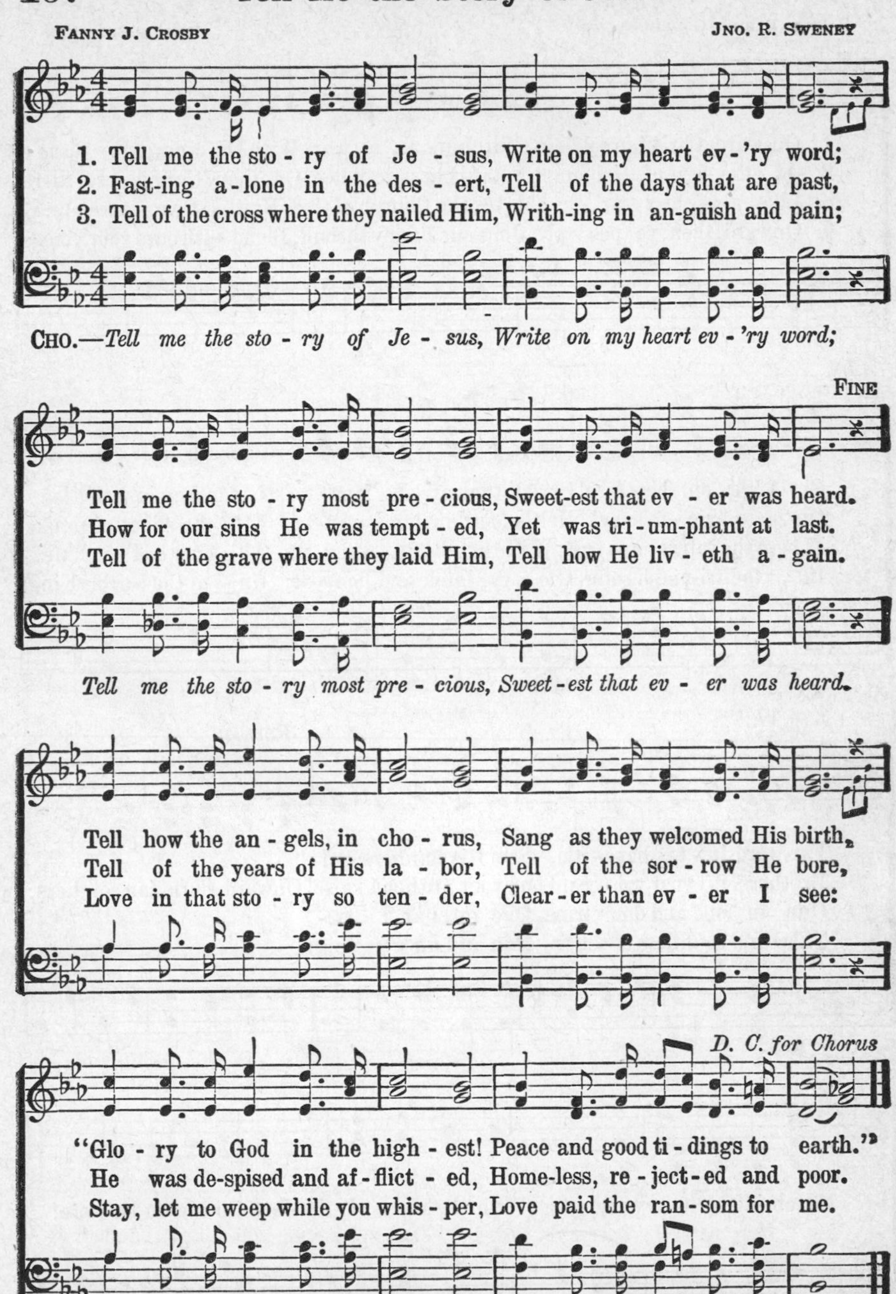
1. Tell me the sto - ry of Je - sus, Write on my heart ev - 'ry word;
2. Fast-ing a-lone in the des - ert, Tell of the days that are past,
3. Tell of the cross where they nailed Him, Writh-ing in an-guish and pain;
CHO.—Tell me the sto - ry of Je - sus, Write on my heart ev - 'ry word;
FINE
Tell me the sto - ry most pre - cious, Sweet-est that ev - er was heard.
How for our sins He was tempt - ed, Yet was tri - um-phant at last.
Tell of the grave where they laid Him, Tell how He liv - eth a - gain.
Tell me the sto - ry most pre - cious, Sweet - est that ev - er was heard.
Tell how the an - gels, in cho - rus, Sang as they welcomed His birth,
Tell of the years of His la - bor, Tell of the sor - row He bore,
Love in that sto - ry so ten - der, Clear - er than ev - er I see:
D. C. for Chorus
"Glo - ry to God in the high - est! Peace and good ti - dings to earth."
He was de-spised and af - flict - ed, Home-less, re - ject - ed and poor.
Stay, let me weep while you whis - per, Love paid the ran - som for me.

198 Onward, Christian Soldiers

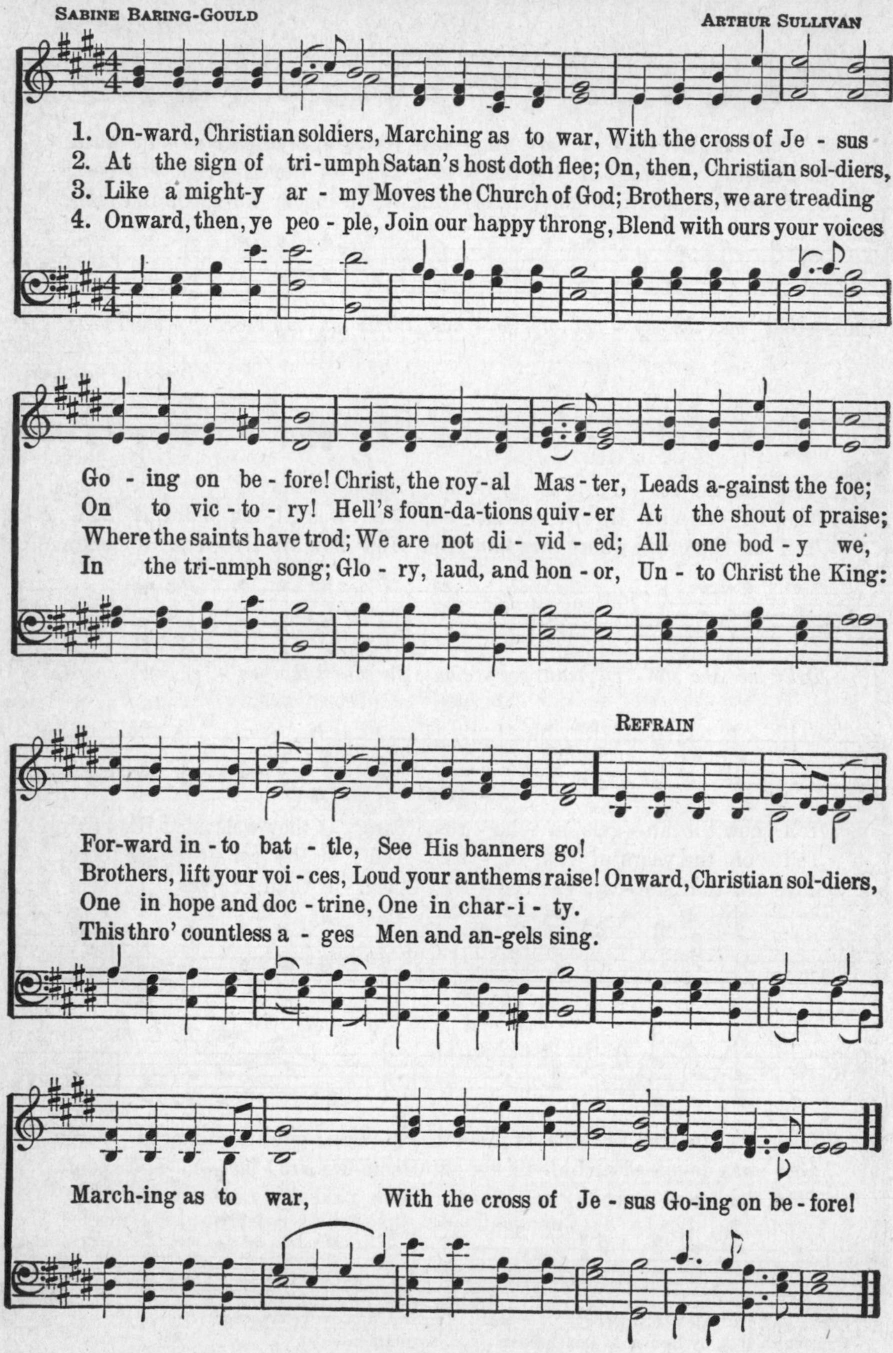

Sabine Baring-Gould
Arthur Sullivan
1. On-ward, Christian soldiers, Marching as to war, With the cross of Je - sus
2. At the sign of tri-umph Satan's host doth flee; On, then, Christian sol-diers,
3. Like a might-y ar - my Moves the Church of God; Brothers, we are treading
4. Onward, then, ye peo - ple, Join our happy throng, Blend with ours your voices
Go - ing on be - fore! Christ, the roy-al Mas-ter, Leads a-gainst the foe;
On to vic - to - ry! Hell's foun-da-tions quiv - er At the shout of praise;
Where the saints have trod; We are not di - vid - ed; All one bod - y we,
In the tri-umph song; Glo - ry, laud, and hon - or, Un - to Christ the King:
Refrain
For-ward in - to bat - tle, See His banners go!
Brothers, lift your voi - ces, Loud your anthems raise! Onward, Christian sol-diers,
One in hope and doc - trine, One in char - i - ty.
This thro' countless a - ges Men and an-gels sing.
March-ing as to war, With the cross of Je - sus Go-ing on be - fore!

199 Wonderful, Unfailing Friend

A. S. R. ALBERT SIMPSON REITZ

1. There nev - er was a tru - er Friend than Je - sus, He hears me when my
2. There nev - er was a tru - er Friend than Je - sus, My sor - rows He will
3. There nev - er was a tru - er Friend than Je - sus, He is my life and
heart for mer-cy pleads(for mer-cy pleads); And no one knows my burdens like my
al - ways with me share(will with me share); And since He bore His cross, my blessed
strength, my all in all (my all in all); Up - on the strong and loving arms of
Je - sus, For He a - lone can un-der-stand my needs.
Je - sus, There is no cross He will not help me bear.
Je - sus My soul shall rest, and nev-er, nev - er fall.
CHORUS
Won-der - ful, Un-
fail-ing Friend is Je-sus, He fills my soul with singing all the day; . . . .
yes, all the day;
Won-der-ful, E-ter-nal Friend is Je-sus, And He'll go with me all the way. . .
all the way.

200 Trust and Obey

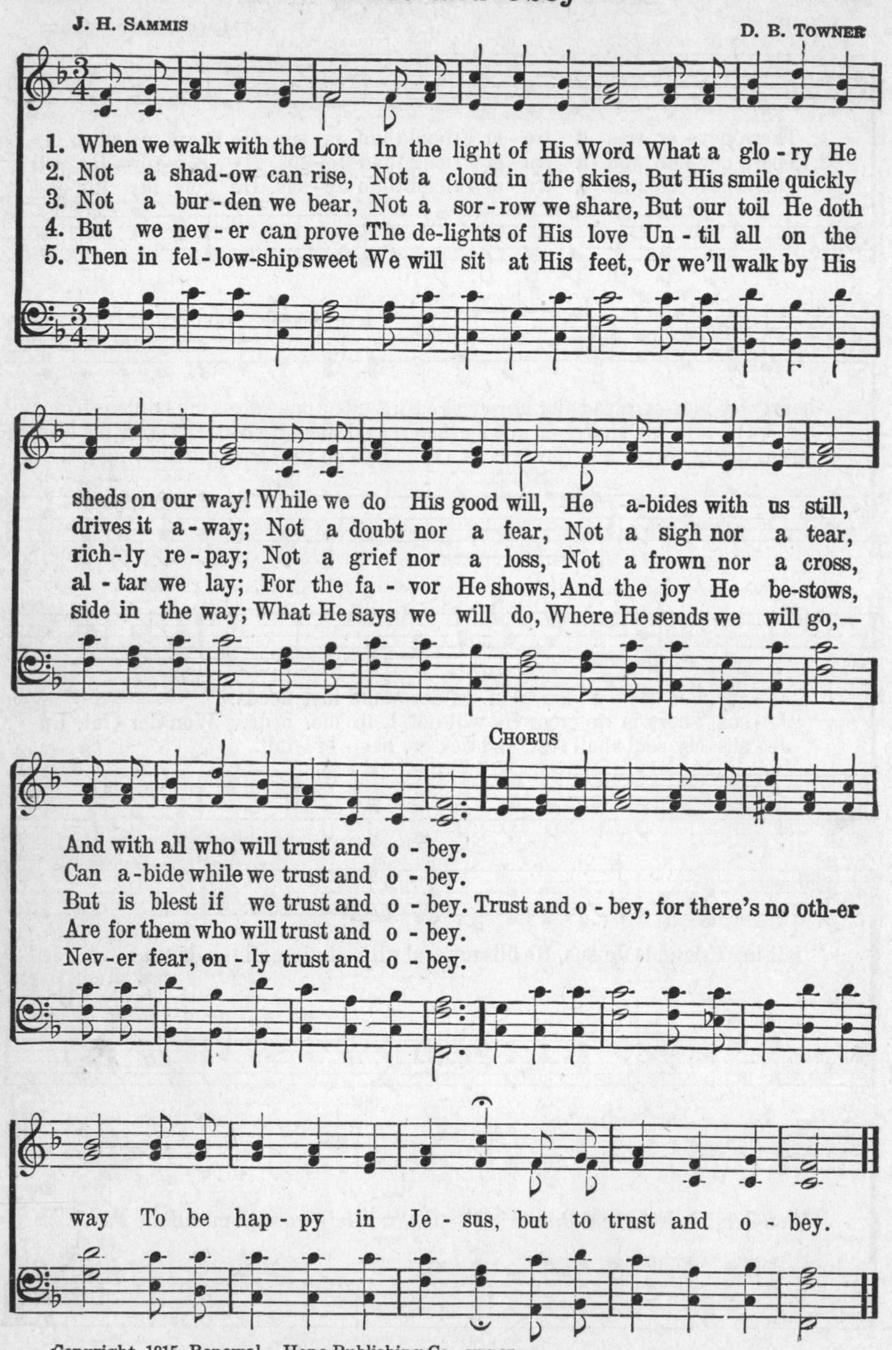
J. H. Sammis
D. B. Towner
1. When we walk with the Lord In the light of His Word What a glo - ry He
2. Not a shad-ow can rise, Not a cloud in the skies, But His smile quickly
3. Not a bur-den we bear, Not a sor-row we share, But our toil He doth
4. But we nev-er can prove The de-lights of His love Un - til all on the
5. Then in fel-low-ship sweet We will sit at His feet, Or we'll walk by His
sheds on our way! While we do His good will, He a-bides with us still,
drives it a-way; Not a doubt nor a fear, Not a sigh nor a tear,
rich-ly re-pay; Not a grief nor a loss, Not a frown nor a cross,
al - tar we lay; For the fa - vor He shows, And the joy He be-stows,
side in the way; What He says we will do, Where He sends we will go,—
Chorus
And with all who will trust and o - bey.
Can a-bide while we trust and o - bey.
But is blest if we trust and o - bey. Trust and o - bey, for there's no oth-er
Are for them who will trust and o - bey.
Nev-er fear, on - ly trust and o - bey.
way To be hap - py in Je - sus, but to trust and o - bey.

201 Meet Me in the Homeland

Ada R. Habershon — Robert Harkness

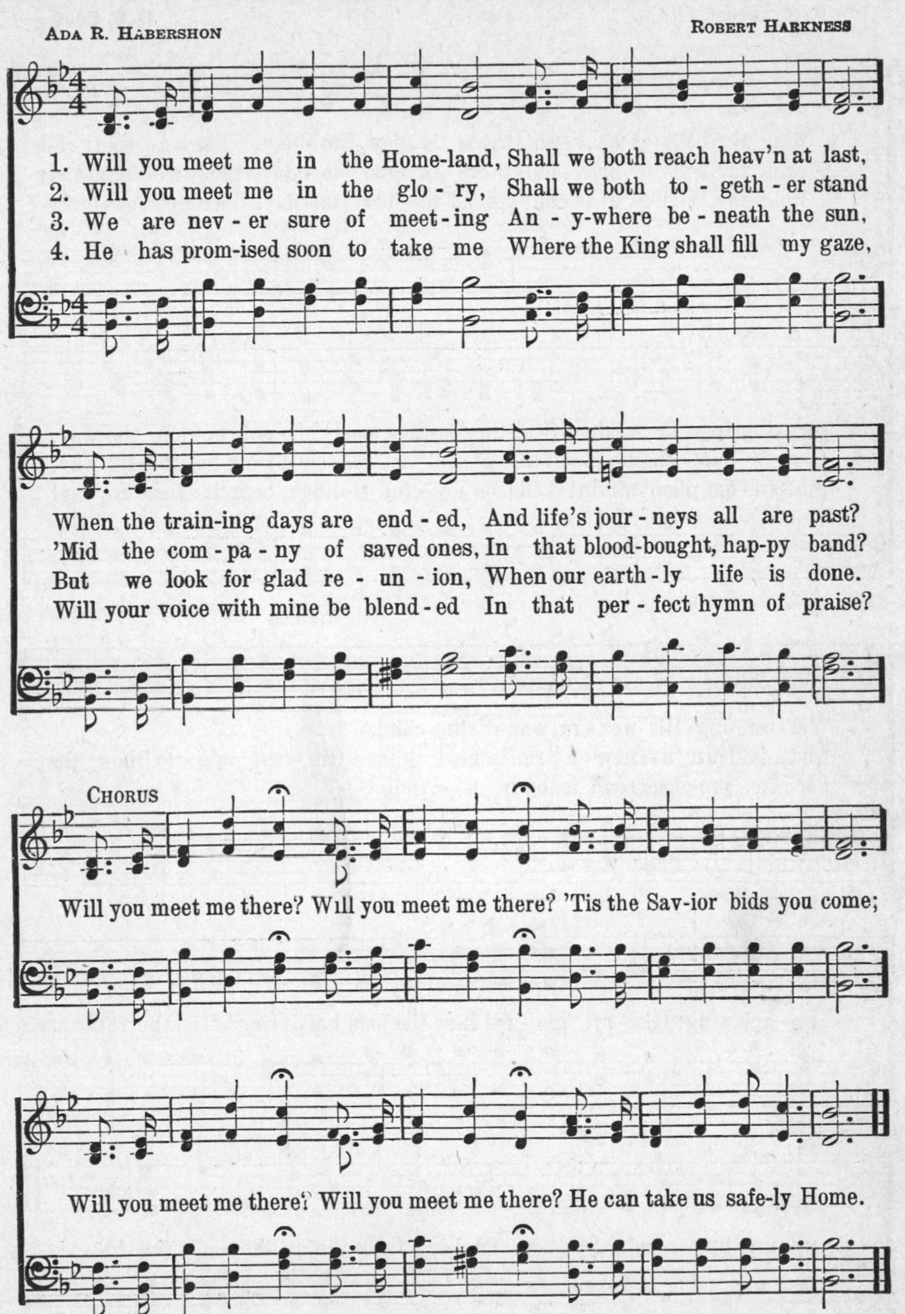
1. Will you meet me in the Home-land, Shall we both reach heav'n at last,
2. Will you meet me in the glo - ry, Shall we both to - geth - er stand
3. We are nev - er sure of meet-ing An - y-where be - neath the sun,
4. He has prom-ised soon to take me Where the King shall fill my gaze,
When the train-ing days are end - ed, And life's jour - neys all are past?
'Mid the com - pa - ny of saved ones, In that blood-bought, hap-py band?
But we look for glad re - un - ion, When our earth - ly life is done.
Will your voice with mine be blend - ed In that per - fect hymn of praise?
Chorus
Will you meet me there? Will you meet me there? 'Tis the Sav-ior bids you come;
Will you meet me there? Will you meet me there? He can take us safe-ly Home.

202 Ring the Bells of Heaven

W. O. CUSHING — G. F. ROOT

Joyfully
1. Ring the bells of heav-en! there is joy to-day, For a soul re-
2. Ring the bells of heav-en! there is joy to-day, For the wan-d'rer
3. Ring the bells of heav-en! spread the feast to-day, An-gels, swell the
turn-ing from the wild; See! the Fa-ther meets him out up-on the way,
now is rec-on-ciled; Yes, a soul is res-cued from his sin-ful way,
glad tri-um-phant strain! Tell the joy-ful ti-dings, bear it far a-way!
Wel-com-ing His wea-ry, wan-d'ring child.
And is born a-new a ran-somed child.
For a pre-cious soul is born a-gain.
CHORUS
Glo-ry! glo-ry! how the
an-gels sing; Glo-ry! glo-ry! how the loud harps ring! 'Tis the ran-somed
ar-my, like a might-y sea, Peal-ing forth the an-them of the free.

203 Jesus, I Come

W. T. Sleeper
Geo. C. Stebbins
1. Out of my bond-age, sor-row and night, Je-sus, I come, Je-sus, I come;
2. Out of my shame-ful fail-ure and loss, Je-sus, I come, Je-sus, I come;
3. Out of un-rest and ar-ro-gant pride, Je-sus, I come, Je-sus, I come;
4. Out of the fear and dread of the tomb, Je-sus, I come, Je-sus, I come;
In-to Thy free-dom, glad-ness and light, Je-sus, I come to Thee;
In-to the glo-rious gain of Thy cross, Je-sus, I come to Thee;
In-to Thy bless-ed will to a-bide, Je-sus, I come to Thee;
In-to the joy and light of Thy home, Je-sus, I come to Thee;
Out of my sick-ness in-to Thy health, Out of my want and in-to Thy wealth,
Out of earth's sorrows in-to Thy balm, Out of life's storms and in-to Thy calm,
Out of my-self to dwell in Thy love, Out of de-spair in-to rap-tures a-bove,
Out of the depths of ru-in un-told, In-to the peace of Thy sheltering fold,
Out of my sin and in-to Thy-self, Je-sus, I come to Thee.
Out of dis-tress to ju-bi-lant psalm, Je-sus, I come to Thee.
Up-ward for aye on wings like a dove, Je-sus, I come to Thee.
Ev-er Thy glo-rious face to be-hold, Je-sus, I come to Thee.

204 We're Marching to Zion

Isaac Watts
Robert Lowry
Spirited
1. Come, we that love the Lord, And let our joys be known, Join
2. Let those re - fuse to sing Who nev - er knew our God; But
3. The hill of Zi - on yields A thou - sand sa - cred sweets Be-
4. Then let our songs a - bound, And ev - 'ry tear be dry; We're
in a song with sweet ac - cord, Join in a song with sweet ac-cord, And
chil-dren of the heav'n-ly King, But chil-dren of the heav'n-ly King, May
fore we reach the heav'n-ly fields, Be - fore we reach the heav'n-ly fields, Or
marching thro' Immanuel's ground, We're marching thro' Immanuel's ground, To
thus sur - - round the throne, And thus sur-round the throne.
speak their joys a - broad, May speak their joys a - broad.
walk the gold - en streets, Or walk the gold - en streets.
fair - - er worlds on high, To fair - er worlds on high.
thus sur-round the throne, And thus sur - round the throne.
Chorus
We're march - ing to Zi - on, Beau-ti - ful, beau-ti - ful Zi - on; We're
We're march-ing on to Zi - on,
march-ing up-ward to Zi - on, The beau-ti - ful cit - y of God.
Zi - on, Zi - on,

205 Christ Arose

R. L. ROBERT LOWRY

1. Low in the grave He lay— Je - sus my Sav - ior! Wait-ing the com-ing day—
2. Vain-ly they watch His bed—Je - sus my Sav - ior! Vain-ly they seal the dead—
3. Death cannot keep his prey— Je - sus my Sav - ior! He tore the bars a - way—
Je - sus my Lord!
REFRAIN Faster
Up from the grave He a - rose, (He a-rose,) With a might-y tri-umph o'er His foes; (He a - rose!) He a - rose a Vic - tor from the dark do - main, And He lives for - ev - er with His saints to reign. He a-rose! He a - rose! He a - rose! He a - rose! Hal - le - lu - jah! Christ a - rose!
rit.

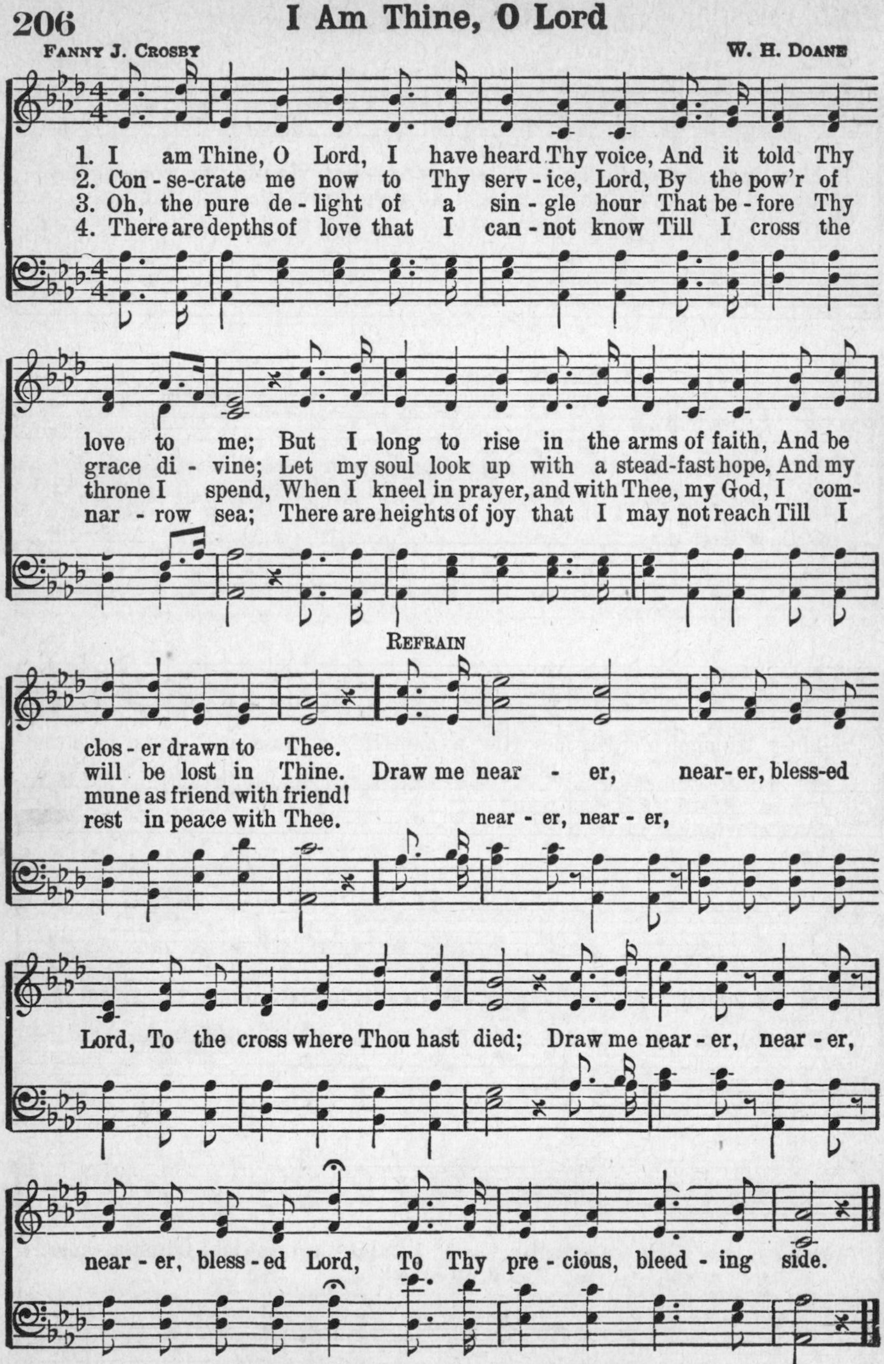
206
I Am Thine, O Lord
Fanny J. Crosby
W. H. Doane
1. I am Thine, O Lord, I have heard Thy voice, And it told Thy love to me; But I long to rise in the arms of faith, And be clos - er drawn to Thee.
2. Con - se-crate me now to Thy serv - ice, Lord, By the pow'r of grace di - vine; Let my soul look up with a stead-fast hope, And my will be lost in Thine.
3. Oh, the pure de - light of a sin - gle hour That be - fore Thy throne I spend, When I kneel in prayer, and with Thee, my God, I com - mune as friend with friend!
4. There are depths of love that I can - not know Till I cross the nar - row sea; There are heights of joy that I may not reach Till I rest in peace with Thee.
Refrain
Draw me near - er, near - er, bless-ed Lord, To the cross where Thou hast died; Draw me near - er, near - er, near - er, bless - ed Lord, To Thy pre - cious, bleed - ing side.
near - er, near - er,

207 He Hideth My Soul

FANNY J. CROSBY — WM. J. KIRKPATRICK

1. A wonderful Savior is Jesus my Lord,
A wonderful Savior to me,
He hideth my soul in the cleft of the rock,
Where rivers of pleasure I see.

2. A wonderful Savior is Jesus my Lord,
He taketh my burden away,
He holdeth me up, and I shall not be moved,
He giveth me strength as my day.

3. With numberless blessings each moment He crowns,
And filled with His fullness divine,
I sing in my rapture, oh, glory to God
For such a Redeemer as mine!

4. When clothed in His brightness, transported I rise
To meet Him in clouds of the sky,
His perfect salvation, His wonderful love,
I'll shout with the millions on high.

CHORUS

He hideth my soul in the cleft of the rock
That shadows a dry, thirsty land;
He hideth my life in the depths of His love,
And covers me there with His hand,
And covers me there with His hand.

208 There Shall Be Showers of Blessing

El Nathan — James McGranahan

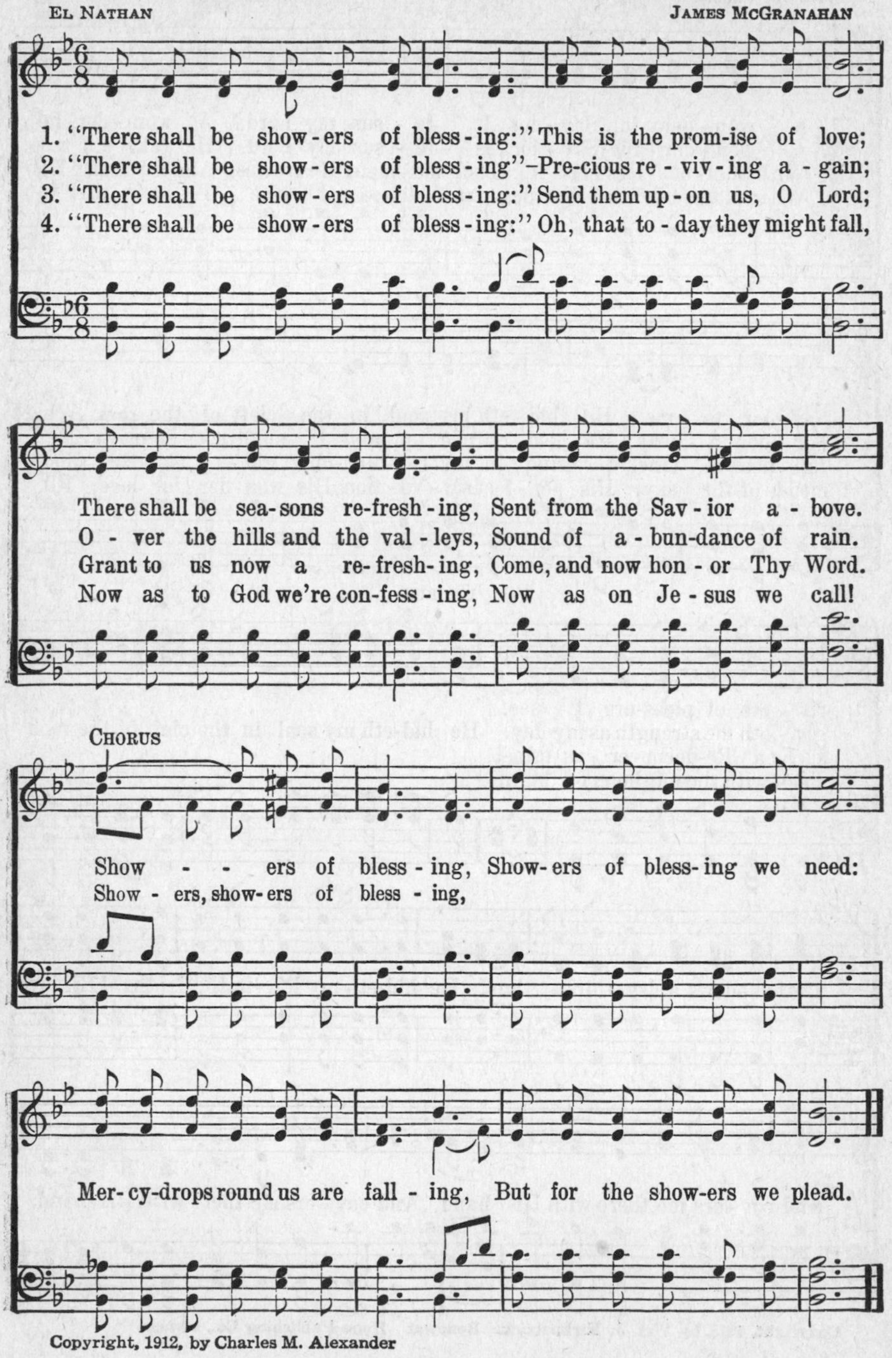
1. "There shall be show-ers of bless-ing:" This is the prom-ise of love;
2. "There shall be show-ers of bless-ing"–Pre-cious re-viv-ing a-gain;
3. "There shall be show-ers of bless-ing:" Send them up-on us, O Lord;
4. "There shall be show-ers of bless-ing:" Oh, that to-day they might fall,
There shall be sea-sons re-fresh-ing, Sent from the Sav-ior a-bove.
O-ver the hills and the val-leys, Sound of a-bun-dance of rain.
Grant to us now a re-fresh-ing, Come, and now hon-or Thy Word.
Now as to God we're con-fess-ing, Now as on Je-sus we call!
Chorus
Show - - ers of bless-ing, Show-ers of bless-ing we need:
Show-ers, show-ers of bless-ing,
Mer-cy-drops round us are fall-ing, But for the show-ers we plead.

209 Since I Have Been Redeemed

E. O. E. E. O. Excell

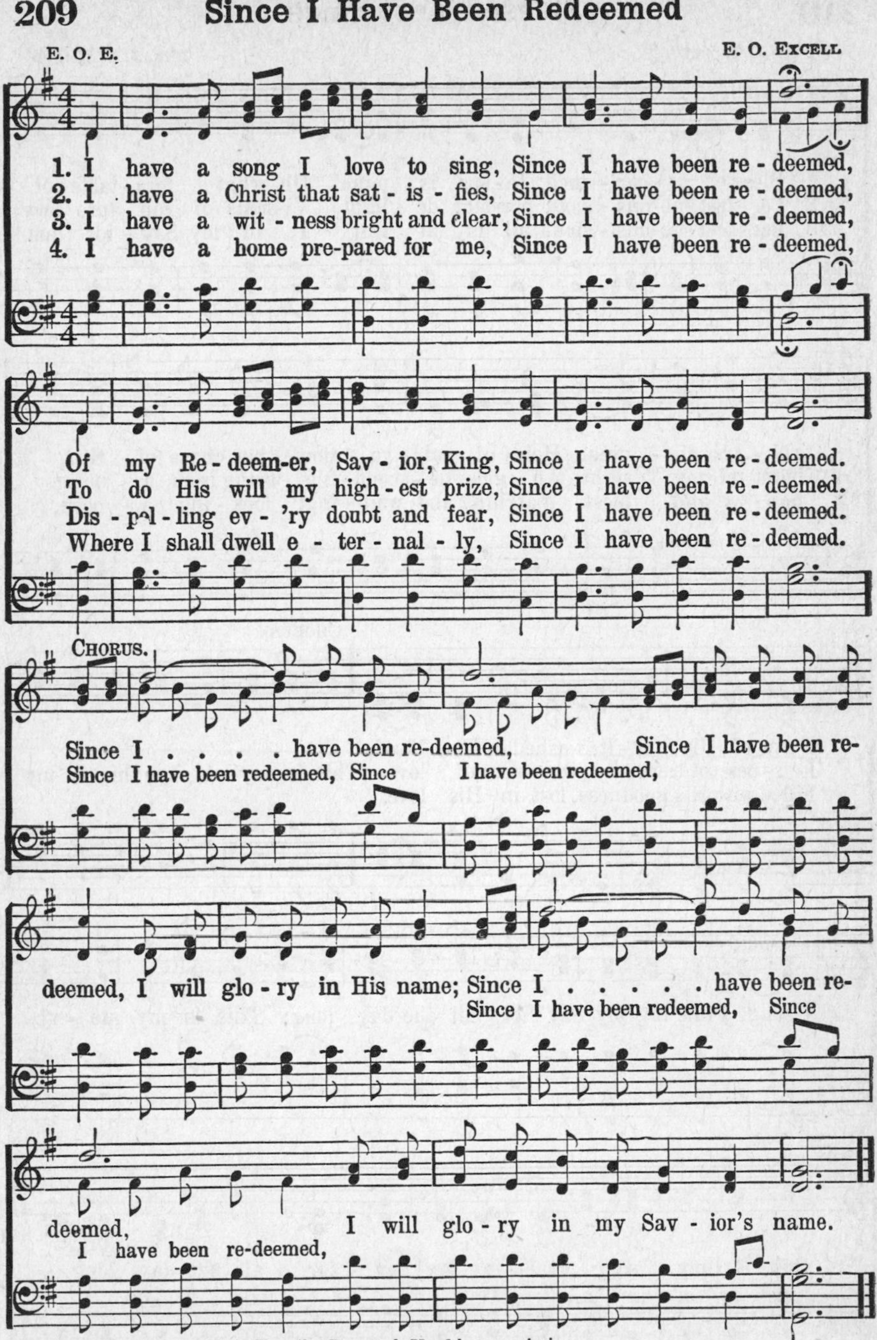
1. I have a song I love to sing, Since I have been re-deemed,
2. I have a Christ that sat-is-fies, Since I have been re-deemed,
3. I have a wit-ness bright and clear, Since I have been re-deemed,
4. I have a home pre-pared for me, Since I have been re-deemed,
Of my Re-deem-er, Sav-ior, King, Since I have been re-deemed.
To do His will my high-est prize, Since I have been re-deemed.
Dis-pel-ling ev-'ry doubt and fear, Since I have been re-deemed.
Where I shall dwell e-ter-nal-ly, Since I have been re-deemed.
Chorus.
Since I . . . . . have been re-deemed, Since I have been re-
Since I have been redeemed, Since I have been redeemed,
deemed, I will glo-ry in His name; Since I . . . . . have been re-
Since I have been redeemed, Since
deemed, I will glo-ry in my Sav-ior's name.
I have been re-deemed,

Blessed Assurance

FANNY J. CROSBY — MRS. J. F. KNAPP

1. Bless-ed as-sur-ance, Je-sus is mine! Oh, what a fore-taste of glo-ry di-vine! Heir of sal-va-tion, pur-chase of God, Born of His Spir-it, washed in His blood.
2. Per-fect sub-mis-sion, per-fect de-light, Vi-sions of rap-ture now burst on my sight; An-gels de-scend-ing, bring from a-bove Ech-oes of mer-cy, whis-pers of love.
3. Per-fect sub-mis-sion, all is at rest, I in my Sav-ior am hap-py and blest; Watching and wait-ing, look-ing a-bove, Filled with His goodness, lost in His love.
CHORUS
This is my sto-ry, this is my song, Prais-ing my Sav-ior all the day long; This is my sto-ry, this is my song, Prais-ing my Sav-ior all the day long.

211 Grace, Enough For Me

E. O. E.
E. O. Excell
1. In look-ing thro' my tears one day, I saw Mount Cal-va-ry; Be-neath the cross there flowed a stream Of grace, e-nough for me.
2. While standing there, my trem-bling heart, Once full of ag-o-ny, Could scarce be-lieve the sight I saw Of grace, e-nough for me.
3. When I be-held my ev-'ry sin Nailed to the cru-el tree, I felt a flood go thro' my soul Of grace, e-nough for me.
4. When I am safe with-in the veil, My por-tion there will be, To sing thro' all the years to come Of grace, e-nough for me.
e-nough for me.
Chorus
Grace is flow-ing from Cal-va-ry, . . .
Grace is flow-ing from Cal-va-ry for me,
Grace as fath-om-less as the sea, . . Grace for time and e-ter-ni-ty, ... Grace . . . e-nough for me.
Grace as fath-om-less as the roll-ing sea, Grace for time and e-ter-ni-ty, His a-bun-dant grace I see, e-nough for me.

212 Beloved, Now Are We

Maj. D. W. Whittle (El Nathan) JAMES McGRANAHAN

Moderato
1. Sons of God, be - loved in Je - sus! O the won-drous word of grace;
2. Bless-ed hope now bright-ly beam - ing, On our God we soon shall gaze;
3. By the pow'r of grace trans-form-ing, We shall then His im - age bear;
In His Son the Fa - ther sees us, And as sons He gives us place.
And in light ce - les - tial gleam-ing, We shall see our Sav - ior's face.
Christ His prom-ised word per-form - ing, We shall then His glo - ry share.
CHORUS I John 3: 2
Be - lov - ed, now are we the sons of God, And it doth not yet ap-
pear what we shall be; But we know . . . that when He shall ap-
But we know, we know, we
pear; . . . . We know . . that when He shall ap-
know that when He shall ap - pear; We know, we know, we

Beloved, Now Are We
ff
pear, ... We shall be like Him, we shall be
know that when He shall ap - pear,
rit.
like Him, For we shall see . . Him as . . . He is." . . . .
213
In Jesus
Jas. Procter
Robert Harkness
1. I've tried in vain a thou-sand ways My fears to quell, my hopes to
2. My soul is night, my heart is steel—I can-not see, I can-not
3. He died, He lives, He reigns, He pleads; There's love in all His words and
4. Tho' some should sneer, and some should blame, I'll go with all my guilt and
raise; But what I need, the Bi-ble says, Is ev-er, on-ly Je-sus.
feel; For light, for life I must ap-peal In sim-ple faith to Je-sus.
deeds; There's all a guilt-y sin-ner needs For-ev-er-more in Je-sus.
shame; I'll go to Him be-cause His name, A-bove all names, is Je-sus.

214 Oh, What a Change!

Ada R. Habershon

Robert Harkness

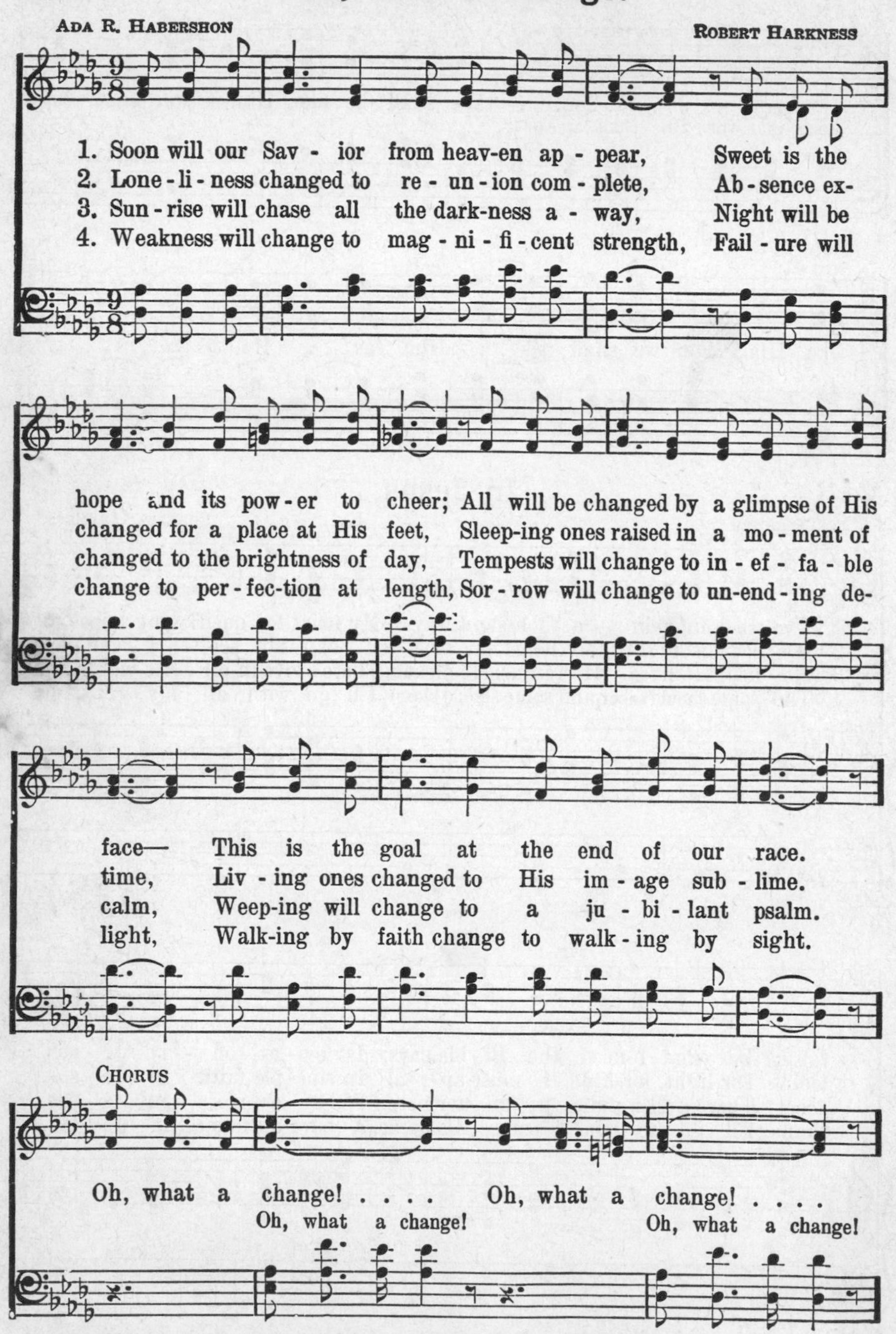

1. Soon will our Sav - ior from heav-en ap - pear, Sweet is the
2. Lone - li - ness changed to re - un - ion com - plete, Ab - sence ex-
3. Sun - rise will chase all the dark-ness a - way, Night will be
4. Weakness will change to mag - ni - fi - cent strength, Fail - ure will
hope and its pow - er to cheer; All will be changed by a glimpse of His
changed for a place at His feet, Sleep-ing ones raised in a mo - ment of
changed to the brightness of day, Tempests will change to in - ef - fa - ble
change to per - fec-tion at length, Sor - row will change to un-end - ing de-
face— This is the goal at the end of our race.
time, Liv - ing ones changed to His im - age sub - lime.
calm, Weep-ing will change to a ju - bi - lant psalm.
light, Walk-ing by faith change to walk - ing by sight.
Chorus
Oh, what a change! . . . . Oh, what a change! . . . .
Oh, what a change! Oh, what a change!

Oh, What a Change!

When I shall see His won-der-ful face! Oh, what a change! . . .
Oh, what a change!
Oh, what a change! . . . When I shall see His face!
Oh, what a change!
215
The Old-Time Religion
CHO.—'Tis the old - time re - lig - ion, 'Tis the old - time re - lig - ion,
1. It was good for our moth-ers, It was good for our moth-ers,
2. It has saved our . . fa - thers, I has saved our . . fa - thers,
3. Makes me love ev - 'ry - bod - y, Makes me love ev - 'ry - bod - y,
4. It will do when I am dy - ing, It will do when I am dy - ing,
5. It will take us all to heav - en, It will take us all to heav - en,
'Tis the old - time re - lig - ion, And it's good e-nough for me.
It was good for our moth - ers, And it's good e-nough for me.
It has saved our . . fa - thers, And it's good e-nough for me.
Makes me love ev - 'ry - bod - y, And it's good e-nough for me.
It will do when I am dy - ing, And it's good e-nough for me.
It will take us all to heav - en, And it's good e-nough for me.

216 Lean On His Arms

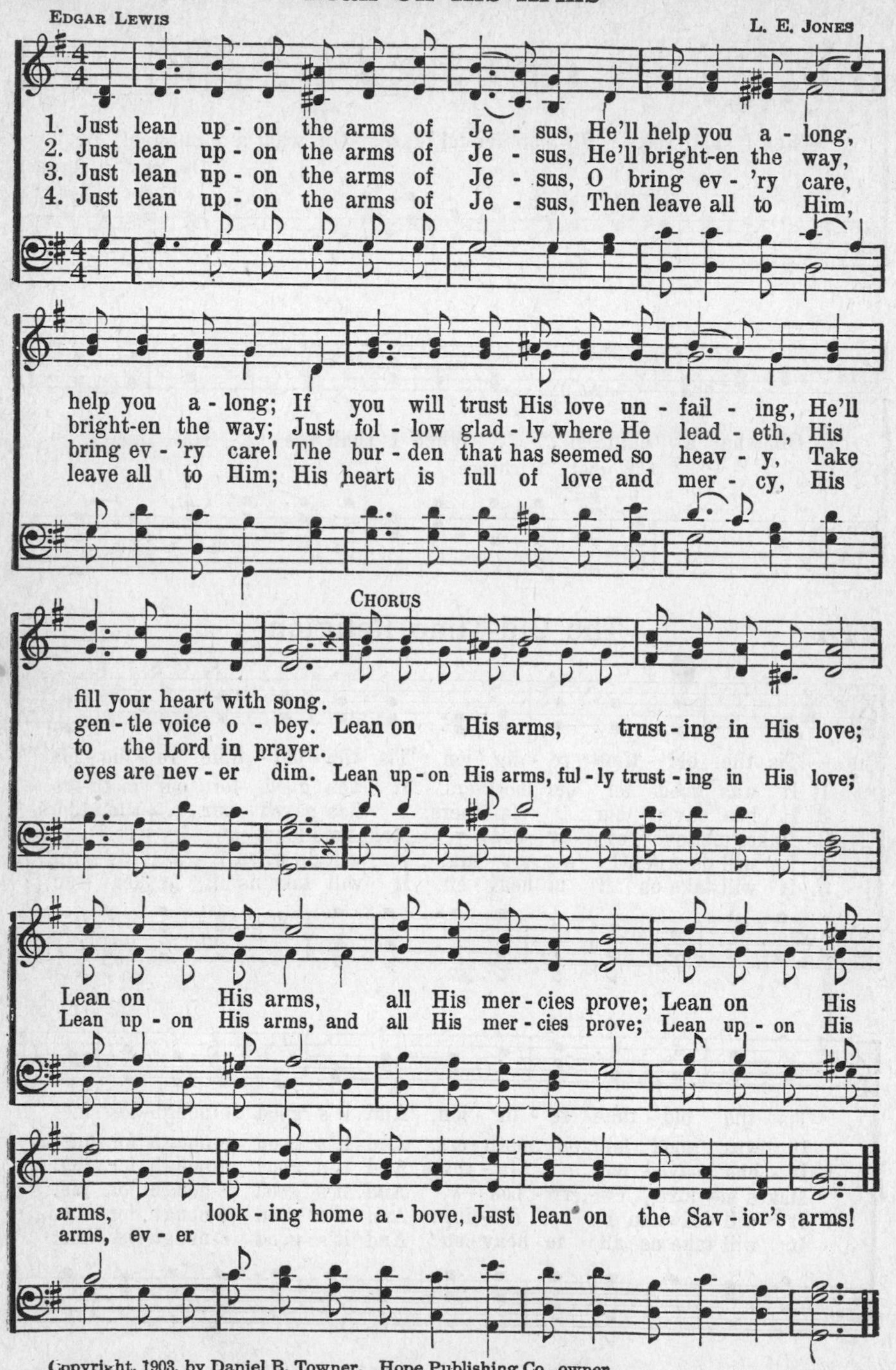

Edgar Lewis
L. E. Jones
1. Just lean up - on the arms of Je - sus, He'll help you a - long, help you a - long; If you will trust His love un - fail - ing, He'll fill your heart with song.
2. Just lean up - on the arms of Je - sus, He'll bright-en the way, bright-en the way; Just fol - low glad - ly where He lead - eth, His gen-tle voice o - bey.
3. Just lean up - on the arms of Je - sus, O bring ev - 'ry care, bring ev - 'ry care! The bur - den that has seemed so heav - y, Take to the Lord in prayer.
4. Just lean up - on the arms of Je - sus, Then leave all to Him, leave all to Him; His heart is full of love and mer - cy, His eyes are nev - er dim.
CHORUS
Lean on His arms, trust-ing in His love;
Lean up-on His arms, ful-ly trust-ing in His love;
Lean on His arms, all His mer-cies prove;
Lean up - on His arms, and all His mer-cies prove;
Lean on His arms, look-ing home a - bove, Just lean on the Sav-ior's arms!
Lean up - on His arms, ev - er

217 That Beautiful Name

Jean Perry, alt.

Mabel Johnston Camp

1. I know of a Name, A beau-ti-ful Name, That an-gels bro't down to earth; They whis-pered it low, One night long a-go, To a maid-en of low-ly birth.
2. I know of a Name, A beau-ti-ful Name, That un-to a Babe was given; The stars glit-tered bright Thro'-out that glad night, And an-gels praised God in heav'n.
3. The One of that Name, My Sav-ior be-came, My Sav-ior of Cal-va-ry; My sins nailed Him there, My bur-dens He bare, He suf-fered all this for me.
4. I love that blest Name, That won-der-ful Name, Made high-er than all in heav'n; 'Twas whis-pered, I know, In my heart long a-go— To Je-sus my life I've giv'n.
Chorus
That beau-ti-ful Name, That beau-ti-ful Name, From sin has pow'r to free us! That beau-ti-ful Name, That won-der-ful Name, That match-less Name is Je-sus!
rit.
cres.
ad lib.

218 Open My Eyes That I May See

C. H. S. CHAS. H. SCOTT

1. O - pen my eyes, that I may see Glimps-es of truth Thou hast for me;
2. O - pen my ears, that I may hear Voi - ces of truth Thou send-est clear;
3. O - pen my mouth, and let me bear Glad - ly the warm truth ev-'ry-where;
Place in my hands the won-der-ful key That shall un-clasp, and set me free.
And while the wave-notes fall on my ear, Ev - 'ry-thing false will dis - ap-pear.
O - pen my heart, and let me pre-pare Love with Thy chil-dren thus to share.
Si-lent-ly now I wait for Thee, Read-y, my God, Thy will to see;
Si-lent-ly now I wait for Thee, Read-y, my God, Thy will to see;
Si-lent-ly now I wait for Thee, Read-y, my God, Thy will to see;
O - pen my eyes, il - lu - mine me, Spir - it di - vine!
O - pen my ears, il - lu - mine me, Spir - it di - vine!
O - pen my heart, il - lu - mine me, Spir - it di - vine!

219 No, Not One!

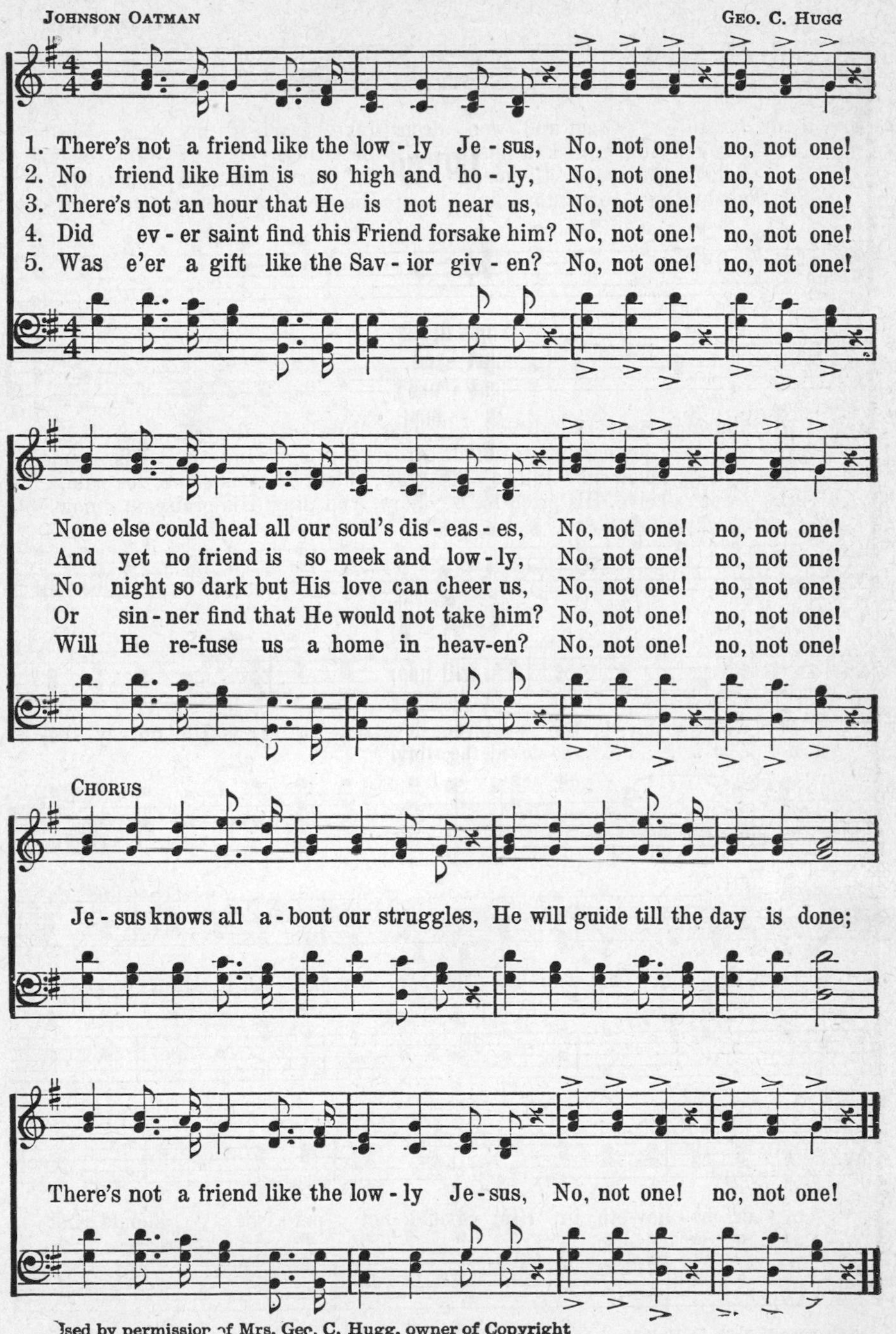
JOHNSON OATMAN
GEO. C. HUGG
1. There's not a friend like the low - ly Je - sus, No, not one! no, not one!
2. No friend like Him is so high and ho - ly, No, not one! no, not one!
3. There's not an hour that He is not near us, No, not one! no, not one!
4. Did ev - er saint find this Friend forsake him? No, not one! no, not one!
5. Was e'er a gift like the Sav - ior giv - en? No, not one! no, not one!
None else could heal all our soul's dis - eas - es, No, not one! no, not one!
And yet no friend is so meek and low - ly, No, not one! no, not one!
No night so dark but His love can cheer us, No, not one! no, not one!
Or sin - ner find that He would not take him? No, not one! no, not one!
Will He re-fuse us a home in heav-en? No, not one! no, not one!
CHORUS
Je - sus knows all a - bout our struggles, He will guide till the day is done;
There's not a friend like the low - ly Je - sus, No, not one! no, not one!

220 For God So Loved the World

E. E. HEWITT

J. LINCOLN HALL

1. A sto - ry sweet and won - drous, Like heav'n-ly mu - sic swells;
2. When, grieving, bro - ken-heart - ed, Be - cause of sin and shame,
3. This love, be - yond all meas - ure Of earth or sea or sky,
4. Come, broth-er, come to Je - sus; His word was meant for you;
In chim-ings clear to all who will hear, Ring out the gos - pel bells.
We find a joy earth can-not de-stroy, Be - liev - ing on His name.
Could on - ly show its full o - ver-flow, When Je - sus came to die.
His grace re-ceive, His prom-ise be - lieve, And sing His praise a - new.
CHORUS
For God so loved the world . . . that He gave His on - ly be-
For God . . . . so loved the world
got - ten Son, That who - so - ev - er be - liev-eth in Him, Who - so-
ev - er be - liev-eth in Him Should not per - ish, should not

For God So Loved the World
per - ish, But have ev - er - last - ing life. . . . .
ev - er - last - ing life.
221
Hold the Fort
P. P. B.
P. P. Bliss
1. Ho, my com - rades! see the sig - nal Wav - ing in the sky!
2. See the might - y host ad - vanc - ing, Sa - tan lead - ing on;
3. See the glo - rious ban - ner wav - ing! Hear the trump - et blow!
4. Fierce and long the bat - tle rag - es, But our help is near;
Re - in - force - ments now ap - pear - ing, Vic - to - ry is nigh.
Might - y men a - round us fall - ing, Cour - age al - most gone!
In our Lead - er's name we tri - umph O - ver ev - 'ry foe.
On - ward comes our great Com - mand - er, Cheer, my com - rades, cheer!
Chorus
"Hold the fort, for I am com - ing," Je - sus sig - nals still;
Wave the an - swer back to heav - en, "By Thy grace we will."

222 Leave It There

C. Albert Tindley
Arr. by Chas. A. Tindley, Jr.
Moderato
1. If the world from you with-hold of its sil - ver and its gold, And you
2. If your bod - y suf - fers pain and your health you can't re-gain, And your
3. When your en - e - mies as - sail and your heart be - gins to fail, Don't for-
4. When your youthful days are gone and old age is steal-ing on, And your
have to get a-long with mea-ger fare, Just re-mem-ber, in His word, how He
soul is al-most sink-ing in de - spair, Je - sus knows the pain you feel, He can
get that God in heav-en answers prayer; He will make a way for you and will
bod - y bends beneath the weight of care; He will nev - er leave you then, He'll go
feeds the lit - tle bird; Take your bur - den to the Lord and leave it there.
save and He can heal; Take your bur - den to the Lord and leave it there.
lead you safe - ly thro'; Take your bur - den to the Lord and leave it there.
with you to the end; Take your bur - den to the Lord and leave it there.
Chorus
Leave it there, . . . leave it there, ... Take your bur-den to the
Leave it there, leave it there,
Lord and leave it there; . . . . If you trust and nev - er doubt, He will
leave it there;

Leave It There

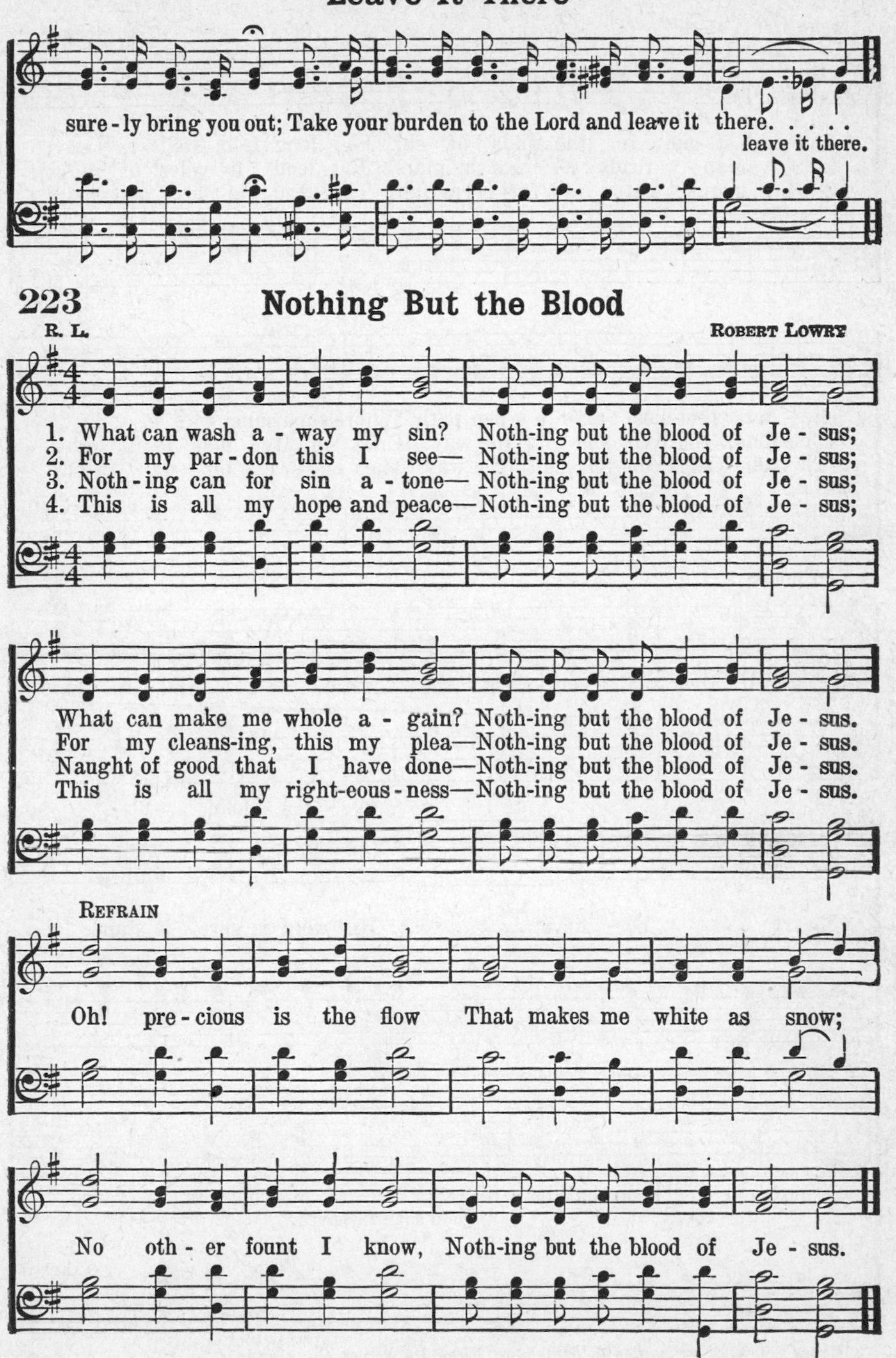

sure - ly bring you out; Take your burden to the Lord and leave it there. . . . .
leave it there.

223

Nothing But the Blood

R. L.

Robert Lowry

1. What can wash a - way my sin? Noth-ing but the blood of Je - sus;
2. For my par - don this I see— Noth-ing but the blood of Je - sus;
3. Noth - ing can for sin a - tone— Noth-ing but the blood of Je - sus;
4. This is all my hope and peace—Noth-ing but the blood of Je - sus;

What can make me whole a - gain? Noth-ing but the blood of Je - sus.
For my cleans-ing, this my plea—Noth-ing but the blood of Je - sus.
Naught of good that I have done—Noth-ing but the blood of Je - sus.
This is all my right-eous - ness—Noth-ing but the blood of Je - sus.

Refrain

Oh! pre - cious is the flow That makes me white as snow;

No oth - er fount I know, Noth-ing but the blood of Je - sus.

224 If Thou Shalt Confess

JOHN R. CLEMENTS B. D. ACKLEY

1. O lost one in the wilds of sin, So long from God a - way;
2. So man - y roads a - cross the marsh But lead to vales of night;
3. How man - y paths at first seem fair, That lead to loss and pain!
Be - fore thee lies an o - pen path, Where thou canst walk to - day.
This one, "the true and liv - ing way," Ends in the fade - less light.
This one yields com - fort all the way, The end e - ter - nal gain.
CHORUS
For if thou shalt con - fess the Lord, ... And in thine
the Lord,
heart be - lieve; . . . . His word is sure, it stands se-
thine heart
And in thine heart be - lieve,
rit.
cure, ... "Thou shalt be saved," . . . . "Thou shalt be saved."
se - cure,
"Thou shalt be saved,"

225 There is a Green Hill Far Away

Cecil F. Alexander — Geo. C. Stebbins

1. There is a green hill far a-way, With-out a cit-y wall,
2. We may not know, we can-not tell What pains He had to bear;
3. He died that we might be for-giv'n, He died to make us good,
4. There was no oth-er good e-nough, To pay the price of sin;
Where the dear Lord was cru-ci-fied, Who died to save us all.
But we be-lieve it was for us He hung and suf-fered there.
That we might go at last to Heav'n, Saved by His pre-cious blood.
He on-ly could un-lock the gate Of Heav'n and let us in.
Chorus
Oh, dear-ly, dear-ly has He loved, And we must love Him, too;
rit . . .
And trust in His re-deem-ing blood, And try His works to do.

226 What a Savior is Mine!
E. E. H.
E. E. Hewitt
1. Beth - le - hem, Cal - va - ry, Ol - i - vet, tell, Oh, what a
2. There, on the cross, where He died for my sin, Oh, what a
3. Ris - ing a - gain in His in - fi - nite grace, Oh, what a
4. Lift - ing my bur - dens, re - liev - ing my care, Oh, what a
Sav - ior is mine! Moun-tain and plain with His prais - es shall swell,
Sav - ior is mine! Giv - ing His life a poor wan-d'rer to win,
Sav - ior is mine! Shed-ding up - on me the light of His face,
Sav - ior is mine! Giv - ing me cour - age to do and to dare,
Oh, what a Sav - ior is mine!
Chorus
Oh, what a Sav - ior!
Oh, what a Sav - ior! Oh, what a Sav - ior is mine! Un - to the
ut - ter-most, won-der-ful, glo - ri - ous! Oh, what a Sav - ior is mine!

227 I Will Praise Him

M. J. H.
Mrs. M. J. Harris
1. When I saw the cleansing foun-tain O - pen wide for all my sin,
2. Tho' the way seems straight and narrow, All I claimed was swept a - way;
3. Then God's fire up - on the al - tar Of my heart was set a - flame;
4. Bless - ed be the name of Je - sus! I'm so glad He took me in;
5. Glo - ry, glo - ry to the Fa - ther! Glo - ry, glo - ry to the Son!
I o - beyed the Spir - it's woo - ing, When He said, Wilt thou be clean?
My am - bi-tions, plans, and wish-es, At my feet in ash - es lay.
I shall nev - er cease to praise Him, Glo - ry, glo - ry to His name!
He's for - giv - en my trans-gres-sions, He has cleansed my heart from sin.
Glo - ry, glo - ry to the Spir - it! Glo - ry to the Three in One!
Chorus Faster
I will praise Him! I will praise Him! Praise the Lamb for sinners slain;
for sin-ners slain;
Give Him glo-ry, all ye peo - ple, For His blood can wash a-way each stain.

228 Oh, Wonderful Love!

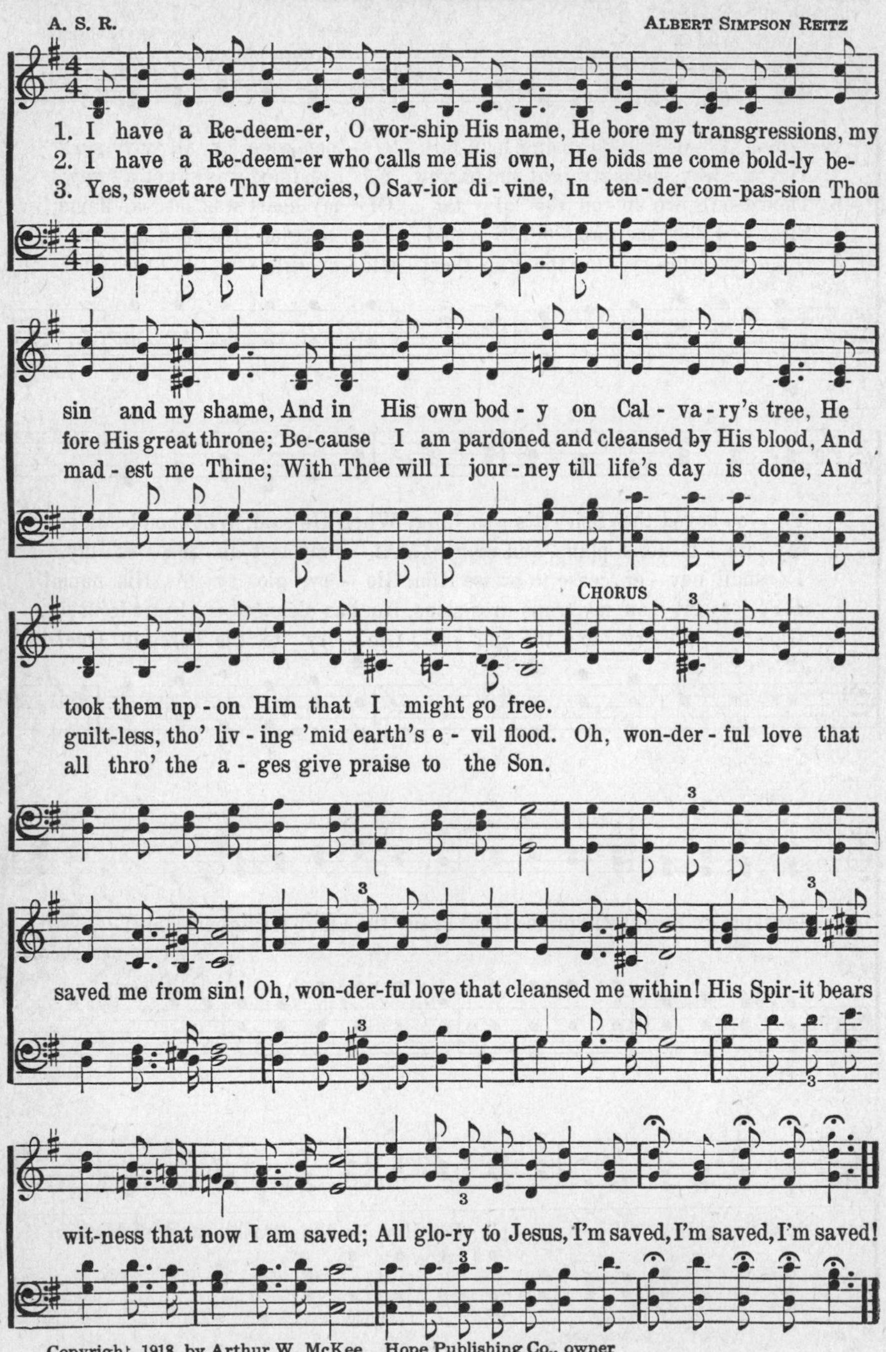
A. S. R.
Albert Simpson Reitz
1. I have a Re-deem-er, O wor-ship His name, He bore my transgressions, my sin and my shame, And in His own bod - y on Cal - va - ry's tree, He took them up - on Him that I might go free.
2. I have a Re-deem-er who calls me His own, He bids me come bold-ly be-fore His great throne; Be-cause I am pardoned and cleansed by His blood, And guilt-less, tho' liv - ing 'mid earth's e - vil flood.
3. Yes, sweet are Thy mercies, O Sav-ior di - vine, In ten - der com-pas-sion Thou mad - est me Thine; With Thee will I jour - ney till life's day is done, And all thro' the a - ges give praise to the Son.
Chorus
Oh, won-der - ful love that saved me from sin! Oh, won-der-ful love that cleansed me within! His Spir-it bears wit-ness that now I am saved; All glo-ry to Jesus, I'm saved, I'm saved, I'm saved!
3
3
3
3
3
3
3

229 Will Jesus Find Us Watching?

FANNY J. CROSBY
W. H. DOANE
1. When Je - sus comes to re - ward His serv-ants, Wheth-er it be
2. If, at the dawn of the ear - ly morn-ing, He shall call us
3. Have we been true to the trust He left us? Do we seek to
4. Bless - ed are those whom the Lord finds watch-ing, In His glo - ry
noon or night, Faith - ful to Him will He find us watch-ing,
one by one, When to the Lord we re - store our tal - ents,
do our best? If in our hearts there is naught con - demns us,
they shall share; If He shall come at the dawn or mid - night,
rit.
With our lamps all trimmed and bright?
Will He an - swer thee—"Well done"?
We shall have a glo - rious rest.
Will He find us watch - ing there?
CHORUS
Oh, can we say we are
read - y, broth-er? Read - y for the soul's bright home? Say, will He
find you and me still watch-ing, Wait-ing, wait-ing when the Lord shall come?

230 Let Him In

J. B. ATCHINSON — E. O. EXCELL

1. There's a Stran-ger at the door, Let Him in;
2. O - pen now to Him your heart, Let Him in;
3. Hear you now His lov - ing voice? Let Him in;
4. Now ad - mit the heav'n-ly Guest, Let Him in;
Let the Sav-ior in, Let the Sav-ior in;
He has been there oft be - fore, Let Him in;
If you wait He will de - part, Let Him in;
Now, oh, now make Him your choice, Let Him in;
He will make for you a feast, Let Him in;
Let the Sav-ior in, Let the Sav-ior in;
Let Him in, ere He is gone, Let Him in, the Ho - ly One, Je - sus
Let Him in, He is your Friend, He your soul will sure de - fend, He will
He is stand-ing at your door, Joy to you He will re - store, And His
He will speak your sins for-giv'n, And when earth ties all are riv'n, He will
Christ, the Fa - ther's Son, Let Him in.
keep you to the end, Let Him in.
name you will a - dore, Let Him in.
take you home to heav'n, Let Him in.
Let the Sav-ior in, Let the Sav-ior in.

231 The Ninety and Nine

ELIZABETH C. CLEPHANE — IRA D. SANKEY

1. There were ninety and nine that safe - ly lay In the shel-ter of the
2. "Lord, Thou hast here Thy nine-ty and nine; Are they not enough for
3. But none of the ransomed ev - er knew How deep were the waters
4. "Lord, whence are those blood-drops all the way That mark out the mountain's
5. But all thro' the mountains, thun-der-riv'n, And up from the rock-y

fold, But one was out on the hills a-way, Far off from the
Thee?" But the Shep-herd made answer: "This of mine Has wan-dered a-
crossed; Nor how dark was the night that the Lord passed thro' Ere He found His
track?" "They were shed for one who had gone a-stray Ere the Shepherd could
steep, There a-rose a glad cry to the gate of heav'n, "Re - joice! I have

rit.

gates of gold— A - way on the moun - tains wild and bare, A-
way from me, And al - tho' the road be rough and steep, I
sheep that was lost. Out in the des - ert He heard its cry—
bring him back." "Lord, whence are Thy hands so rent and torn?" "They're
found my sheep!" And the an - gels ech-oed a - round the throne, "Re-

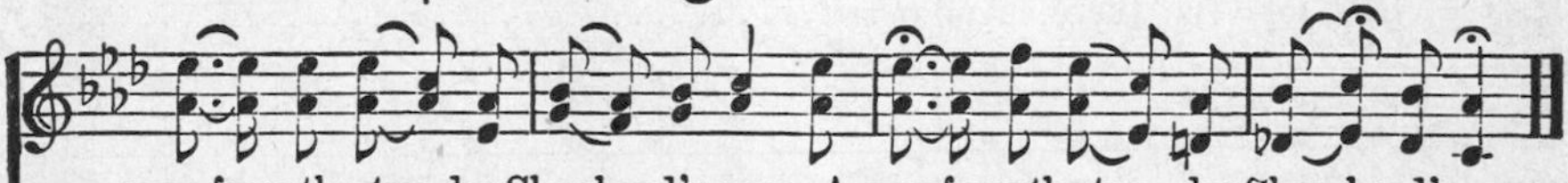

way from the ten-der Shepherd's care, A-way from the ten - der Shep-herd's care.
go to the des-ert to find my sheep, I go to the des-ert to find my sheep."
Sick and helpless, and ready to die; Sick and helpless, and ready to die.
pierced to - night by many a thorn; They're pierced to-night by man-y a thorn."
joice, for the Lord brings back His own! Re-joice, for the Lord brings back His own."

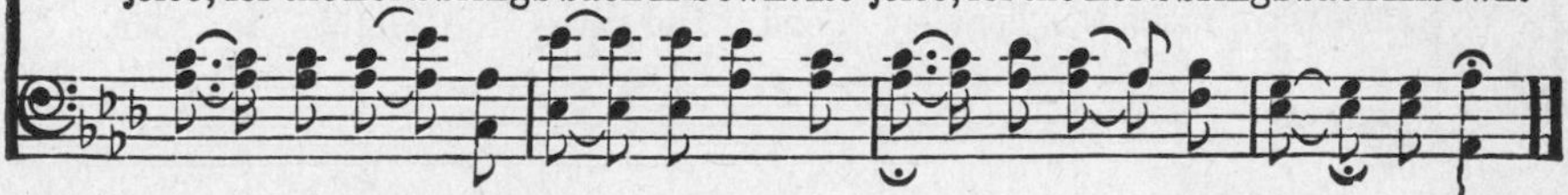

232
All Alone
C. A. M.
C. Austin Miles
1. Have you ev - er tried to bear your bur - dens All a - lone? All a - lone? Don't you know there's One who waits to help you, Who will make all your bur-dens His own?
2. Don't you know He trod the wine-press for you All a - lone? All a - lone? And the bur - den that He bore in meek - ness, Such a bur - den no oth - er has known.
3. Don't you know that He has bought your par-don All a - lone? All a - lone? And your grat - i - tude for such a mer - cy Un - to Je - sus you nev - er have shown.
All a-lone?
All a-lone?
Chorus
When I have bur-dens to bear which no one can share, I take them to Je - sus, The Man of Cal - va - ry;
When I have cross-es to bear, my Sav - ior is there, And (Omit ....)
1
2
al - ways takes the heav - y end, and gives the light to me.

233 Savior, Like a Shepherd Lead Us

DOROTHY A. THRUPP — WILLIAM B. BRADBURY

1. Sav - ior, like a shep-herd lead us, Much we need Thy ten- der care;
2. We are Thine; do Thou be - friend us, Be the Guardian of our way;
3. Thou hast promised to re - ceive us, Poor and sin- ful though we be;
4. Ear - ly let us seek Thy fa - vor; Ear - ly let us do Thy will;
In Thy pleas-ant pas-tures feed us, For our use Thy folds pre-pare:
Keep Thy flock, from sin de - fend us, Seek us when we go a - stray:
Thou hast mer - cy to re - lieve us, Grace to cleanse, and pow'r to free:
Bless - ed Lord and on - ly Sav - ior, With Thy love our bos- oms fill:
Bless-ed Je - sus, Bless-ed Je - sus, Thou hast bought us, Thine we are;
Bless-ed Je - sus, Bless-ed Je - sus, Hear, O hear us when we pray;
Bless-ed Je - sus, Bless-ed Je - sus, Ear - ly let us turn to Thee;
Bless-ed Je - sus, Bless-ed Je - sus, Thou hast loved us, love us still;
Bless-ed Je - sus, Bless-ed Je - sus, Thou hast bought us, Thine we are.
Bless-ed Je - sus, Bless-ed Je - sus, Hear, O hear us when we pray.
Bless-ed Je - sus, Bless-ed Je - sus, Ear - ly let us turn to Thee.
Bless-ed Je - sus, Bless-ed Je - sus, Thou hast loved us, love us still.

234 When They Ring the Golden Bells

Dion De Marbelle

1. There's a land be-yond the riv - er, That we call the sweet for-ev - er, And we
2. We shall know no sin nor sor-row, In that ha - ven of to-mor-row, When our
3. When our days shall know their number, When in death we sweetly slumber, When the
on - ly reach that shore by faith's decree; One by one we'll gain the portals, There to
barque shall sail beyond the sil - ver sea; We shall on-ly know the blessing Of our
King commands the spir-it to be free; Nevermore with anguish la-den, We shall
dwell with the immortals, When they ring the golden bells for you and me.
Father's sweet caressing, When they ring the golden bells for you and me.
reach that love-ly Ai-den, When they ring the golden bells for you and me.
you and me.
Chorus
Don't you hear the bells now ringing? Don't you hear the an-gels singing? 'Tis the
glo - ry hal - le - lu-jah Ju - bi-lee (Ju-bi-lee). In that far-off sweet for-ev-er, Just be-

When They Ring the Golden Bells

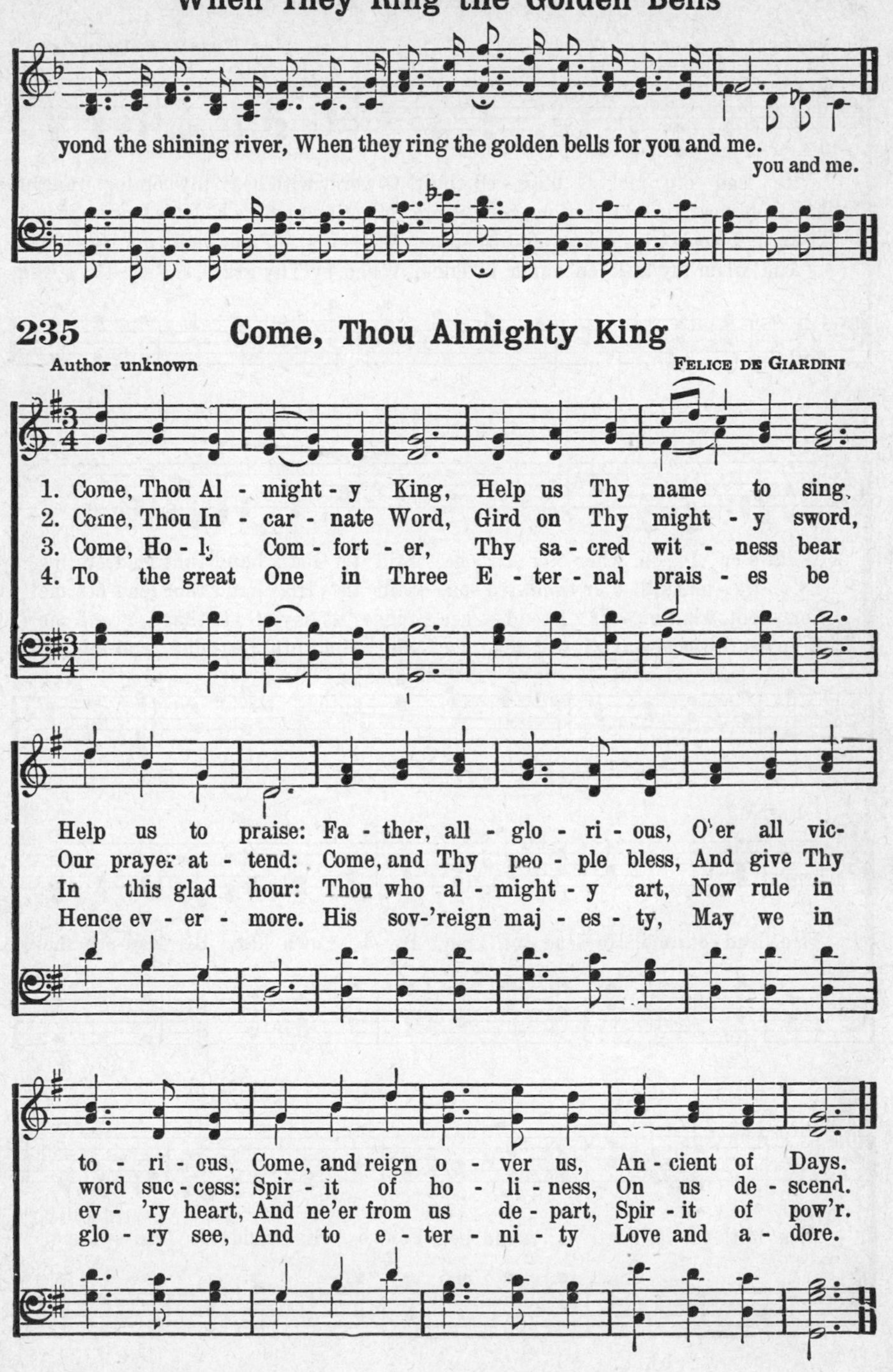
yond the shining river, When they ring the golden bells for you and me.
you and me.
235
Come, Thou Almighty King
Author unknown
FELICE DE GIARDINI
1. Come, Thou Al - might - y King, Help us Thy name to sing,
2. Come, Thou In - car - nate Word, Gird on Thy might - y sword,
3. Come, Ho - ly Com - fort - er, Thy sa - cred wit - ness bear
4. To the great One in Three E - ter - nal prais - es be
Help us to praise: Fa - ther, all - glo - ri - ous, O'er all vic-
Our prayer at - tend: Come, and Thy peo - ple bless, And give Thy
In this glad hour: Thou who al - might - y art, Now rule in
Hence ev - er - more. His sov-'reign maj - es - ty, May we in
to - ri - ous, Come, and reign o - ver us, An - cient of Days.
word suc - cess: Spir - it of ho - li - ness, On us de - scend.
ev - 'ry heart, And ne'er from us de - part, Spir - it of pow'r.
glo - ry see, And to e - ter - ni - ty Love and a - dore.

He Leadeth Me

Joseph H. Gilmore | William B. Bradbury

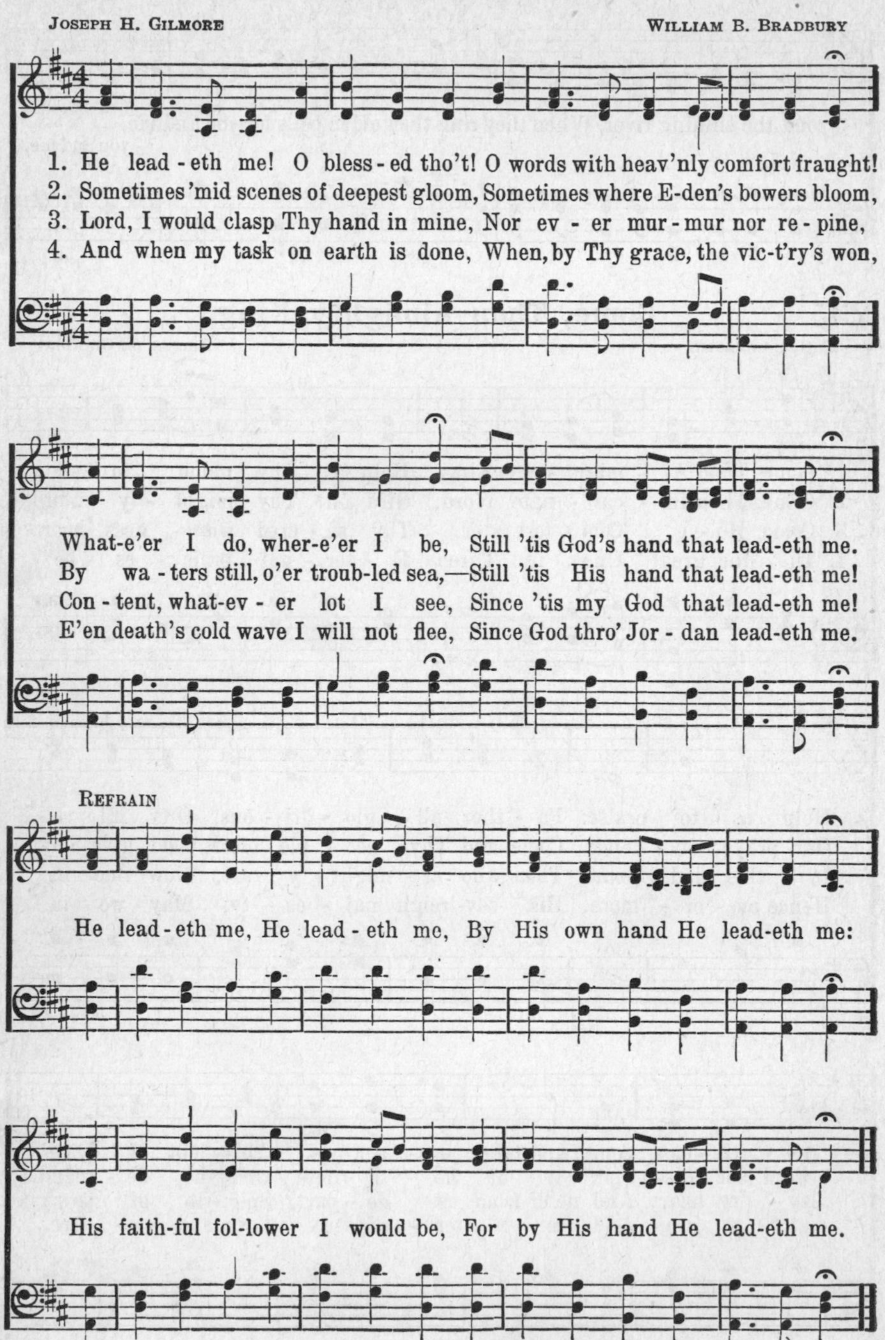
1. He lead - eth me! O bless - ed tho't! O words with heav'nly comfort fraught!
2. Sometimes 'mid scenes of deepest gloom, Sometimes where E-den's bowers bloom,
3. Lord, I would clasp Thy hand in mine, Nor ev - er mur - mur nor re - pine,
4. And when my task on earth is done, When, by Thy grace, the vic-t'ry's won,
What-e'er I do, wher-e'er I be, Still 'tis God's hand that lead-eth me.
By wa - ters still, o'er troub-led sea,—Still 'tis His hand that lead-eth me!
Con - tent, what-ev - er lot I see, Since 'tis my God that lead-eth me!
E'en death's cold wave I will not flee, Since God thro' Jor - dan lead-eth me.
Refrain
He lead - eth me, He lead - eth me, By His own hand He lead-eth me:
His faith-ful fol-lower I would be, For by His hand He lead-eth me.

237 Held In His Mighty Arms

W. M. W. MACOMBER

1. Safe is my ref-uge, sweet is my rest, Ill can-not harm me, nor
2. Press-ing my tear-stained cheek to His own, Hush-ing my grief with His
3. Tem-pests may rage, sin's surg-es may beat, Ne'er can they reach my
foes e'er mo-lest; Je-sus my spir-it so ten-der-ly calms,
sweet gen-tle tone; Touch-ing my heart with His heal-ing balms,
shel-tered re-treat; Free from all dan-ger, from dread a-larms,
Hold-ing me close in His might-y arms.
Hold-ing me still in His might-y arms.
Rest-ing so safe in His might-y arms.
CHORUS
Oh! what won-der-ful,
won-der-ful rest! Trust-ing com-plete-ly in Je-sus I'm blest; Sweet-ly He
com-forts and shields from a-larms, Hold-ing me safe in His might-y arms.

238 A Mighty Fortress Is Our God

MARTIN LUTHER
Tr. F. H. HEDGE

MARTIN LUTHER

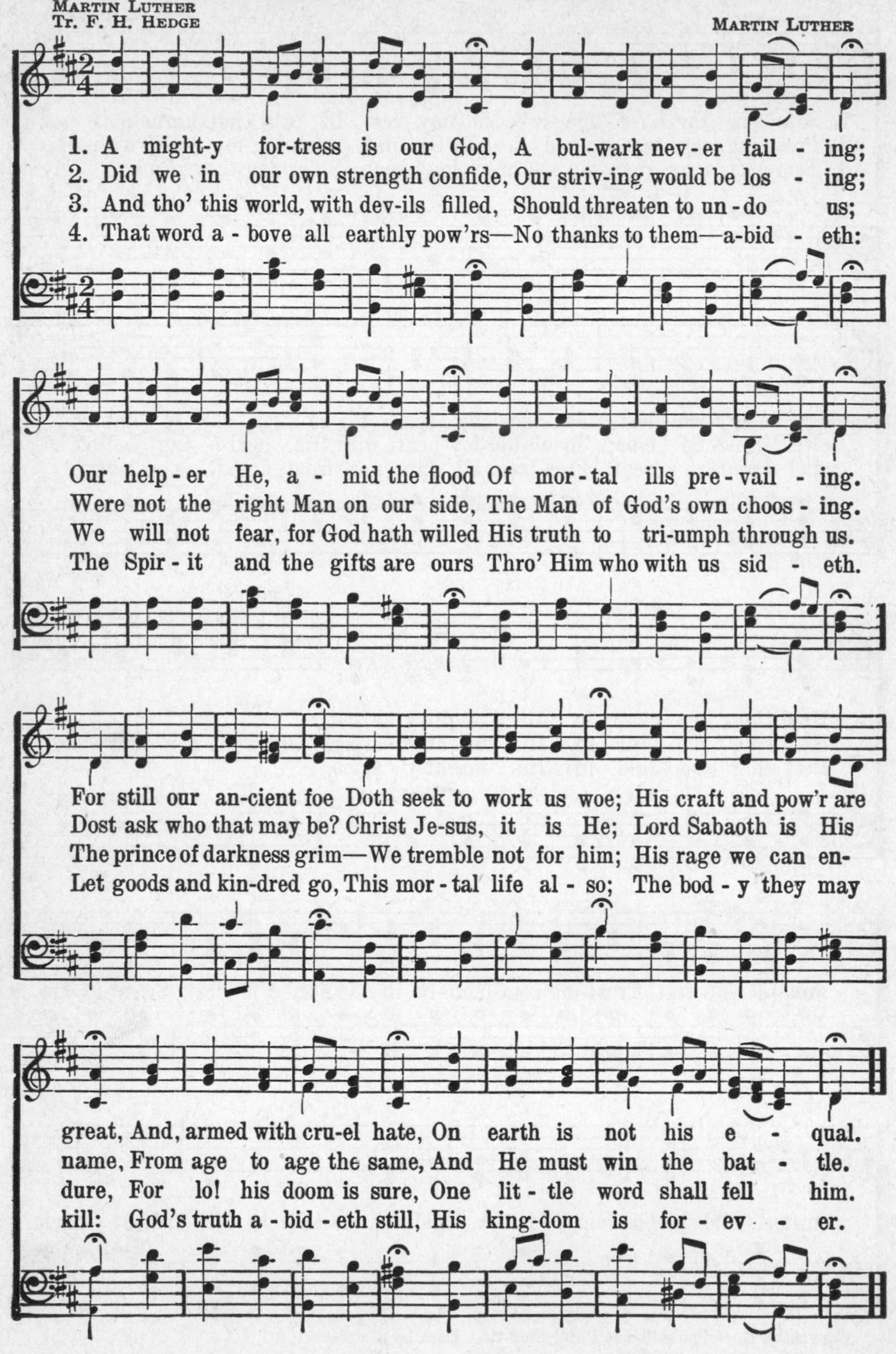
1. A mighty fortress is our God, A bulwark never failing;
2. Did we in our own strength confide, Our striving would be losing;
3. And tho' this world, with devils filled, Should threaten to undo us;
4. That word above all earthly pow'rs—No thanks to them—abideth:
Our helper He, amid the flood Of mortal ills prevailing.
Were not the right Man on our side, The Man of God's own choosing.
We will not fear, for God hath willed His truth to triumph through us.
The Spirit and the gifts are ours Thro' Him who with us sideth.
For still our ancient foe Doth seek to work us woe; His craft and pow'r are
Dost ask who that may be? Christ Jesus, it is He; Lord Sabaoth is His
The prince of darkness grim—We tremble not for him; His rage we can en-
Let goods and kindred go, This mortal life also; The body they may
great, And, armed with cruel hate, On earth is not his equal.
name, From age to age the same, And He must win the battle.
dure, For lo! his doom is sure, One little word shall fell him.
kill: God's truth abideth still, His kingdom is forever.

239 The Regions Beyond

A. B. SIMPSON — MARGARET M. SIMPSON

1. To the re-gions be-yond I must go, I must go, Where the sto-ry has nev-er been told (been told); To the mil-lions that never have heard of His love, I must tell the sweet sto-ry of old (of old).
2. To the hard-est of plac-es He calls me to go, Not think-ing of com-fort or ease (or ease); The world may pronounce me a dreamer, a fool, E-nough if the Mas-ter I please (I please).
3. Oh, ye that are spending your leisure and pow'rs In pleas-ures so fool-ish and fond (and fond); A-wake from your self-ish-ness, fol-ly and sin, And go to the re-gions be-yond (be-yond).
4. There are oth-er "lost sheep" that the Master must bring, And they must the mes-sage be told (be told); He sends me to gath-er them out of all lands, And wel-come them back to His fold (His fold).
CHORUS With spirit
To the re-gions be-yond I must go, I must go, Till the world, all the world, His sal-va-tion shall know.
I must go, I must go, To the re-gions be-yond I must go, Till the world, all the world, His sal-va-tion shall know, shall know.
rit.

240 The Home Over There

D. W. C. HUNTINGTON
TULLIUS C. O'KANE
1. O think of the home o - ver there, By the side of the riv - er of light, Where the saints, all im - mor - tal and fair, Are robed in their garments of white.
2. O think of the friends o - ver there, Who be - fore us the jour - ney have trod, Of the songs that they breathe on the air, In their home in the pal - ace of God.
3. My Sav - ior is now o - ver there, There my kin - dred and friends are at rest; Then a - way from my sor - row and care, Let me fly to the land of the blest.
4. I'll soon be at home o - ver there, For the end of my jour - ney I see; Man - y dear to my heart, o - ver there, Are watch - ing and wait - ing for me.
o - ver there,
REFRAIN
O - ver there, o - ver there, O think of the home o - ver there, O - ver
O - ver there, o - ver there, O think of the friends o - ver there, O - ver
O - ver there, o - ver there, My Sav - ior is now o - ver there, O - ver
O - ver there, o - ver there, I'll soon be at home o - ver there, O - ver
o - ver there. O - ver there, o - ver there, o - ver there,

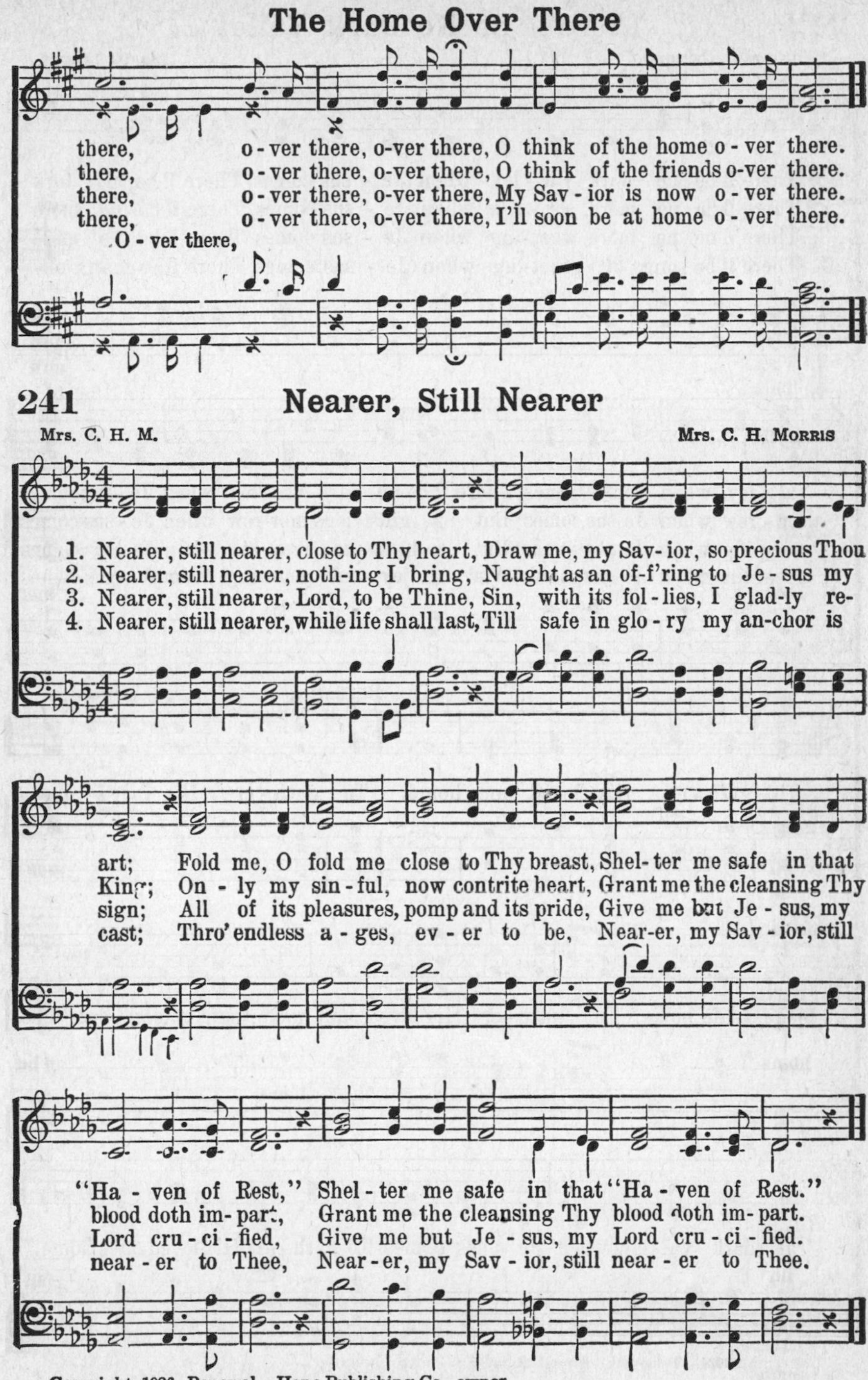

The Home Over There
there, o - ver there, o-ver there, O think of the home o - ver there.
there, o - ver there, o-ver there, O think of the friends o-ver there.
there, o - ver there, o-ver there, My Sav - ior is now o - ver there.
there, o - ver there, o-ver there, I'll soon be at home o - ver there.
O - ver there,
241
Nearer, Still Nearer
Mrs. C. H. M.
Mrs. C. H. Morris
1. Nearer, still nearer, close to Thy heart, Draw me, my Sav- ior, so precious Thou
2. Nearer, still nearer, noth-ing I bring, Naught as an of-f'ring to Je - sus my
3. Nearer, still nearer, Lord, to be Thine, Sin, with its fol - lies, I glad-ly re-
4. Nearer, still nearer, while life shall last, Till safe in glo - ry my an-chor is
art; Fold me, O fold me close to Thy breast, Shel- ter me safe in that
King; On - ly my sin - ful, now contrite heart, Grant me the cleansing Thy
sign; All of its pleasures, pomp and its pride, Give me but Je - sus, my
cast; Thro' endless a - ges, ev - er to be, Near-er, my Sav - ior, still
"Ha - ven of Rest," Shel - ter me safe in that "Ha - ven of Rest."
blood doth im- part, Grant me the cleansing Thy blood doth im- part.
Lord cru - ci - fied, Give me but Je - sus, my Lord cru - ci - fied.
near - er to Thee, Near - er, my Sav - ior, still near - er to Thee.
Copyright, 1926, Renewal. Hope Publishing Co., owner

242 There'll Be No Dark Valley

WILLIAM O. CUSHING IRA D. SANKEY

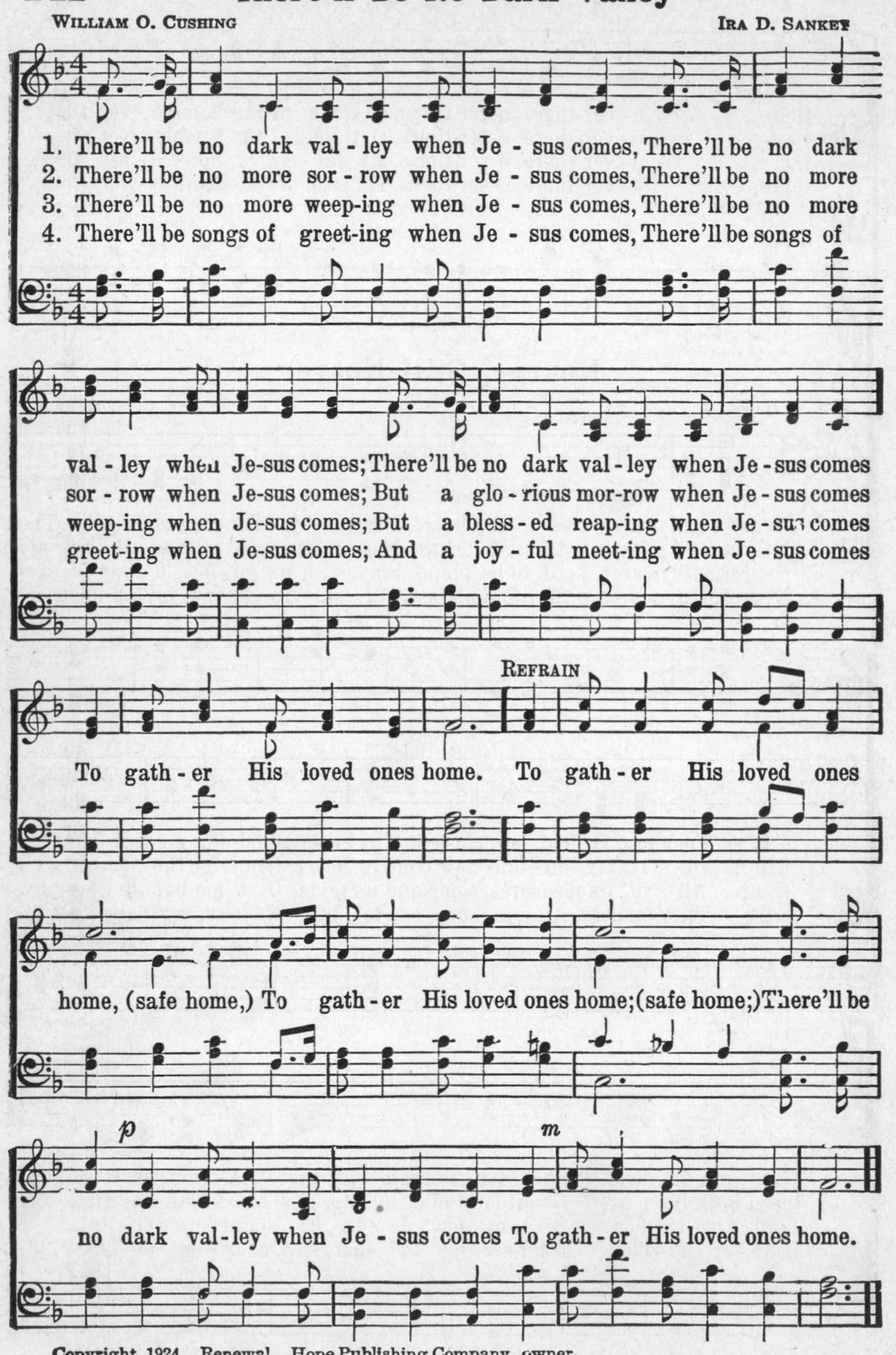

243 Thou Didst Leave Thy Throne

EMILY E. S. ELLIOTT — TIMOTHY R. MATTHEWS

1. Thou didst leave Thy throne And Thy king - ly crown When Thou
2. Heav-en's arch - es rang When the an - gels sang, Pro - - -
3. The fox - es found rest, And the birds their nest In the
4. Thou cam - est, O Lord, With the liv - ing word That should
5. When the heav - ens shall ring, And the an - gels sing, At Thy
cam - est to earth for me; But in Beth - le - hem's home
claim - ing Thy roy - al de - gree; But of low - ly birth
shade of the for - est tree; But Thy couch was the sod,
set Thy peo - ple free; But with mock - ing scorn,
com - ing to vic - to - ry. Let Thy voice call me home,
Was there found no room For Thy ho - ly na - tiv - i - ty:
Didst Thou come to earth, And in great - est hu - mil - i - ty:
O Thou Son of God, In the des - erts of Gal - i - lee:
And with crown of thorn, They bore Thee to Cal - va - ry:
Say - ing, "Yet there is room, There is room at My side for thee:"
REFRAIN
1-4. O come to my heart, Lord Je - sus, There is room in my heart for Thee.
5. My heart shall rejoice, Lord Je - sus, When Thou comest and call-est for me.

244 Him That Cometh Unto Me

E. E. Hewitt — Wm. J. Kirkpatrick

1. Lis - ten to the bless - ed in - vi - ta - tion, Sweet - er than the notes of an - gel-song, Chim-ing soft - ly with a heav'n-ly ca - dence, Call - ing to the pass - ing throng.
2. Wea - ry toil - er, sad and heav - y - la - den, Joy - ful - ly the great sal - va - tion see; Close be - side thee stands the Bur-den Bear - er, Strong to bear thy load and thee.
3. Come, ye thirst - y, to the liv - ing wa - ters, Hun - gry, come and on His boun-ty feed; Not thy fit - ness is the plea to bring Him, But thy press-ing ut - most need.
4. "Him that com-eth," blind or maimed or sin - ful, Com - ing for His heal - ing touch di - vine, For the cleans-ing of the blood so pre - cious, Prove a - new this gra - cious line.
5. Com - ing hum - bly, dai - ly to this Sav - ior, Breath-ing all the heart to Him in prayer; Com - ing some day to the heav'n-ly man - sions, He will give thee wel - come there.

CHORUS

Him that com - eth un - to me, (un - to me,) Him that com - eth un - to me, (un - to me,) Him that com - eth un - to me, ... (un - to me,) I will in no wise cast out.

245 Blessed Be the Name

W. H. Clark — Arr. by Wm. J. Kirkpatrick

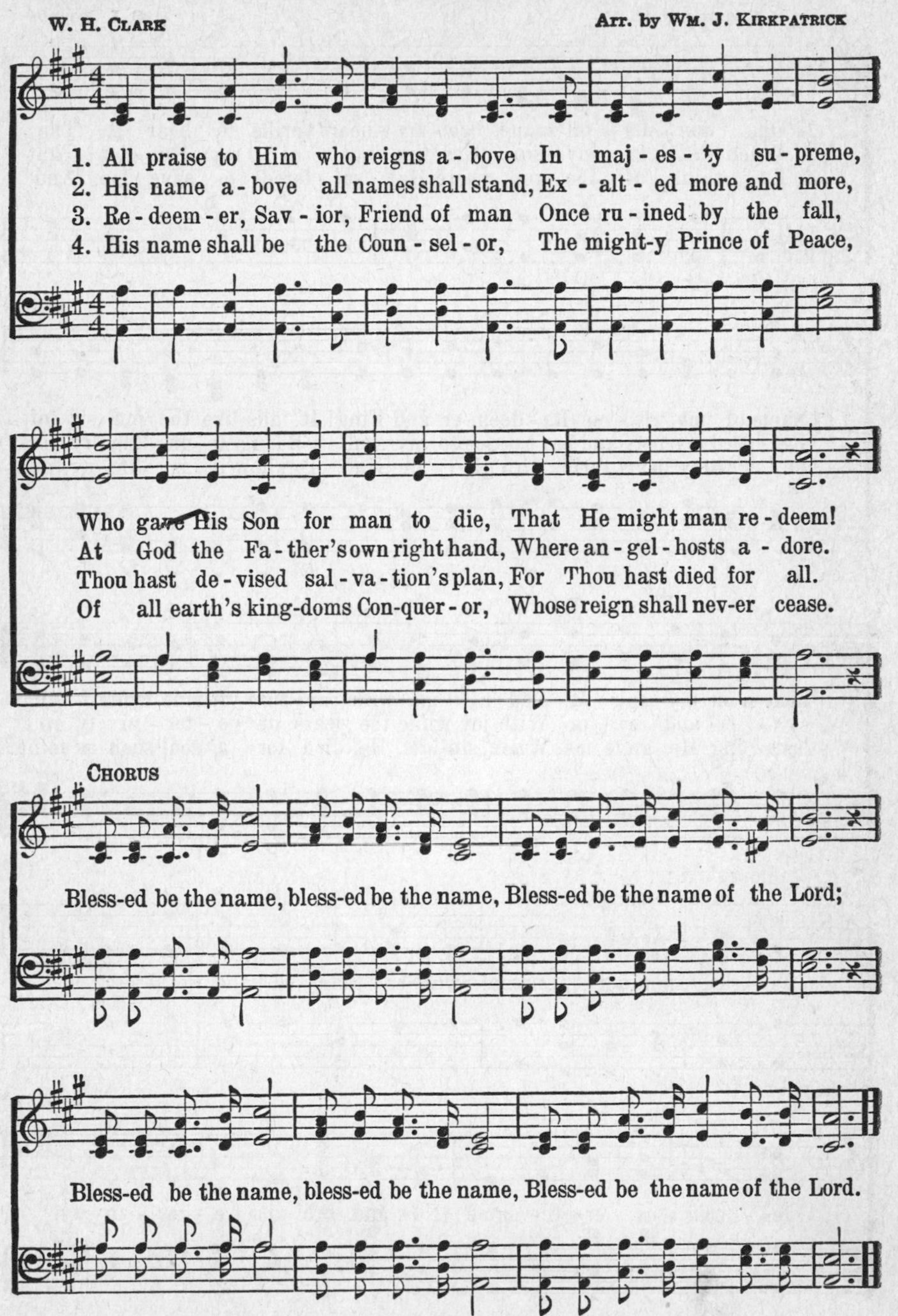

1. All praise to Him who reigns a - bove In maj - es - ty su - preme,
2. His name a - bove all names shall stand, Ex - alt - ed more and more,
3. Re - deem - er, Sav - ior, Friend of man Once ru - ined by the fall,
4. His name shall be the Coun - sel - or, The might-y Prince of Peace,
Who gave His Son for man to die, That He might man re - deem!
At God the Fa - ther's own right hand, Where an - gel - hosts a - dore.
Thou hast de - vised sal - va - tion's plan, For Thou hast died for all.
Of all earth's king-doms Con-quer - or, Whose reign shall nev-er cease.
Chorus
Bless-ed be the name, bless-ed be the name, Bless-ed be the name of the Lord;
Bless-ed be the name, bless-ed be the name, Bless-ed be the name of the Lord.

246 Jesus! Wonderful Name!

Avis B. Christiansen — C. L. Dorris

1. Oh, won-der-ful name, how my heart thrills to hear it— The name of my ris-en Re-deem-er and King! It falls like the mu-sic of heav'n on my spir-it, And fills me with rap-ture di-vine while I sing.
2. When lost in my sin, 'twas the name of my Sav-ior That ban-ished my fear and bro't peace to my soul; I'll sing it in glo-ry for-ev-er and ev-er With joy while the years of e-ter-ni-ty roll.
3. I think of the cross where He suf-fered to save me, And oh, how my heart thrills with glo-ry di-vine To know it is life ev-er-last-ing He gave me, When, sin-less, He died for a soul such as mine.
rit.
Chorus
Je-sus! won-der-ful name! Sweet-er than all the world to me;
Je-sus! ev-er the same—Now and thro' all e-ter-ni-ty.

247 What a Wonderful Savior

E. A. H. ELISHA A. HOFFMAN

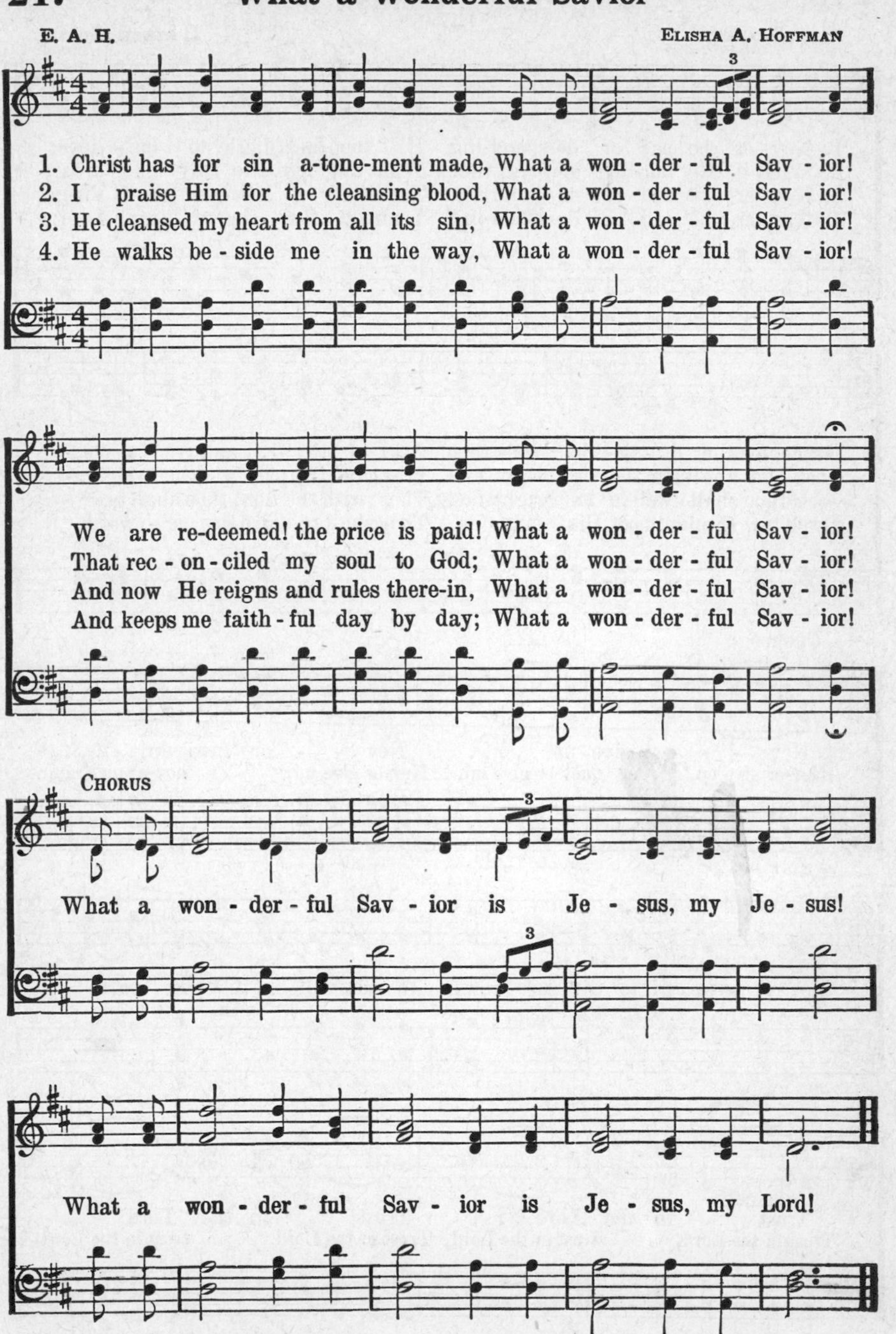
1. Christ has for sin a-tone-ment made, What a won - der - ful Sav - ior!
2. I praise Him for the cleansing blood, What a won - der - ful Sav - ior!
3. He cleansed my heart from all its sin, What a won - der - ful Sav - ior!
4. He walks be - side me in the way, What a won - der - ful Sav - ior!
We are re-deemed! the price is paid! What a won - der - ful Sav - ior!
That rec - on - ciled my soul to God; What a won - der - ful Sav - ior!
And now He reigns and rules there-in, What a won - der - ful Sav - ior!
And keeps me faith - ful day by day; What a won - der - ful Sav - ior!
CHORUS
What a won - der - ful Sav - ior is Je - sus, my Je - sus!
What a won - der - ful Sav - ior is Je - sus, my Lord!

By permission of Rev. E. A. Hoffman

248 Never Give Up

FANNY J. CROSBY — I. ALLAN SANKEY

1. Nev-er be sad or de-spond-ing If thou hast faith to be-lieve;
2. What if thy bur-dens op-press thee; What tho' thy life may be drear;
3. Nev-er be sad or de-spond-ing, There is a mor-row for thee;
4. Nev-er be sad or de-spond-ing, Lean on the arm of thy Lord;
Grace, for the du-ties be-fore thee, Ask of thy God and re-ceive.
Look on the side that is bright-est, Pray, and thy path will be clear.
Soon thou shalt dwell in its bright-ness, There with the Lord thou shalt be.
Dwell in the depths of His mer-cy, Thou shalt re-ceive thy re-ward.
CHORUS
Nev - - er give up, ... Nev - - er give up, ...
Nev-er give up, nev-er give up, Nev-er give up, nev-er give up,
Nev-er give up to thy sor-rows, Je-sus will bid them de-part;
Trust . . . . in the Lord, ... Trust . . . in the Lord, . . .
Trust in the Lord, trust in the Lord, Trust in the Lord, trust in the Lord,

Never Give Up

Sing when your tri - als are great - est, Trust in the Lord and take heart.

249 Look to the Lamb of God

H. G. JACKSON
JAMES M. BLACK

1. If you from sin are long-ing to be free, Look to the Lamb of God;
2. When Satan tempts, and doubts and fears assail, Look to the Lamb of God;
3. Are you a-wea - ry, does the way seem long? Look to the Lamb of God;
4. Fear not when shadows on your path-way fall, Look to the Lamb of God;

He, to re-deem you, died on Cal - va - ry, Look to the Lamb of God.
You in His strength shall o-ver all pre-vail, Look to the Lamb of God.
His love will cheer and fill your heart with song, Look to the Lamb of God.
In joy or sor - row Christ is all in all, Look to the Lamb of God.

CHORUS
Look to the Lamb of God, Look to the Lamb of God,
the Lamb of God, the Lamb of God,

For He a - lone is a - ble to save you, Look to the Lamb of God.

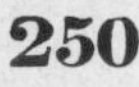

Alive Again

P. R. PAUL RADER

1. Ma - ry be-held Him, and "Master!" cried, Aft - er He came from the tomb;
2. Pe - ter be-held Him there on the shore, Ate with Him there by the sea;
3. Thom-as be-held Him there in the room, Called Him his Master and Lord,
Sud - den - ly Je - sus stood in their midst, En - tered the tight-shut room.
Je - sus was say - ing, with lips once dead, "Pe - ter, dost thou love Me?"
Put forth his fin - gers in - to the holes Made by the nails and sword.
CHORUS Spirito
He who was dead is a - live a - gain! He who was dead is a - live a - gain!
maestoso
a tempo
Bro-ken the stout, i - cy clutch-es of death—He who was dead is a - live a - gain!

251 Guide Me, O Thou Great Jehovah

WILLIAM WILLIAMS THOMAS HASTINGS

1. { Guide me, O Thou great Je-ho-vah, Pil-grim thro' this bar-ren land: / I am weak, but Thou art mighty; Hold me with Thy pow'rful hand: } Bread of heav-en,
2. { O - pen now the crys-tal foun-tain, Whence the healing waters flow; / Let the fier - y, cloud-y pil - lar Lead me all my jour-ney thro'; } Strong De-liv-'rer,
3. { When I tread the verge of Jor-dan, Bid my anx-ious fears sub-side; / Bear me thro' the swell-ing cur-rent, Land me safe on Ca-naan's side: } Songs of prais-es

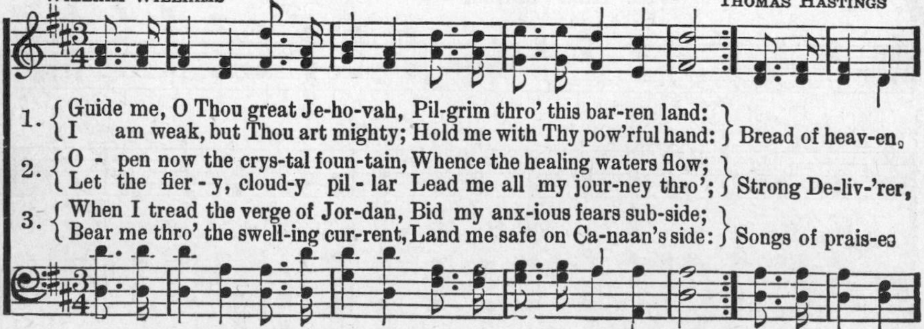

Guide Me, O Thou Great Jehovah

Feed me till I want no more; Bread of heav-en, Feed me till I want no more.
Be Thou still my strength and shield; Strong De-liv-'rer, Be Thou still my strength and shield.
I will ev - er give to Thee; Songs of prais - es I will ev - er give to Thee.
252
Traveling Home
R. H.
ROBERT HARKNESS
1. Thro' a land of sin and shame, Led by Je - sus we are trav-'ling Home;
2. To a land of peace and rest, Led by Je - sus we are trav-'ling Home;
3. Joy un-ceas-ing we shall share, Led by Je - sus we are trav-'ling Home;
4. Sor - rows will for - got - ten be, Led by Je - sus we are trav-'ling Home;
Trust-ing in the Sav-ior's name, Led by Je - sus we are trav-'ling Home.
Where no soul can be dis-tressed, Led by Je - sus we are trav-'ling Home.
With the loved ones wait-ing there, Led by Je - sus we are trav-'ling Home.
O - ver for e - ter - ni - ty, Led by Je - sus we are trav-'ling Home.
CHORUS
Trav-'ling Home, trav-'ling Home, Led by Je - sus we are trav - 'ling Home;
Trav-'ling Home, trav-'ling Home, Led by Je - sus we are trav-'ling Home.

253 Anywhere With Jesus

JESSIE H. BROWN and MRS. C. M. ALEXANDER — D. B. TOWNER

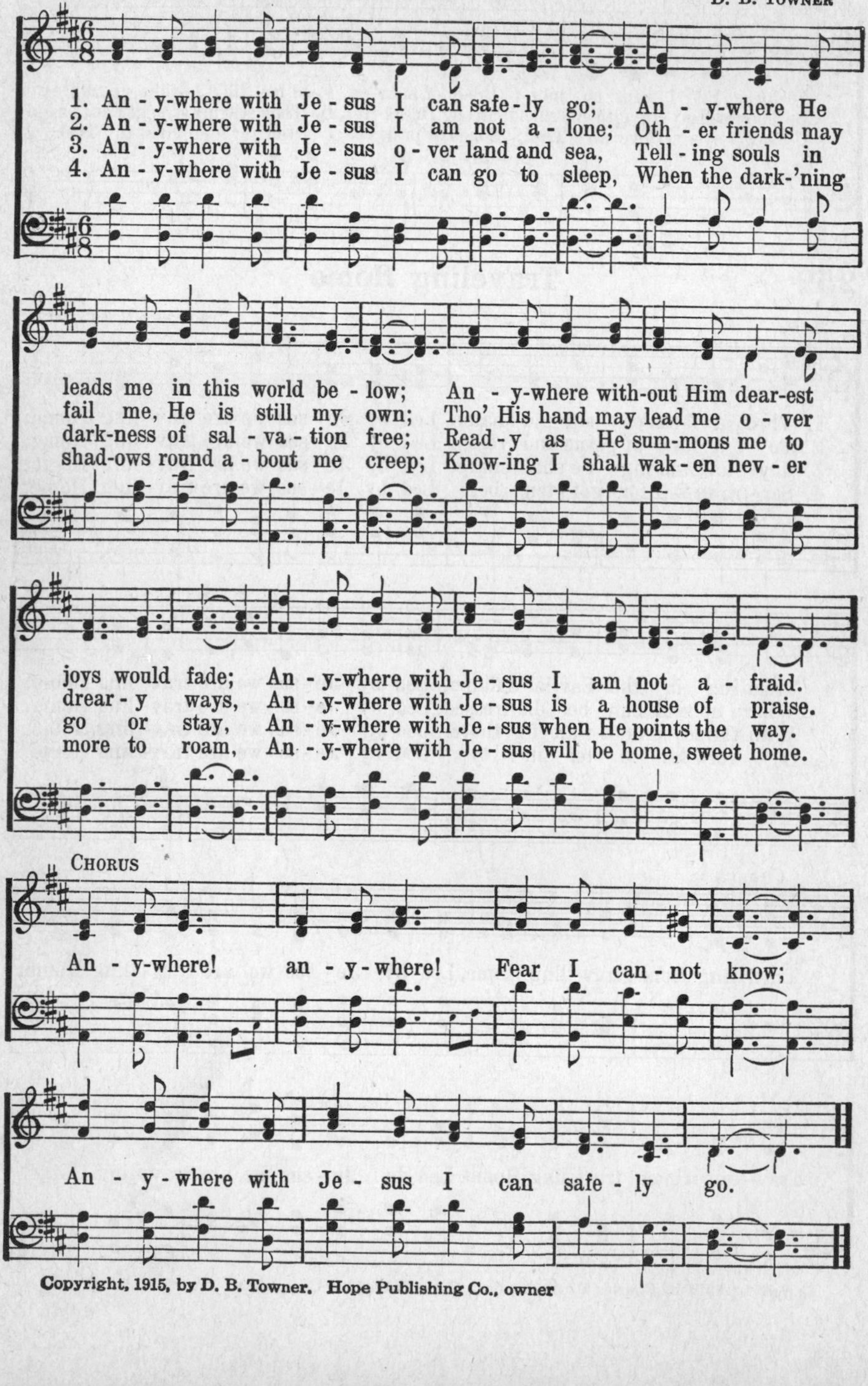

1. An - y-where with Je - sus I can safe - ly go; An - y-where He leads me in this world be - low; An - y-where with-out Him dear-est joys would fade; An - y-where with Je - sus I am not a - fraid.

2. An - y-where with Je - sus I am not a - lone; Oth - er friends may fail me, He is still my own; Tho' His hand may lead me o - ver drear - y ways, An - y-where with Je - sus is a house of praise.

3. An - y-where with Je - sus o - ver land and sea, Tell - ing souls in dark-ness of sal - va - tion free; Read - y as He sum-mons me to go or stay, An - y-where with Je - sus when He points the way.

4. An - y-where with Je - sus I can go to sleep, When the dark-'ning shad-ows round a - bout me creep; Know-ing I shall wak - en nev - er more to roam, An - y-where with Je - sus will be home, sweet home.

CHORUS

An - y-where! an - y-where! Fear I can - not know; An - y - where with Je - sus I can safe - ly go.

Joy to the World!

ISAAC WATTS

Arr. from GEORGE F. HANDEL

1. Joy to the world! the Lord is come; Let earth re-
2. Joy to the world! the Sav - ior reigns; Let men their
3. No more let sins and sor - rows grow, Nor thorns in-
4. He rules the world with truth and grace, And makes the
ceive her King; Let ev - 'ry heart pre - pare Him room,
songs em - ploy; While fields and floods, rocks, hills and plains
fest the ground; He comes to make His bless-ings flow
na - tions prove The glo - ries of His right-eous - ness,
And heav'n and na - ture sing, And heav'n and na - ture
Re - peat the sound-ing joy, Re - peat the sound - ing
Far as the curse is found, Far as the curse is
And won-ders of His love, And won-ders of His
1. And heav'n and na - ture sing,.......... And
sing, And heav'n, and heav'n and na - ture sing.
joy, Re - peat, re - peat the sound-ing joy.
found, Far as, far as the curse is found.
love, And won-ders, and won - ders of His love.
heav'n and na - ture sing,

255 Hark! the Herald Angels Sing

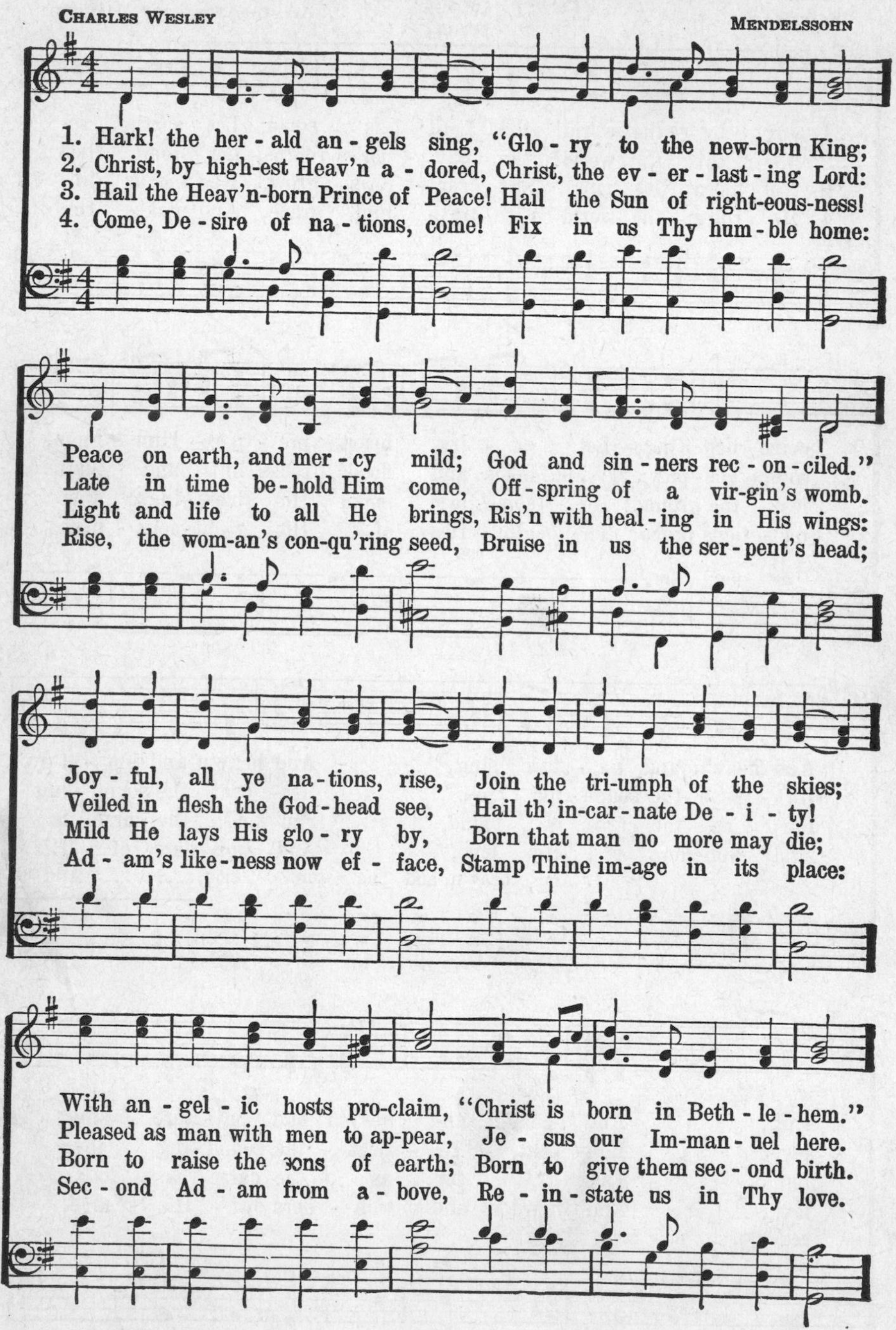

Charles Wesley
Mendelssohn
1. Hark! the her-ald an-gels sing, "Glo-ry to the new-born King;
2. Christ, by high-est Heav'n a-dored, Christ, the ev-er-last-ing Lord:
3. Hail the Heav'n-born Prince of Peace! Hail the Sun of right-eous-ness!
4. Come, De-sire of na-tions, come! Fix in us Thy hum-ble home:
Peace on earth, and mer-cy mild; God and sin-ners rec-on-ciled."
Late in time be-hold Him come, Off-spring of a vir-gin's womb.
Light and life to all He brings, Ris'n with heal-ing in His wings:
Rise, the wom-an's con-qu'ring seed, Bruise in us the ser-pent's head;
Joy-ful, all ye na-tions, rise, Join the tri-umph of the skies;
Veiled in flesh the God-head see, Hail th' in-car-nate De-i-ty!
Mild He lays His glo-ry by, Born that man no more may die;
Ad-am's like-ness now ef-face, Stamp Thine im-age in its place:
With an-gel-ic hosts pro-claim, "Christ is born in Beth-le-hem."
Pleased as man with men to ap-pear, Je-sus our Im-man-uel here.
Born to raise the sons of earth; Born to give them sec-ond birth.
Sec-ond Ad-am from a-bove, Re-in-state us in Thy love.

Hark! the Herald Angels Sing

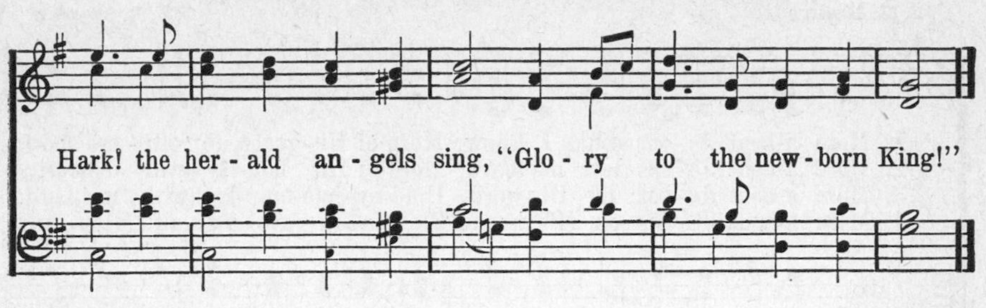

Hark! the her - ald an - gels sing, "Glo - ry to the new - born King!"

256 Silent Night! Holy Night!

JOSEPH MOHR

FRANZ GRUBER

1. Si - lent night! Ho - ly night! All is dark, save the light
2. Si - lent night! Peace - ful night! Dark - ness flies, all is light;
3. Si - lent night! Ho - ly night! Guid - ing Star, lend thy light!
4. Si - lent night! Ho - li - est night! Won - drous Star, lend thy light!

Yon - der, where they sweet vig - ils keep, O'er the Babe who in si - lent sleep
Shepherds hear the an - gels sing, "Al - le - lu - ia! hail the King!
See the East - ern wise men bring Gifts and hom - age to our King!
With the an - gels let us sing Al - le - lu - ia to our King!

Rests in heav - en - ly peace, Rests in heav - en - ly peace.
Christ the Sav - ior is born, Je - sus the Sav - ior is born."
Christ the Sav - ior is born, Je - sus the Sav - ior is born!
Christ the Sav - ior is born, Je - sus the Sav - ior is born!

257 More About Jesus

E. E. Hewitt — Jno. R. Sweney

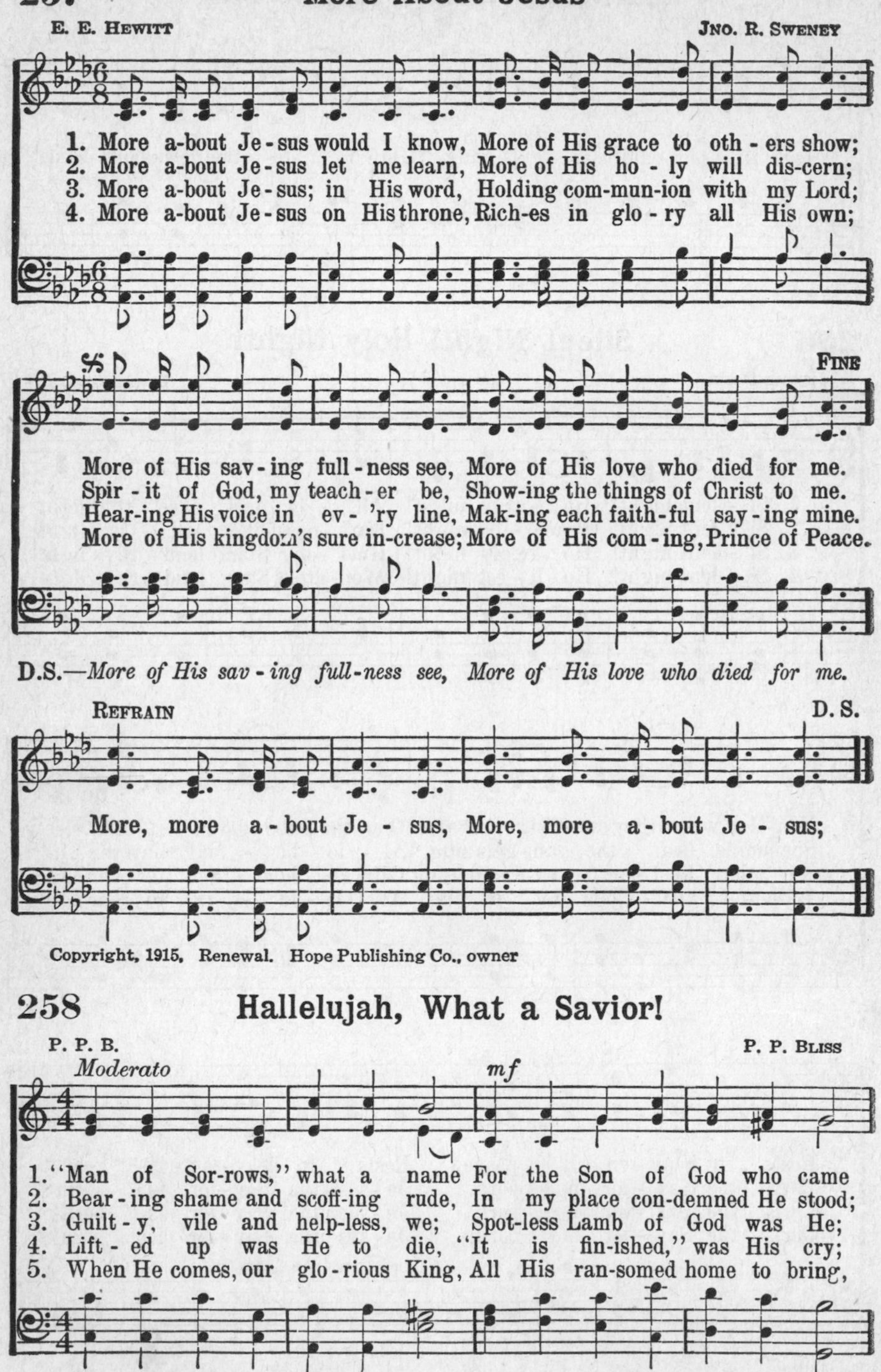

1. More a-bout Je-sus would I know, More of His grace to oth-ers show;
2. More a-bout Je-sus let me learn, More of His ho-ly will dis-cern;
3. More a-bout Je-sus; in His word, Holding com-mun-ion with my Lord;
4. More a-bout Je-sus on His throne, Rich-es in glo-ry all His own;
Fine
More of His sav-ing full-ness see, More of His love who died for me.
Spir-it of God, my teach-er be, Show-ing the things of Christ to me.
Hear-ing His voice in ev-'ry line, Mak-ing each faith-ful say-ing mine.
More of His kingdom's sure in-crease; More of His com-ing, Prince of Peace.
D.S.—More of His sav-ing full-ness see, More of His love who died for me.
Refrain
D. S.
More, more a-bout Je-sus, More, more a-bout Je-sus;

258 Hallelujah, What a Savior!

P. P. B. — P. P. Bliss

Moderato
mf
1. "Man of Sor-rows," what a name For the Son of God who came
2. Bear-ing shame and scoff-ing rude, In my place con-demned He stood;
3. Guilt-y, vile and help-less, we; Spot-less Lamb of God was He;
4. Lift-ed up was He to die, "It is fin-ished," was His cry;
5. When He comes, our glo-rious King, All His ran-somed home to bring,

Hallelujah, What a Savior!
f
ff
Ru - ined sin - ners to re-claim! Hal - le - lu - jah! what a Sav - ior!
Sealed my par - don with His blood; Hal - le - lu - jah! what a Sav - ior!
"Full a - tone-ment!" can it be? Hal - le - lu - jah! what a Sav - ior!
Now in heav'n ex - alt - ed high; Hal - le - lu - jah! what a Sav - ior!
Then a - new this song we'll sing: Hal - le - lu - jah! what a Sav - ior!
259 O Love That Wilt Not Let Me Go
GEORGE MATHESON
A. L. PEACE
p
1. O Love that wilt not let me go, I rest my wea - ry soul on Thee; I give Thee back the life I owe, That in Thine o - cean depths its flow May rich - er, full - er be.
2. O Light that fol - low'st all my way, I yield my flick-'ring torch to Thee; My heart re - stores its bor - rowed ray, That in Thy sun-shine's glow its day May bright-er, fair - er be.
3. O Joy that seek - est me thro' pain, I can - not close my heart to Thee; I trace the rain - bow thro' the rain, And feel the prom - ise is not vain That morn shall tear - less be.
4. O Cross that lift - est up my head, I dare not ask to hide from Thee; I lay in dust life's glo - ry dead, And from the ground there blossoms red Life that shall end - less be.

260 Why Do You Wait?

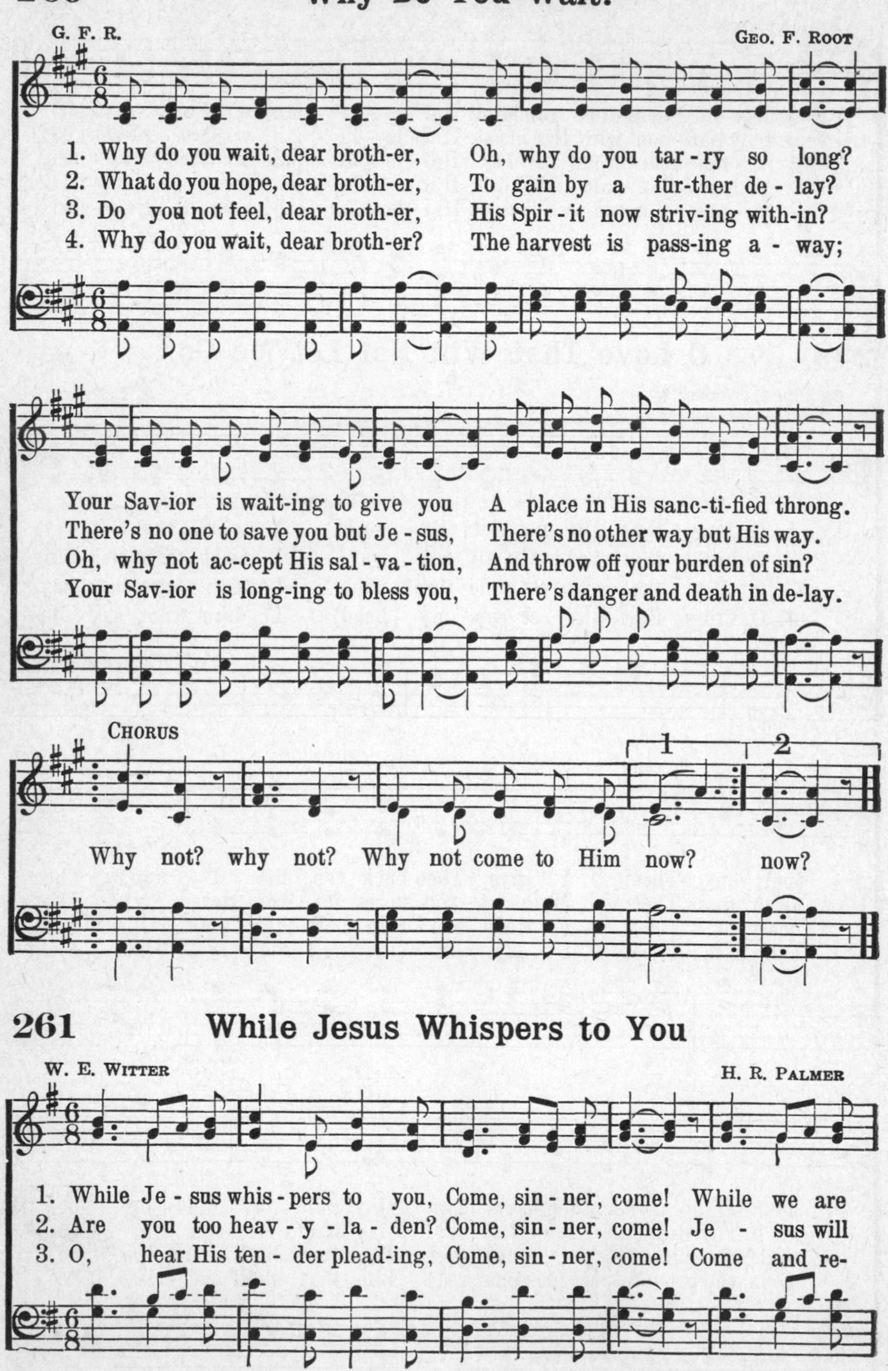
G. F. R.
Geo. F. Root
1. Why do you wait, dear broth-er, Oh, why do you tar-ry so long?
2. What do you hope, dear broth-er, To gain by a fur-ther de-lay?
3. Do you not feel, dear broth-er, His Spir-it now striv-ing with-in?
4. Why do you wait, dear broth-er? The harvest is pass-ing a-way;
Your Sav-ior is wait-ing to give you A place in His sanc-ti-fied throng.
There's no one to save you but Je-sus, There's no other way but His way.
Oh, why not ac-cept His sal-va-tion, And throw off your burden of sin?
Your Sav-ior is long-ing to bless you, There's danger and death in de-lay.
Chorus
1
2
Why not? why not? Why not come to Him now? now?
261 While Jesus Whispers to You
W. E. Witter
H. R. Palmer
1. While Je-sus whis-pers to you, Come, sin-ner, come! While we are
2. Are you too heav-y-la-den? Come, sin-ner, come! Je-sus will
3. O, hear His ten-der plead-ing, Come, sin-ner, come! Come and re-

While Jesus Whispers to You
pray-ing for you, Come, sin - ner, come! Now is the time to own Him,
bear your bur-den, Come, sin - ner, come! Je - sus will not de-ceive you,
ceive the bl-ss-ing, Come, sin - ner, come! While Je - sus whis-pers to you,
Come, sin-ner, come! Now is the time to know Him, Come, sin-ner, come!
Come, sin-ner, come! Je - sus can now re-ceive you, Come, sin-ner, come!
Come, sin-ner, come! While we are pray-ing for you, Come, sin-ner, come!
262
Oh, How I Love Jesus
1. There is a name I love to hear, I love to sing its worth; It sounds like
2. It tells me of a Sav-ior's love, Who died to set me free; It tells me
3. It tells me what my Fa-ther hath In store for ev - 'ry day, And tho' I
4. It tells of One whose loving heart Can feel my deep-est woe, Who in each
CHORUS
mu - sic in mine ear, The sweetest name on earth.
of His precious blood, The sin-ner's per-fect plea. Oh, how I love Je - sus,
tread a darksome path, Yields sunshine all the way.
sor - row bears a part, That none can bear be-low.
Oh, how I love Je - sus, Oh, how I love Je - sus, Be-cause He first loved me!

263 Jesus Paid It All

Mrs. H. M. Hall
John T. Grape
1. I hear the Sav - ior say, "Thy strength in - deed is small, Child of
2. Lord, now in - deed I find Thy pow'r, and Thine a - lone, Can
3. For noth - ing good have I Where-by Thy grace to claim— I'll
4. And when, be - fore the throne, I stand in Him com-plete, "Je - sus
Chorus
weakness, watch and pray, Find in Me thine all in all."
change the lep-er's spots, And melt the heart of stone. Je - sus paid it all,
wash my garments white In the blood of Cal-v'ry's Lamb.
died my soul to save," My lips shall still re - peat.
All to Him I owe; Sin had left a crimson stain, He washed it white as snow.
264 Lord, I'm Coming Home
W. J. K.
Wm. J. Kirkpatrick
1. I've wan-dered far a - way from God, Now I'm com - ing home;
2. I've wast - ed man - y pre - cious years, Now I'm com - ing home;
3. I've tired of sin and stray - ing, Lord, Now I'm com - ing home;
4. My soul is sick, my heart is sore, Now I'm com - ing home;

Lord, I'm Coming Home

FINE
The paths of sin too long I've trod, Lord, I'm com-ing home.
I now re-pent with bit-ter tears, Lord, I'm com-ing home.
I'll trust Thy love, be-lieve Thy word, Lord, I'm com-ing home.
My strength re-new, my hope re-store, Lord, I'm com-ing home.
D. S.—O-pen wide Thine arms of love, Lord, I'm com-ing home.
CHORUS
D. S.
Com-ing home, com-ing home, Nev-er-more to roam,
265
I Am Coming Home
L. H.
L. HARTSOUGH
1. I hear Thy welcome voice, That calls me, Lord, to Thee For cleansing in Thy precious blood That flowed on Cal-va-ry.
2. Tho' coming weak and vile, Thou dost my strength assure; Thou dost my vileness ful-ly cleanse, Till spot-less all and pure.
3. 'Tis Je-sus calls me on To per-fect faith and love, To per-fect hope, and peace, and trust, For earth and heav'n a-bove.
CHORUS
I am com-ing, Lord! Com-ing now to Thee! Wash me, cleanse me in the blood That flowed on Cal-va-ry!

266 Take Time to Be Holy

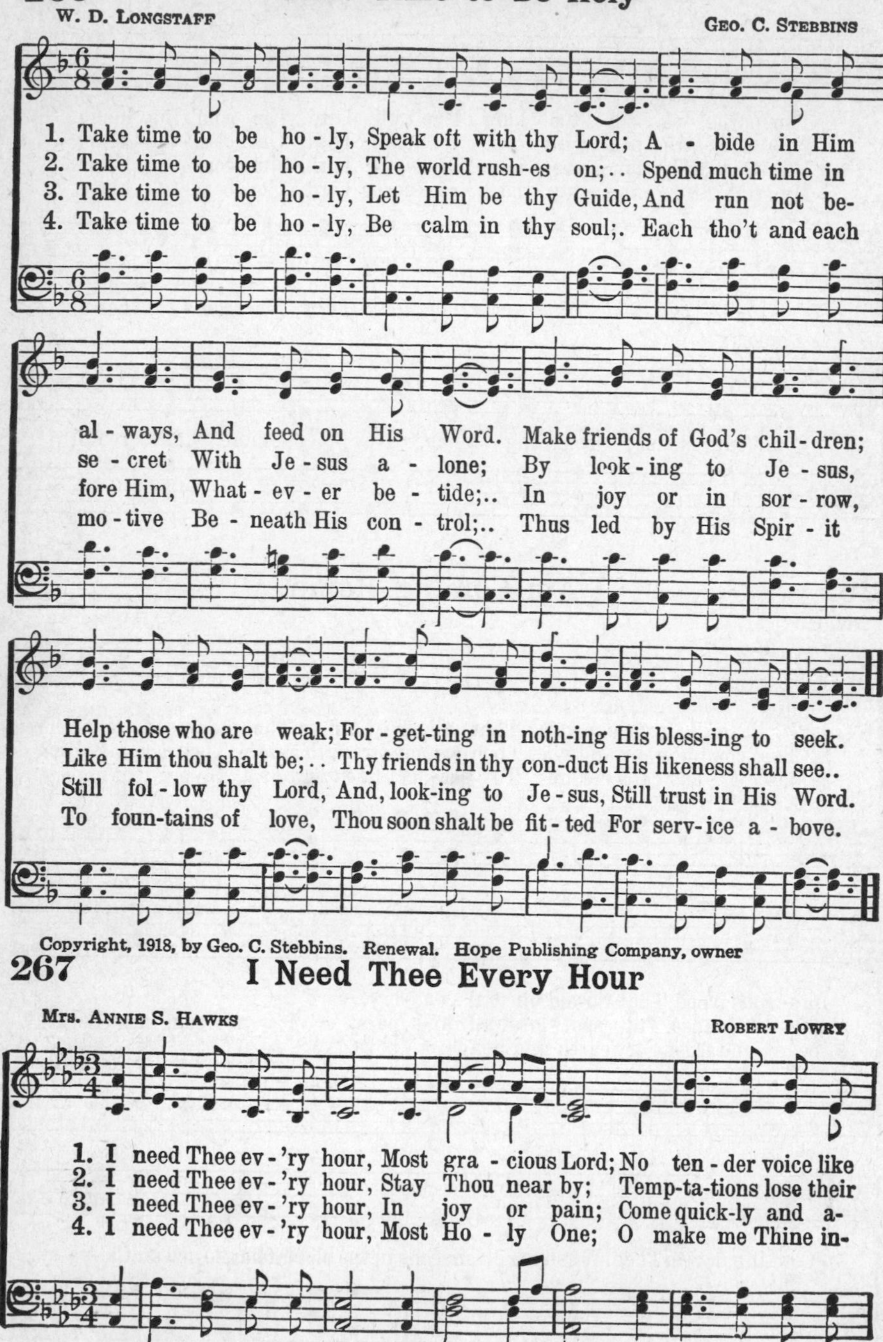
W. D. LONGSTAFF
GEO. C. STEBBINS
1. Take time to be ho - ly, Speak oft with thy Lord; A - bide in Him al - ways, And feed on His Word. Make friends of God's chil - dren; Help those who are weak; For - get-ting in noth-ing His bless-ing to seek.
2. Take time to be ho - ly, The world rush-es on; Spend much time in se - cret With Je - sus a - lone; By look - ing to Je - sus, Like Him thou shalt be; Thy friends in thy con-duct His likeness shall see.
3. Take time to be ho - ly, Let Him be thy Guide, And run not be - fore Him, What - ev - er be - tide; In joy or in sor - row, Still fol - low thy Lord, And, look-ing to Je - sus, Still trust in His Word.
4. Take time to be ho - ly, Be calm in thy soul; Each tho't and each mo - tive Be - neath His con - trol; Thus led by His Spir - it To foun-tains of love, Thou soon shalt be fit - ted For serv-ice a - bove.
Copyright, 1918, by Geo. C. Stebbins. Renewal. Hope Publishing Company, owner
267
I Need Thee Every Hour
Mrs. ANNIE S. HAWKS
ROBERT LOWRY
1. I need Thee ev - 'ry hour, Most gra - cious Lord; No ten - der voice like
2. I need Thee ev - 'ry hour, Stay Thou near by; Temp-ta-tions lose their
3. I need Thee ev - 'ry hour, In joy or pain; Come quick-ly and a-
4. I need Thee ev - 'ry hour, Most Ho - ly One; O make me Thine in-

I Need Thee Every Hour
Chorus
Thine Can peace af - ford.
pow'r When Thou art nigh. I need Thee, O I need Thee; Ev - 'ry hour I
bide, Or life is vain.
deed, Thou bless-ed Son!
need Thee! O bless me now, my Sav - ior, I come to Thee!
268
Jesus Won My Heart
Alfred Barratt
Harry Dixon Loes
Je-sus won my heart, . . Je-sus won my heart; . . By His love so
He won my heart, He won my heart;
full and free, And the grace He gave to me, Je - sus won my heart, . .
He won my
Je-sus won my heart; . . By His love so full and free, Je-sus won my heart.
heart, He won my heart;
ad lib.

269
Just As I Am
Charlotte Elliott
William B. Bradbury
1. Just as I am, with-out one plea, But that Thy blood was shed for me,
2. Just as I am, and wait-ing not To rid my soul of one dark blot,
3. Just as I am, tho' tossed a-bout With many a con-flict, many a doubt,
4. Just as I am, poor, wretched, blind; Sight, riches, heal-ing of the mind,
5. Just as I am, Thou wilt re-ceive, Wilt welcome, pardon, cleanse, relieve;
And that Thou bidd'st me come to Thee, O Lamb of God, I come! I come!
To Thee whose blood can cleanse each spot, O Lamb of God, I come! I come!
Fight-ings and fears with-in, with-out, O Lamb of God, I come! I come!
Yea, all I need, in Thee to find, O Lamb of God, I come! I come!
Be - cause Thy prom-ise I be-lieve, O Lamb of God, I come! I come!
270
O Happy Day
Philip Doddridge
E. F. Rimbault
1. O hap-py day that fixed my choice On Thee, my Sav - ior and my God!
Well may this glow-ing heart re-joice, And tell its rap-tures all a-broad.
2. O hap-py bond, that seals my vows To Him who mer-its all my love!
Let cheer-ful an-thems fill His house, While to that sa-cred shrine I move.
3. 'Tis done: the great trans-ac-tion's done; I am my Lord's, and He is mine;
He drew me and I fol-lowed on, Charmed to confess the voice di-vine.
4. Now rest, my long-di-vid-ed heart; Fixed on this bliss-ful cen-ter, rest;
Nor ev-er from my Lord de-part, With Him of ev-'ry good possessed.
Fine
Hap-py day, hap-py day, When Je-sus washed my sins a-way!

O Happy Day

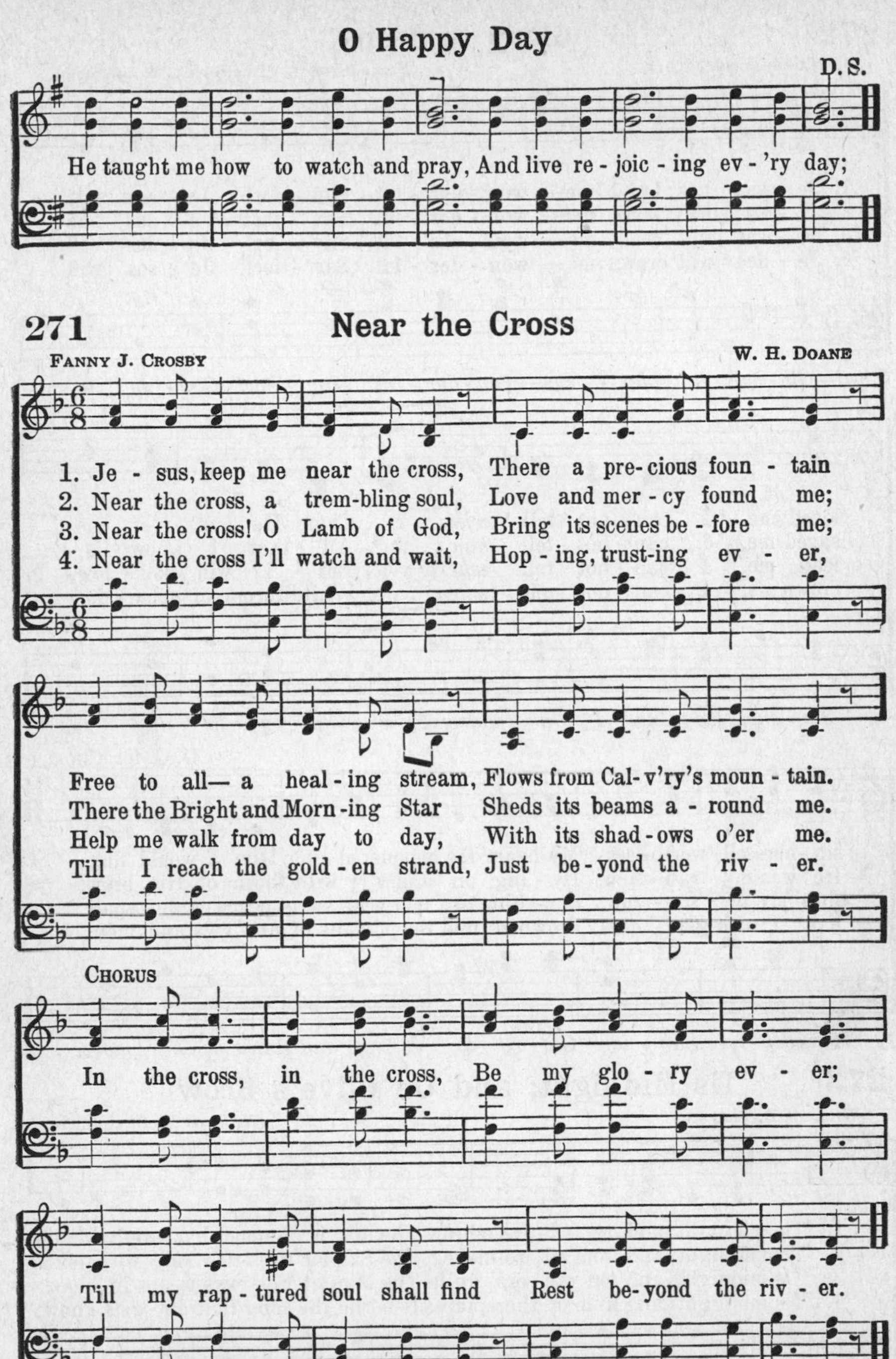
D.S.
He taught me how to watch and pray, And live re - joic - ing ev - 'ry day;

271 Near the Cross

FANNY J. CROSBY

W. H. DOANE

1. Je - sus, keep me near the cross, There a precious foun - tain
2. Near the cross, a trem-bling soul, Love and mer - cy found me;
3. Near the cross! O Lamb of God, Bring its scenes be - fore me;
4. Near the cross I'll watch and wait, Hop - ing, trust-ing ev - er,
Free to all— a heal - ing stream, Flows from Cal-v'ry's moun - tain.
There the Bright and Morn - ing Star Sheds its beams a - round me.
Help me walk from day to day, With its shad - ows o'er me.
Till I reach the gold - en strand, Just be - yond the riv - er.
CHORUS
In the cross, in the cross, Be my glo - ry ev - er;
Till my rap - tured soul shall find Rest be - yond the riv - er.

272 Glory to Jesus

J. WAKEFIELD MACGILL — From BATISTE. Har. by C. W. and E. M.

1. Je - sus has loved me— won - der - ful Sav - ior! Je - sus has
2. Je - sus has saved me— won - der - ful Sav - ior! Je - sus has
3. Je - sus will lead me— won - der - ful Sav - ior! Je - sus will
4. Je - sus will crown me— won - der - ful Sav - ior! Je - sus will

CHO.—*Glo - ry to Je - sus—won - der - ful Sav - ior! Glo - ry to*

loved me, I can - not tell *why;* . . . . Came He to res - cue
saved me, I can - not tell *how;* . . . . All that I know is,
lead me, I can - not tell *where;* . . . But I will fol - low,
crown me, I can - not tell *when;* . . . White throne of splen - dor

Je - sus, the One I a - dore; . . . . *Glo - ry to Je - sus—*

D. C. for CHORUS

sin - ners all worth - less, My heart He conquered—for Him I would die.
He was my ran - som, Dy - ing on Cal - v'ry with thorns on His brow.
thro' joy or sor - row, Sun - shine or tem - pest, sweet peace or de - spair.
hail I with glad - ness, Crowned 'mid the plaudits of an - gels and men.

won - der - ful Sav - ior! Glo - ry to Je - sus, and praise ev - er - more.

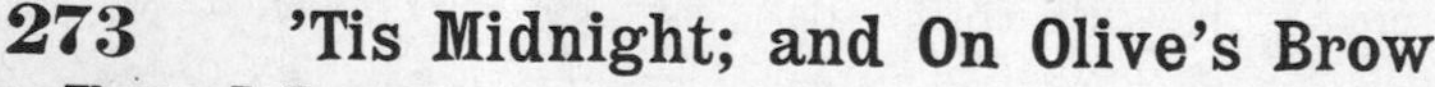

273 'Tis Midnight; and On Olive's Brow

WILLIAM B. TAPPAN — WILLIAM B. BRADBURY

1. 'Tis midnight; and on Ol - ive's brow The star is dimmed that late - ly shone:
2. 'Tis midnight; and from all re - moved, The Sav - ior wres - tles lone with fears;
3. 'Tis midnight; and for oth - ers' guilt The Man of Sor - rows weeps in blood;
4. 'Tis midnight; and from e - ther - plains Is borne the song that an - gels know;

'Tis Midnight; and On Olive's Brow

'Tis mid-night in the gar - den now, The suf-f'ring Sav-ior prays a - lone.
E'en that dis-ci - ple whom He loved Heeds not His Master's grief and tears.
Yet He that hath in an - guish knelt Is not for-sak - en by His God.
Un-heard by mor-tals are the strains That sweetly soothe the Sav-ior's woe.
274 Break Thou the Bread of Life
Mary Ann Lathbury
William F. Sherwin
1. Break Thou the bread of life, Dear Lord, to me, As Thou didst
2. Bless Thou the truth, dear Lord, To me— to me— As Thou didst
3. Thou art the bread of life, O Lord, to me, Thy ho - ly
4. O send Thy Spir - it, Lord, Now un - to me, That He may
break the loaves Be - side the sea; Be - yond the sa - cred page
bless the bread By Gal - i - lee; Then shall all bond- age cease,
Word the truth That sav - eth me; Give me to eat and live
touch my eyes, And make me see: Show me the truth con-cealed
I seek Thee, Lord; My spir - it pants for Thee, O liv - ing Word.
All fet - ters fall; And I shall find my peace, My All in all.
With Thee a - bove; Teach me to love Thy truth, For Thou art love.
With- in Thy Word, And in Thy book re-vealed I see the Lord.

275 My Faith Looks Up to Thee

RAY PALMER — LOWELL MASON

1. My faith looks up to Thee, Thou Lamb of Cal - va - ry, Sav - ior di - vine! Now hear me while I pray, Take all my guilt a - way, O let me from this day Be whol - ly Thine!
2. May Thy rich grace im - part Strength to my faint - ing heart, My zeal in - spire; As Thou hast died for me, O may my love to Thee Pure, warm, and changeless be, A liv - ing fire!
3. While life's dark maze I tread, And griefs a - round me spread, Be Thou my Guide; Bid dark - ness turn to day, Wipe sor - row's tears a - way, Nor let me ev - er stray From Thee a - side.
4. When ends life's tran-sient dream, When death's cold, sul - len stream Shall o'er me roll; Blest Sav - ior, then, in love, Fear and dis- trust re - move; O bear me safe a - bove, A ran - somed soul!

276 O For a Thousand Tongues

CHARLES WESLEY — CARL G. GLASER, Arr. by LOWELL MASON

1. O for a thou - sand tongues to sing My great Re-deem - er's praise,
2. My gra-cious Mas - ter and my God, As - sist me to pro - claim,
3. Je - sus! the name that charms our fears, That bids our sor - rows cease;
4. He breaks the pow'r of can - celed sin, He sets the pris - 'ner free;
5. Hear Him, ye deaf; His praise, ye dumb, Your loosened tongues em - ploy;

O For a Thousand Tongues

277 Lead, Kindly Light

The glo-ries of my God and King, The tri-umphs of His grace.
To spread thro' all the earth a-broad, The hon-ors of Thy name.
'Tis mu-sic in the sin-ner's ears, 'Tis life, and health, and peace.
His blood can make the foul-est clean; His blood a-vailed for me.
Ye blind, be-hold your Sav-ior come; And leap, ye lame, for joy.
JOHN H. NEWMAN
JOHN B. DYKES
1. Lead, kindly Light, amid th'encircling gloom, Lead Thou me on! The night is
2. I was not ev-er thus, nor prayed that Thou Shouldst lead me on; I loved to
3. So long Thy pow'r hath blest me, sure it still Will lead me on O'er moor and
dark, and I am far from home; Lead Thou me on! Keep Thou my feet; I
choose and see my path; but now Lead Thou me on! I loved the gar-ish
fen, o'er crag and torrent, till The night is gone, And with the morn those
do not ask to see . . . The dis-tant scene; one step e-nough for me.
day, and, spite of fears, . . Pride ruled my will. Remember not past years!
an-gel fa-ces smile, . Which I have loved long since, and lost a-while!

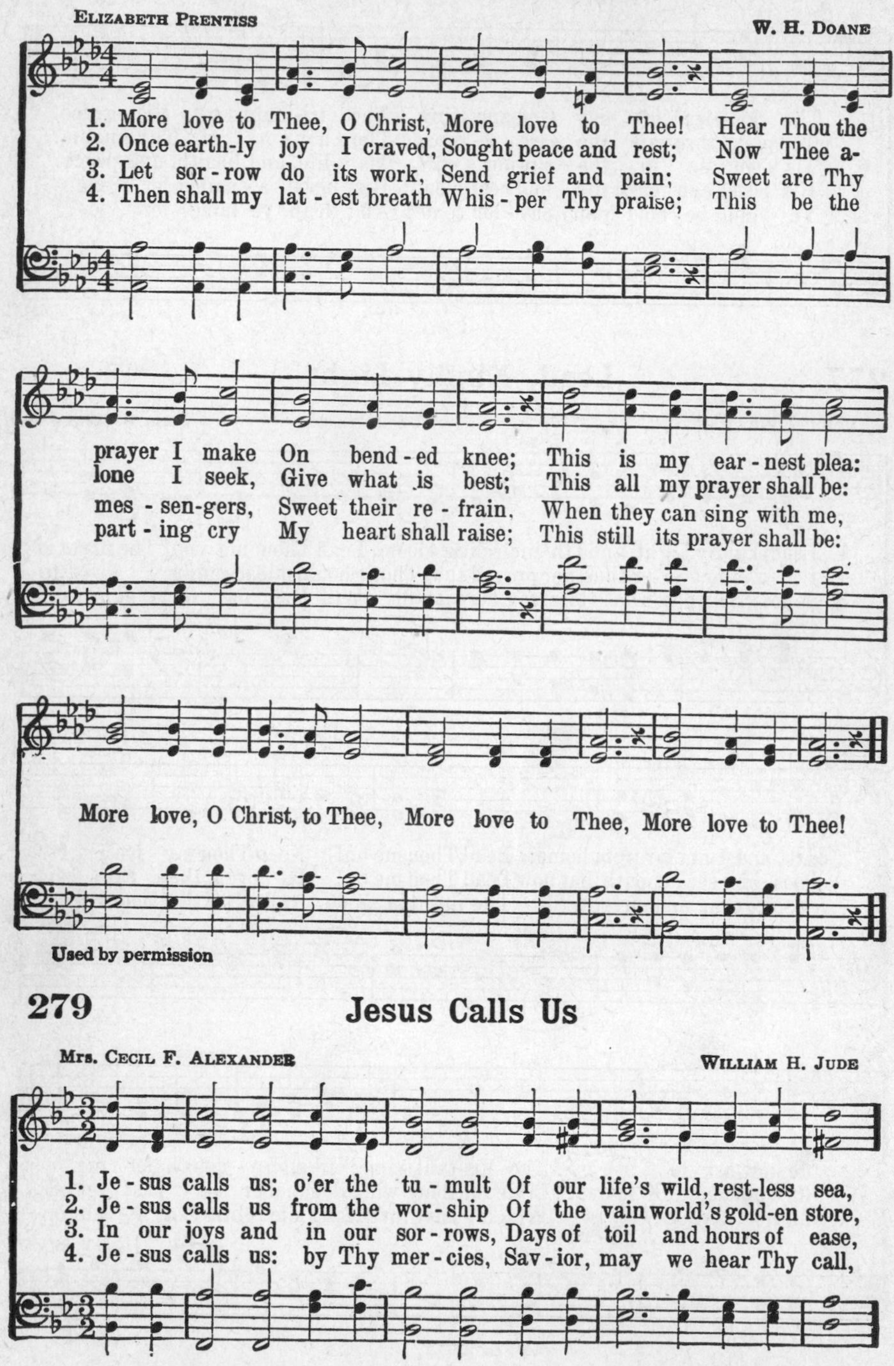
278
More Love to Thee
Elizabeth Prentiss
W. H. Doane
1. More love to Thee, O Christ, More love to Thee! Hear Thou the prayer I make On bend-ed knee; This is my ear-nest plea:
2. Once earth-ly joy I craved, Sought peace and rest; Now Thee a-lone I seek, Give what is best; This all my prayer shall be:
3. Let sor-row do its work, Send grief and pain; Sweet are Thy mes-sen-gers, Sweet their re-frain, When they can sing with me,
4. Then shall my lat-est breath Whis-per Thy praise; This be the part-ing cry My heart shall raise; This still its prayer shall be:
More love, O Christ, to Thee, More love to Thee, More love to Thee!
Used by permission
279
Jesus Calls Us
Mrs. Cecil F. Alexander
William H. Jude
1. Je-sus calls us; o'er the tu-mult Of our life's wild, rest-less sea,
2. Je-sus calls us from the wor-ship Of the vain world's gold-en store,
3. In our joys and in our sor-rows, Days of toil and hours of ease,
4. Je-sus calls us: by Thy mer-cies, Sav-ior, may we hear Thy call,

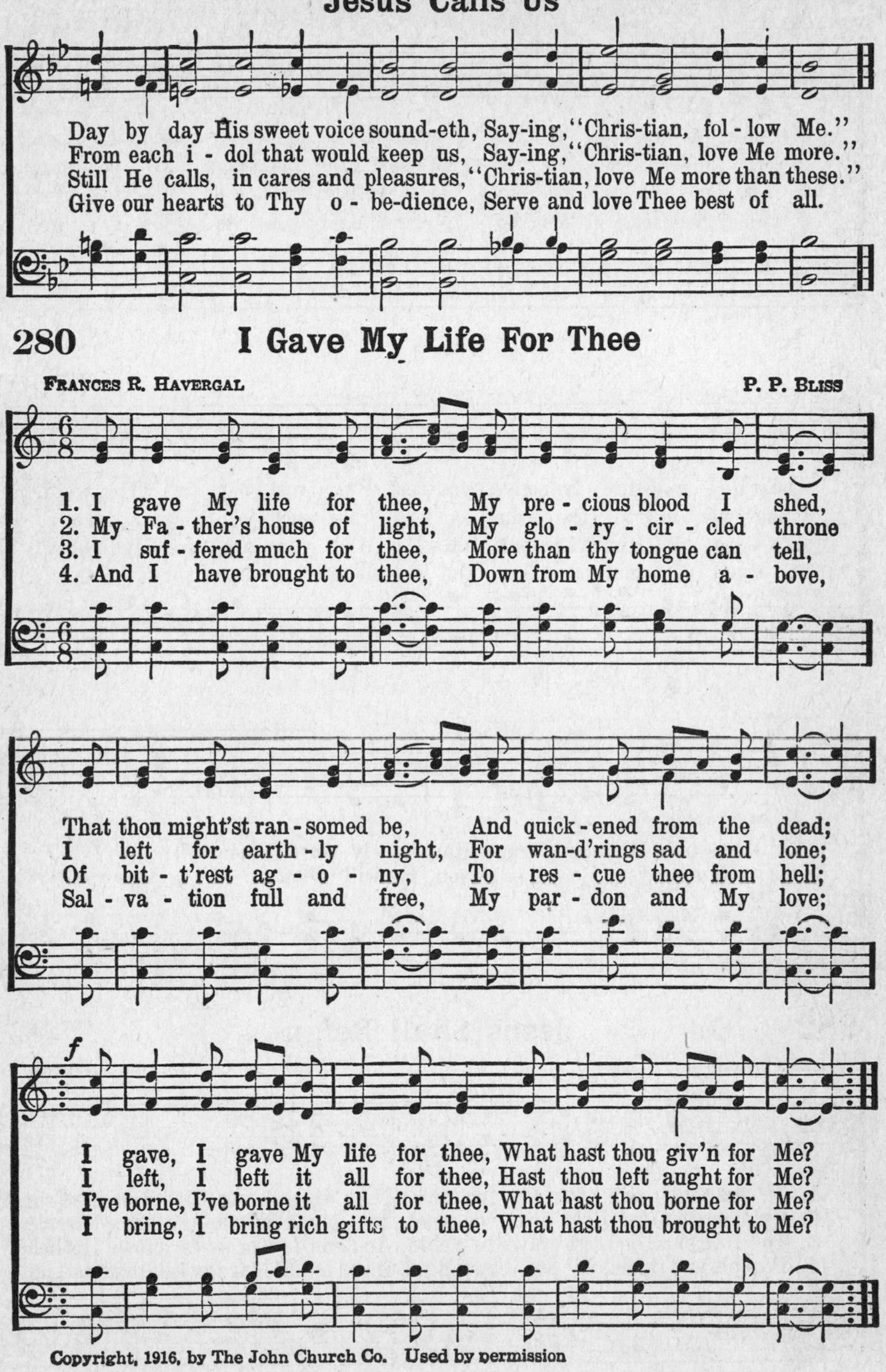
Jesus Calls Us
Day by day His sweet voice sound-eth, Say-ing, "Chris-tian, fol - low Me."
From each i - dol that would keep us, Say-ing, "Chris-tian, love Me more."
Still He calls, in cares and pleasures, "Chris-tian, love Me more than these."
Give our hearts to Thy o - be-dience, Serve and love Thee best of all.
280
I Gave My Life For Thee
Frances R. Havergal
P. P. Bliss
1. I gave My life for thee, My pre - cious blood I shed,
2. My Fa - ther's house of light, My glo - ry - cir - cled throne
3. I suf - fered much for thee, More than thy tongue can tell,
4. And I have brought to thee, Down from My home a - bove,
That thou might'st ran - somed be, And quick - ened from the dead;
I left for earth - ly night, For wan-d'rings sad and lone;
Of bit - t'rest ag - o - ny, To res - cue thee from hell;
Sal - va - tion full and free, My par - don and My love;
f
I gave, I gave My life for thee, What hast thou giv'n for Me?
I left, I left it all for thee, Hast thou left aught for Me?
I've borne, I've borne it all for thee, What hast thou borne for Me?
I bring, I bring rich gifts to thee, What hast thou brought to Me?
Copyright, 1916, by The John Church Co. Used by permission

281 Only Trust Him
J. H. S.
J. H. Stockton
1. Come, ev - 'ry soul by sin op-pressed, There's mer- cy with the Lord,
2. For Je - sus shed His pre-cious blood, Rich bless-ings to be - stow;
3. Yes, Je - sus is the Truth, the Way, That leads you in - to rest:
4. Come, then, and join this ho - ly band, And on to glo - ry go,
And He will sure - ly give you rest By trust - ing in His word.
Plunge now in - to the crim - son flood That wash - es white as snow.
Be - lieve in Him with - out de - lay, And you are ful - ly blest.
To dwell in that ce - les - tial land, Where joys im - mor - tal flow.
1
2
On - ly trust Him, on-ly trust Him, On - ly trust Him now.
He will save you, He will save you, He will (Omit . . . . . save you now.
282 Jesus Shall Reign
Isaac Watts
John Hatton
1. Je - sus shall reign wher-e'er the sun Does his suc - ces - sive jour-neys run;
2. From north to south the prin - ces meet To pay their hom-age at His feet;
3. To Him shall end-less prayer be made, And end-less prais-es crown His head;
4. Peo- ple and realms of ev - 'ry tongue Dwell on His love with sweetest song,

Jesus Shall Reign

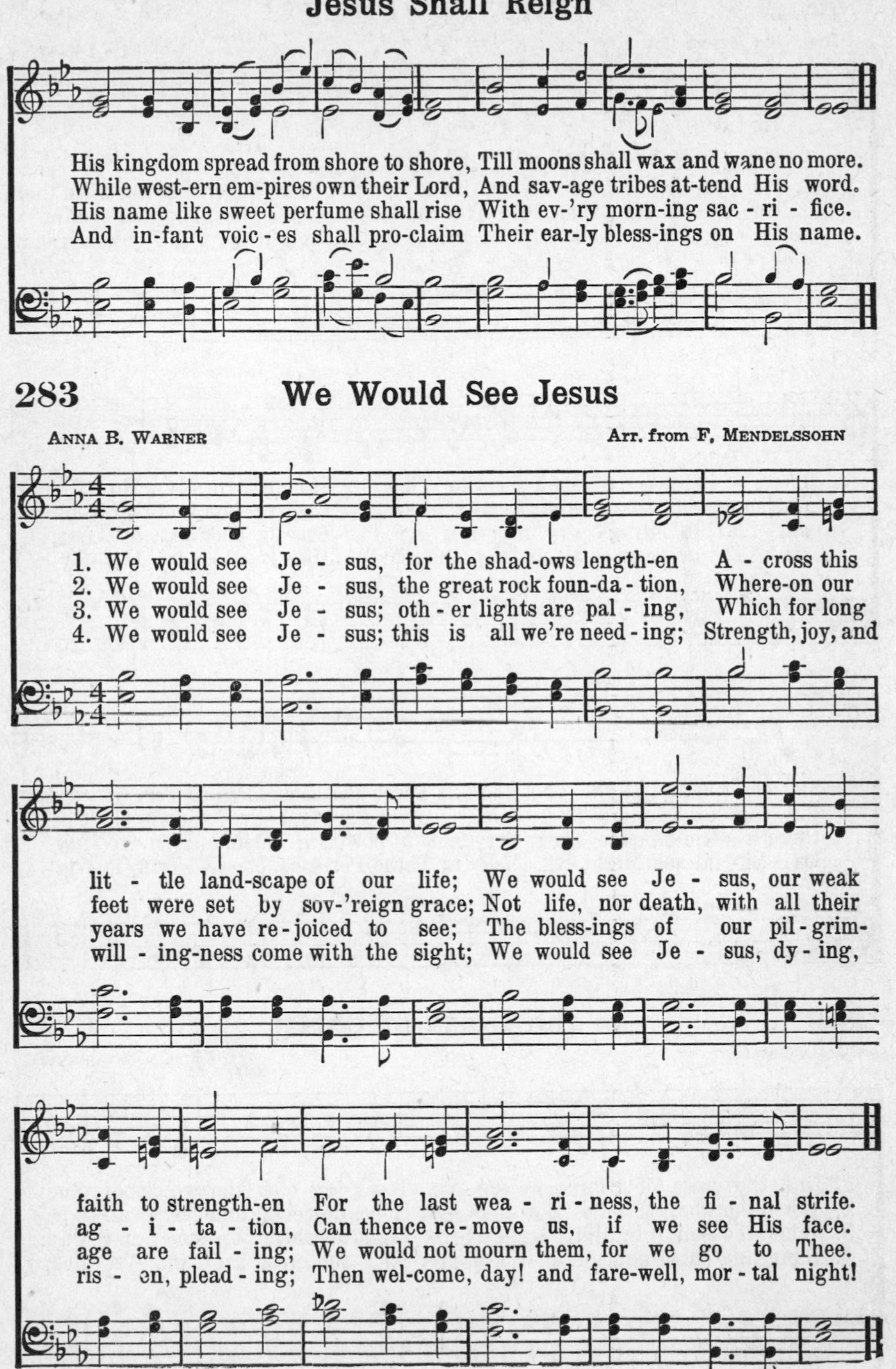

His kingdom spread from shore to shore, Till moons shall wax and wane no more.
While west-ern em-pires own their Lord, And sav-age tribes at-tend His word.
His name like sweet perfume shall rise With ev-'ry morn-ing sac - ri - fice.
And in-fant voic - es shall pro-claim Their ear-ly bless-ings on His name.

283 We Would See Jesus

Anna B. Warner — Arr. from F. Mendelssohn

1. We would see Je - sus, for the shad-ows length-en A - cross this lit - tle land-scape of our life; We would see Je - sus, our weak faith to strength-en For the last wea - ri - ness, the fi - nal strife.
2. We would see Je - sus, the great rock foun-da - tion, Where-on our feet were set by sov-'reign grace; Not life, nor death, with all their ag - i - ta - tion, Can thence re - move us, if we see His face.
3. We would see Je - sus; oth - er lights are pal - ing, Which for long years we have re - joiced to see; The bless-ings of our pil - grim-age are fail - ing; We would not mourn them, for we go to Thee.
4. We would see Je - sus; this is all we're need - ing; Strength, joy, and will - ing-ness come with the sight; We would see Je - sus, dy - ing, ris - en, plead - ing; Then wel-come, day! and fare-well, mor - tal night!

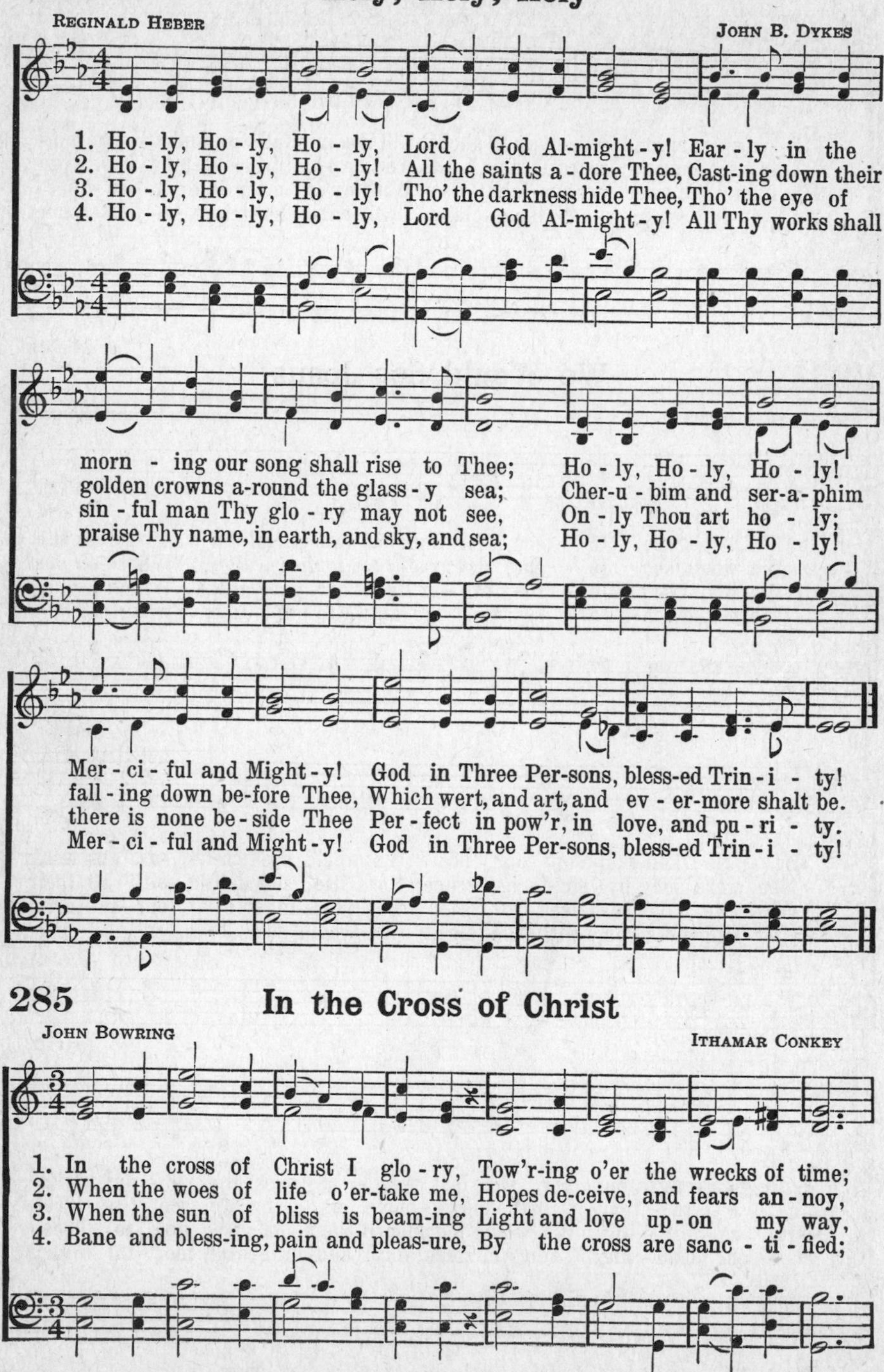
284 Holy, Holy, Holy
Reginald Heber
John B. Dykes
1. Ho - ly, Ho - ly, Ho - ly, Lord God Al-might - y! Ear - ly in the
2. Ho - ly, Ho - ly, Ho - ly! All the saints a - dore Thee, Cast-ing down their
3. Ho - ly, Ho - ly, Ho - ly! Tho' the darkness hide Thee, Tho' the eye of
4. Ho - ly, Ho - ly, Ho - ly, Lord God Al-might - y! All Thy works shall
morn - ing our song shall rise to Thee; Ho - ly, Ho - ly, Ho - ly!
golden crowns a-round the glass - y sea; Cher-u - bim and ser-a - phim
sin - ful man Thy glo - ry may not see, On - ly Thou art ho - ly;
praise Thy name, in earth, and sky, and sea; Ho - ly, Ho - ly, Ho - ly!
Mer - ci - ful and Might - y! God in Three Per-sons, bless-ed Trin - i - ty!
fall - ing down be-fore Thee, Which wert, and art, and ev - er-more shalt be.
there is none be - side Thee Per - fect in pow'r, in love, and pu - ri - ty.
Mer - ci - ful and Might - y! God in Three Per-sons, bless-ed Trin - i - ty!
285 In the Cross of Christ
John Bowring
Ithamar Conkey
1. In the cross of Christ I glo - ry, Tow'r-ing o'er the wrecks of time;
2. When the woes of life o'er-take me, Hopes de-ceive, and fears an - noy,
3. When the sun of bliss is beam-ing Light and love up - on my way,
4. Bane and bless-ing, pain and pleas-ure, By the cross are sanc - ti - fied;

In the Cross of Christ
All the light of sa - cred sto - ry Gath-ers round its head sub-lime.
Nev - er shall the cross for - sake me: Lo! it glows with peace and joy.
From the cross the ra - diance streaming Adds more lus - ter to the day.
Peace is there that knows no meas-ure, Joys that thro' all time a - bide.
286
Hallelujah, 'Tis Done
P. P. B.
P. P. Bliss
1. 'Tis the prom - ise of God, full sal - va - tion to give
2. Tho' the path - way be lone - ly, and dan - ger - ous too,
3. Man - y loved ones have I in yon heav - en - ly throng,
4. There's a part in that cho - rus for you and for me,
Un - to him who on Je - sus, His Son, will be - lieve.
Sure - ly Je - sus is a - ble to car - ry me through.
They are safe now in glo - ry, and this is their song:
And the theme of our prais - es for - ev - er will be:
Refrain
Hal - le - lu - jah, 'tis done! I be-lieve on the Son; I am
1
2
saved by the blood of the cru - ci - fied One; cru - ci - fied One.

287 Glory to His Name

E. A. Hoffman — J. H. Stockton

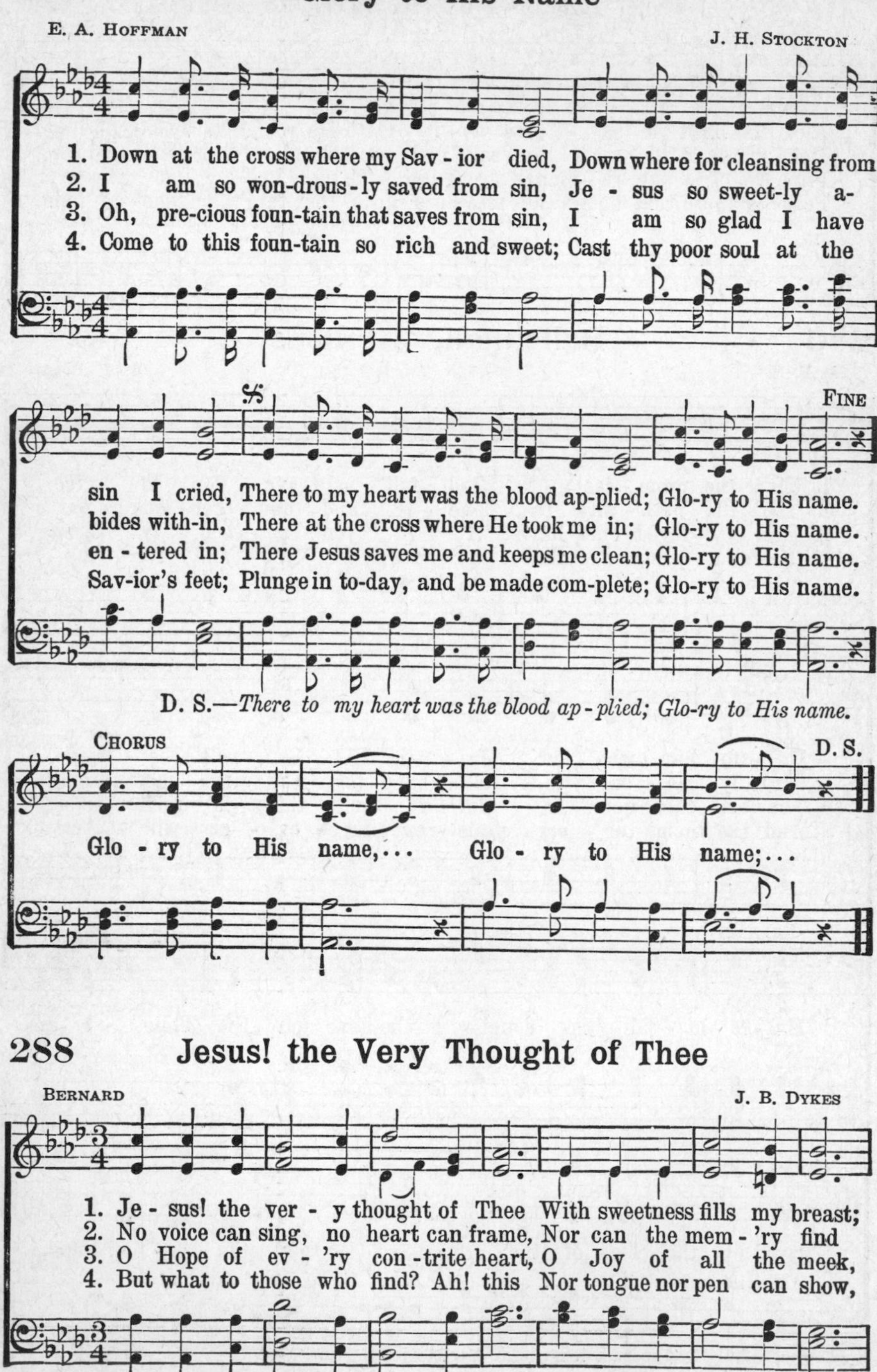

1. Down at the cross where my Sav - ior died, Down where for cleansing from sin I cried, There to my heart was the blood ap-plied; Glo-ry to His name.
2. I am so won-drous-ly saved from sin, Je - sus so sweet-ly a-bides with-in, There at the cross where He took me in; Glo-ry to His name.
3. Oh, pre-cious foun-tain that saves from sin, I am so glad I have en - tered in; There Jesus saves me and keeps me clean; Glo-ry to His name.
4. Come to this foun-tain so rich and sweet; Cast thy poor soul at the Sav-ior's feet; Plunge in to-day, and be made com-plete; Glo-ry to His name.
FINE
D. S.—There to my heart was the blood ap-plied; Glo-ry to His name.
CHORUS
Glo - ry to His name,... Glo - ry to His name;...
D. S.

288 Jesus! the Very Thought of Thee

Bernard — J. B. Dykes

1. Je - sus! the ver - y thought of Thee With sweetness fills my breast;
2. No voice can sing, no heart can frame, Nor can the mem - 'ry find
3. O Hope of ev - 'ry con - trite heart, O Joy of all the meek,
4. But what to those who find? Ah! this Nor tongue nor pen can show,

Jesus! the Very Thought of Thee

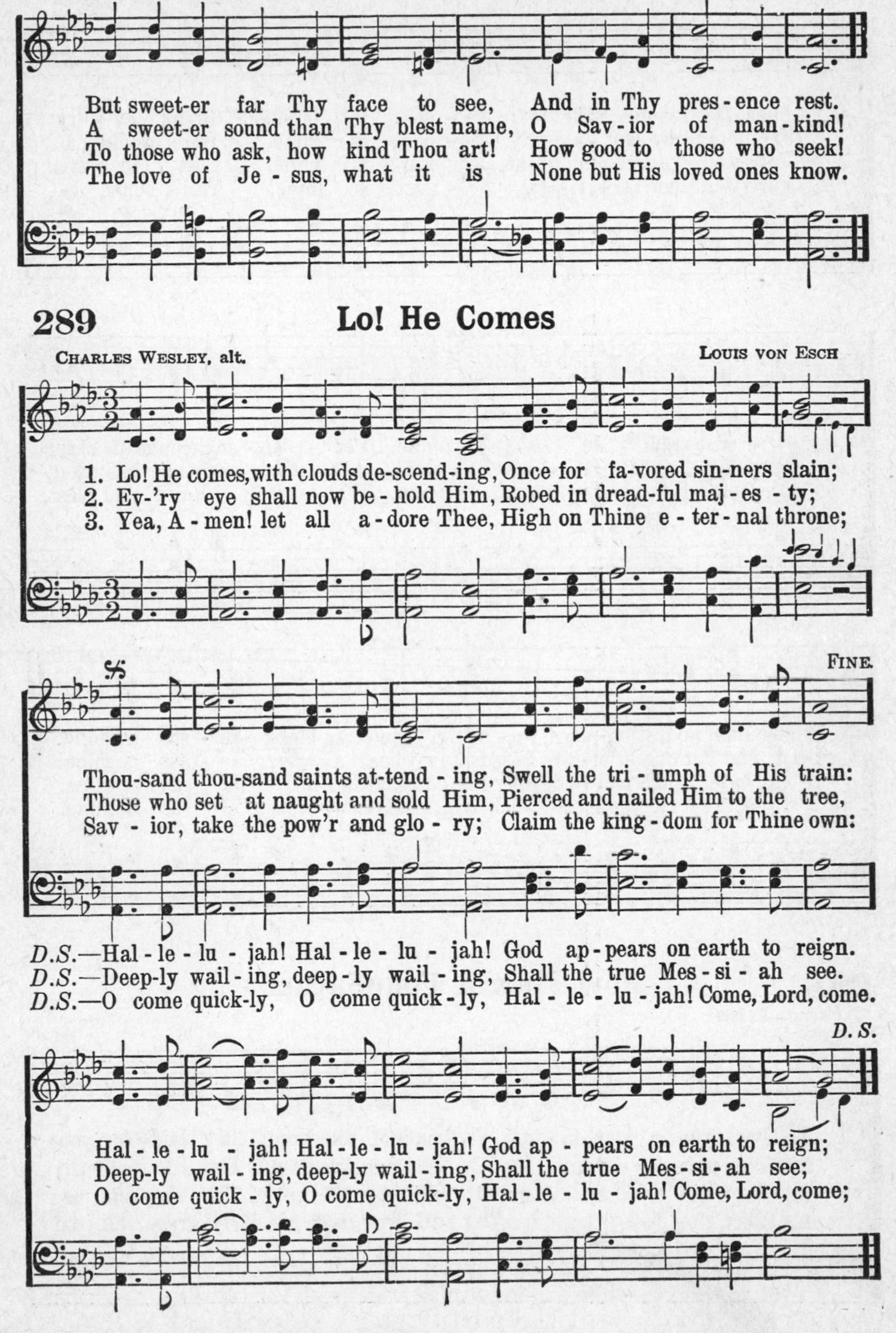

But sweet-er far Thy face to see, And in Thy pres-ence rest.
A sweet-er sound than Thy blest name, O Sav-ior of man-kind!
To those who ask, how kind Thou art! How good to those who seek!
The love of Je-sus, what it is None but His loved ones know.
289
Lo! He Comes
CHARLES WESLEY, alt.
LOUIS VON ESCH
1. Lo! He comes, with clouds de-scend-ing, Once for fa-vored sin-ners slain;
2. Ev-'ry eye shall now be-hold Him, Robed in dread-ful maj-es-ty;
3. Yea, A-men! let all a-dore Thee, High on Thine e-ter-nal throne;
FINE
Thou-sand thou-sand saints at-tend-ing, Swell the tri-umph of His train:
Those who set at naught and sold Him, Pierced and nailed Him to the tree,
Sav-ior, take the pow'r and glo-ry; Claim the king-dom for Thine own:
D.S.—Hal-le-lu-jah! Hal-le-lu-jah! God ap-pears on earth to reign.
D.S.—Deep-ly wail-ing, deep-ly wail-ing, Shall the true Mes-si-ah see.
D.S.—O come quick-ly, O come quick-ly, Hal-le-lu-jah! Come, Lord, come.
D. S.
Hal-le-lu-jah! Hal-le-lu-jah! God ap-pears on earth to reign;
Deep-ly wail-ing, deep-ly wail-ing, Shall the true Mes-si-ah see;
O come quick-ly, O come quick-ly, Hal-le-lu-jah! Come, Lord, come;

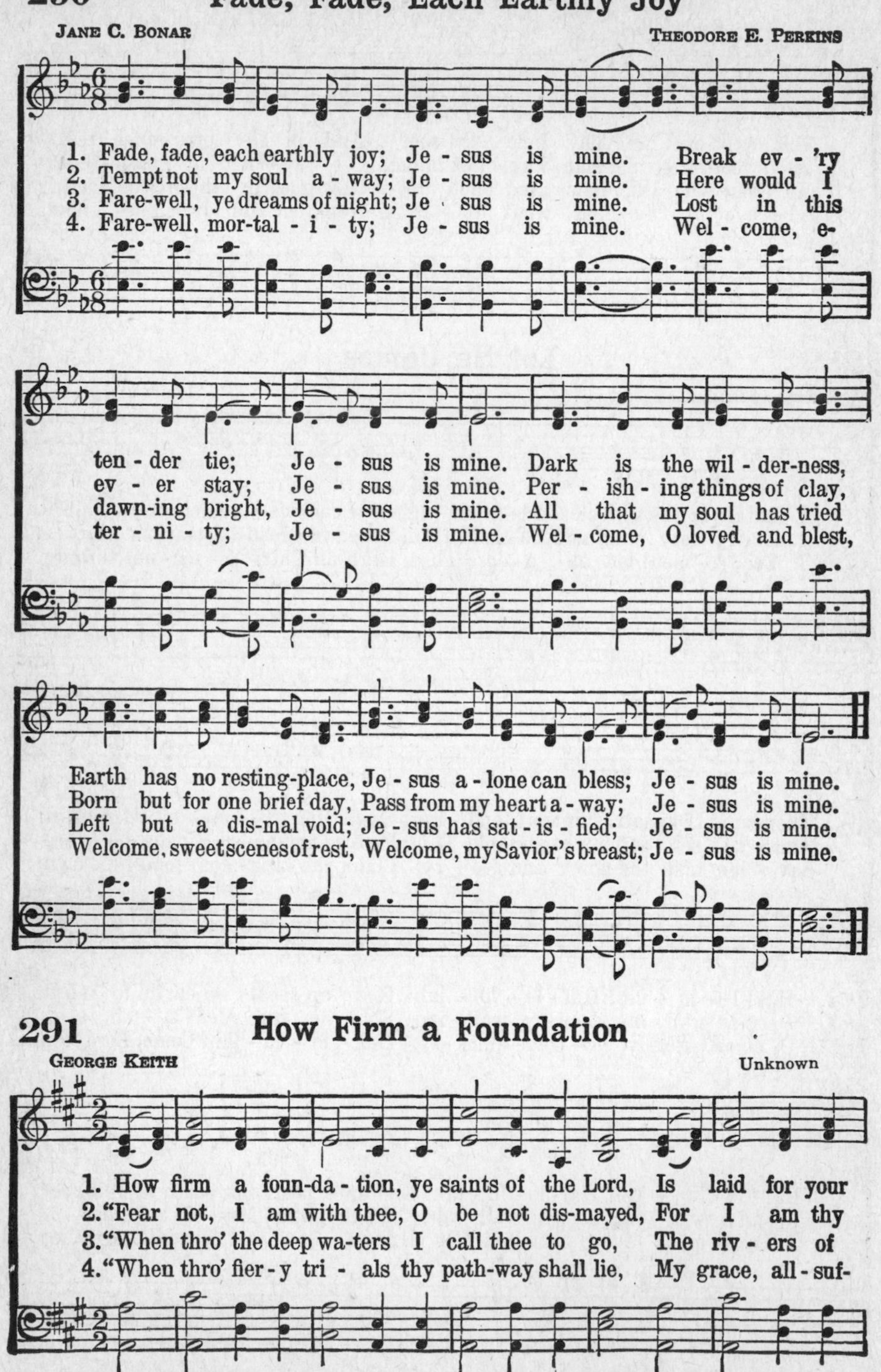
290 Fade, Fade, Each Earthly Joy
Jane C. Bonar
Theodore E. Perkins
1. Fade, fade, each earthly joy; Je - sus is mine. Break ev - 'ry
2. Tempt not my soul a - way; Je - sus is mine. Here would I
3. Fare-well, ye dreams of night; Je - sus is mine. Lost in this
4. Fare-well, mor-tal - i - ty; Je - sus is mine. Wel - come, e-
ten - der tie; Je - sus is mine. Dark is the wil - der-ness,
ev - er stay; Je - sus is mine. Per - ish - ing things of clay,
dawn-ing bright, Je - sus is mine. All that my soul has tried
ter - ni - ty; Je - sus is mine. Wel - come, O loved and blest,
Earth has no resting-place, Je - sus a - lone can bless; Je - sus is mine.
Born but for one brief day, Pass from my heart a - way; Je - sus is mine.
Left but a dis-mal void; Je - sus has sat - is - fied; Je - sus is mine.
Welcome, sweet scenes of rest, Welcome, my Savior's breast; Je - sus is mine.
291 How Firm a Foundation
George Keith
Unknown
1. How firm a foun-da - tion, ye saints of the Lord, Is laid for your
2. "Fear not, I am with thee, O be not dis-mayed, For I am thy
3. "When thro' the deep wa-ters I call thee to go, The riv - ers of
4. "When thro' fier - y tri - als thy path-way shall lie, My grace, all - suf-

How Firm a Foundation

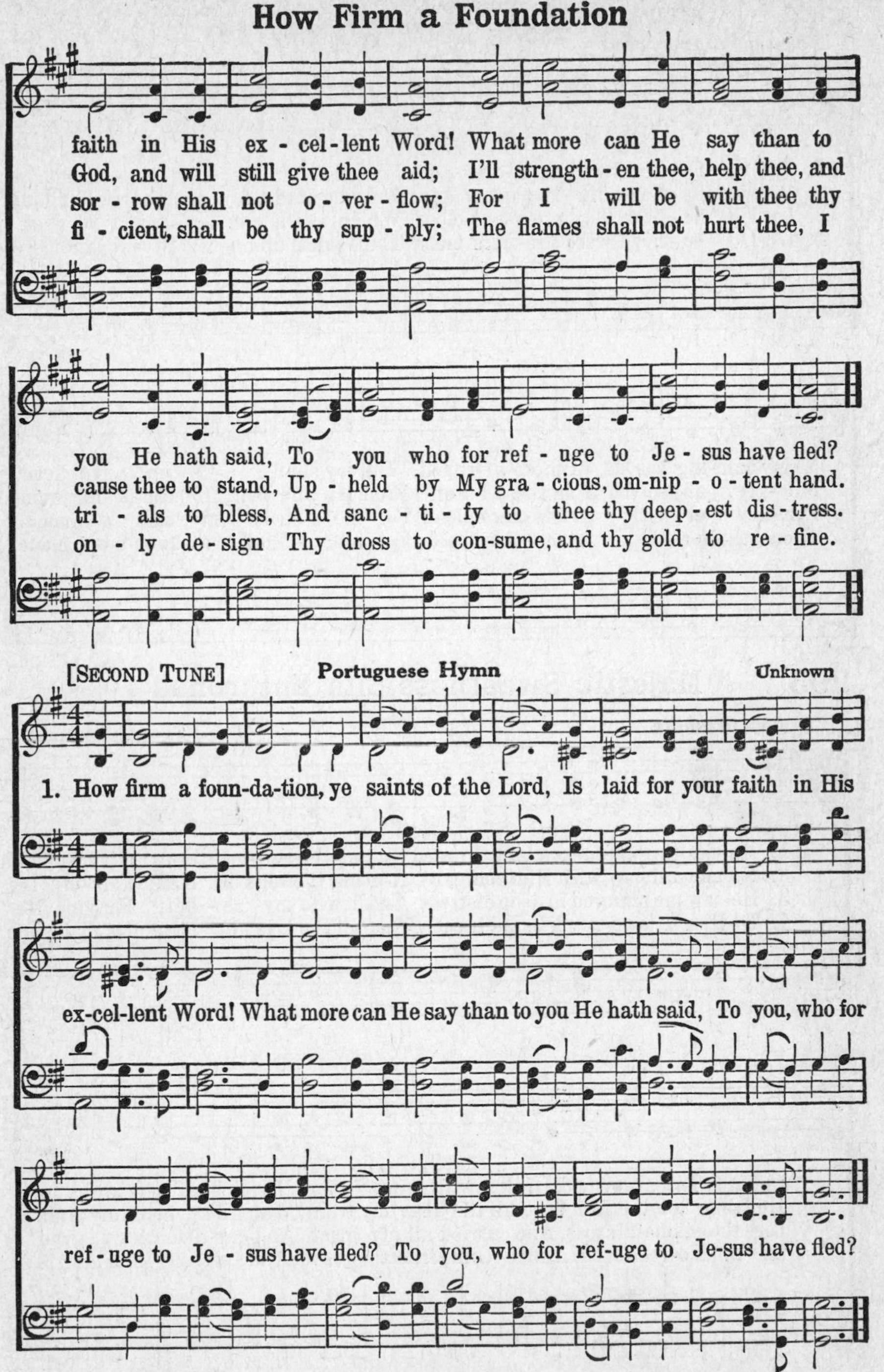
faith in His ex - cel - lent Word! What more can He say than to
God, and will still give thee aid; I'll strength - en thee, help thee, and
sor - row shall not o - ver - flow; For I will be with thee thy
fi - cient, shall be thy sup - ply; The flames shall not hurt thee, I
you He hath said, To you who for ref - uge to Je - sus have fled?
cause thee to stand, Up - held by My gra - cious, om - nip - o - tent hand.
tri - als to bless, And sanc - ti - fy to thee thy deep - est dis - tress.
on - ly de - sign Thy dross to con - sume, and thy gold to re - fine.
[SECOND TUNE]
Portuguese Hymn
Unknown
1. How firm a foun-da-tion, ye saints of the Lord, Is laid for your faith in His
ex-cel-lent Word! What more can He say than to you He hath said, To you, who for
ref - uge to Je - sus have fled? To you, who for ref-uge to Je-sus have fled?

292 Jesus, Thy Blood and Righteousness

NICOLAUS L. ZINZENDORF
Tr. by JOHN WESLEY

LUDWIG VAN BEETHOVEN

293 Majestic Sweetness Sits Enthroned

SAMUEL STENNETT

THOMAS HASTINGS

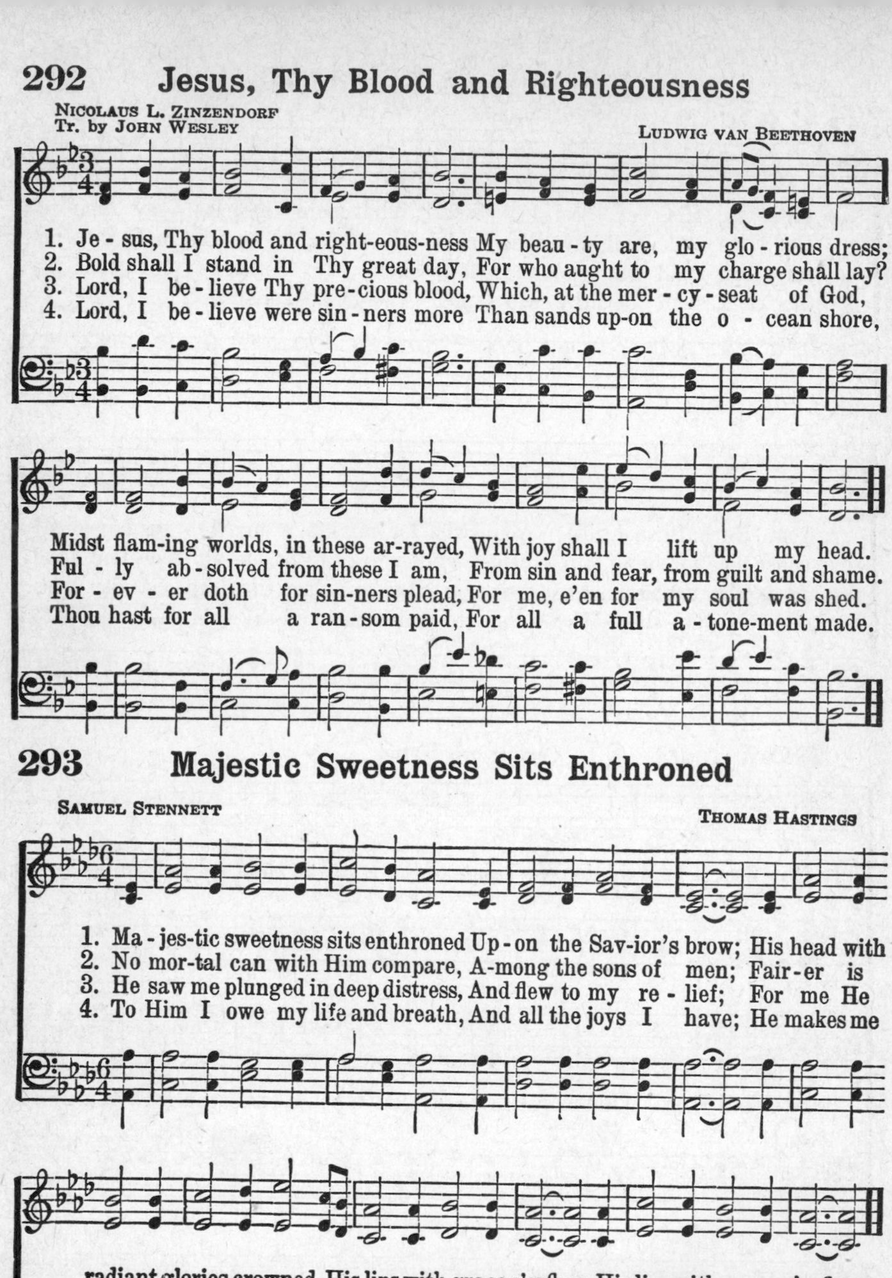
1. Je - sus, Thy blood and right-eous-ness My beau - ty are, my glo - rious dress;
2. Bold shall I stand in Thy great day, For who aught to my charge shall lay?
3. Lord, I be - lieve Thy pre - cious blood, Which, at the mer - cy - seat of God,
4. Lord, I be - lieve were sin - ners more Than sands up-on the o - cean shore,
Midst flam-ing worlds, in these ar-rayed, With joy shall I lift up my head.
Ful - ly ab - solved from these I am, From sin and fear, from guilt and shame.
For - ev - er doth for sin-ners plead, For me, e'en for my soul was shed.
Thou hast for all a ran - som paid, For all a full a - tone-ment made.
1. Ma - jes-tic sweetness sits enthroned Up - on the Sav-ior's brow; His head with
2. No mor-tal can with Him compare, A-mong the sons of men; Fair-er is
3. He saw me plunged in deep distress, And flew to my re - lief; For me He
4. To Him I owe my life and breath, And all the joys I have; He makes me
radiant glories crowned, His lips with grace o'erflow, His lips with grace o'erflow.
He than all the fair Who fill the heav'nly train, Who fill the heav'nly train.
bore the shameful cross, And carried all my grief, And car-ried all my grief.
tri - umph o-ver death, And saves me from the grave, And saves me from the grave.

294 Memories of Mother

FRED. P. MORRIS ROBERT HARKNESS

1. My moth-er's hand is on my brow, Her gen - tle voice is plead-ing now;
2. Once more I see that look of pain, The an-guish in those eyes a - gain;
3. While oth-ers scorned me in their pride She gen - tly drew me to her side;
4. The mem - o - ries of by-gone years, My moth-er's love, my mother's tears,
5. I'm com - ing home, by sin be - set, For Je - sus loves me e - ven yet;

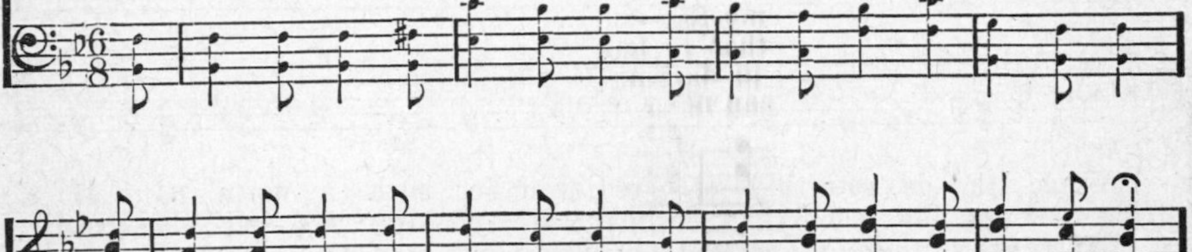

A - cross the years so marred by sin What mem-o-ries of love steal in!
My heart is sad, for well I know My sin has caused this bit - ter woe.
When all the world had turned a-way, My moth - er stood by me that day.
The tho't of all her con-stant care Doth bring the an - swer to her prayer.
My moth-er's love brings home to me The great-er love of Cal - va - ry.

CHORUS

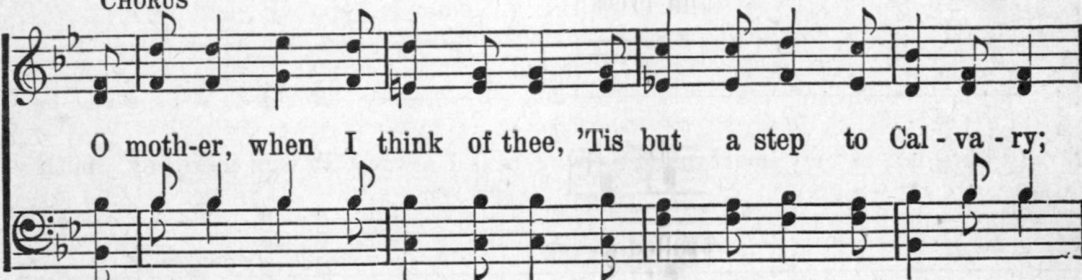

O moth-er, when I think of thee, 'Tis but a step to Cal - va - ry;

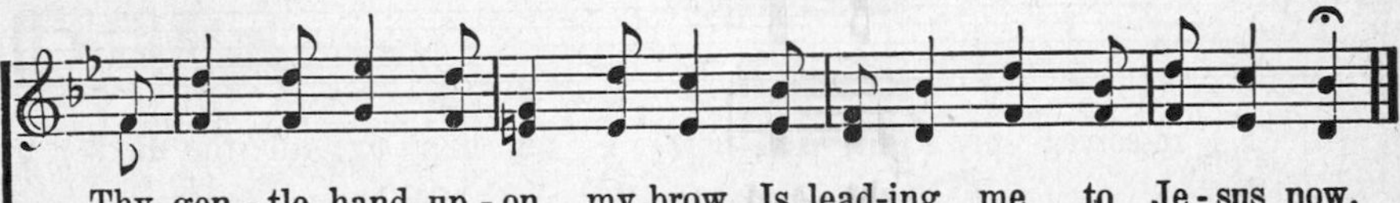

Thy gen - tle hand up - on my brow Is lead-ing me to Je - sus now.

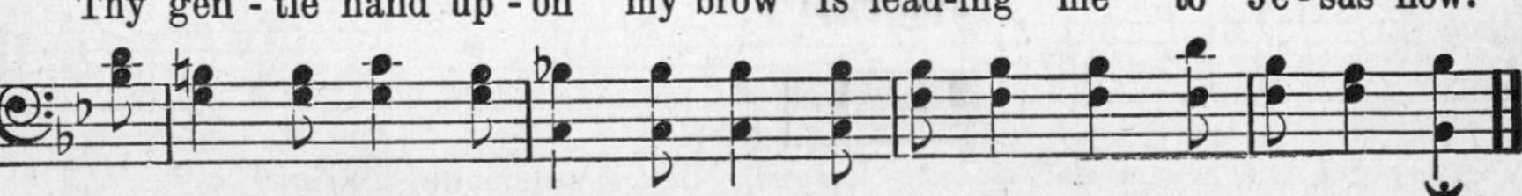

295 At the Cross

Isaac Watts | R. E. Hudson

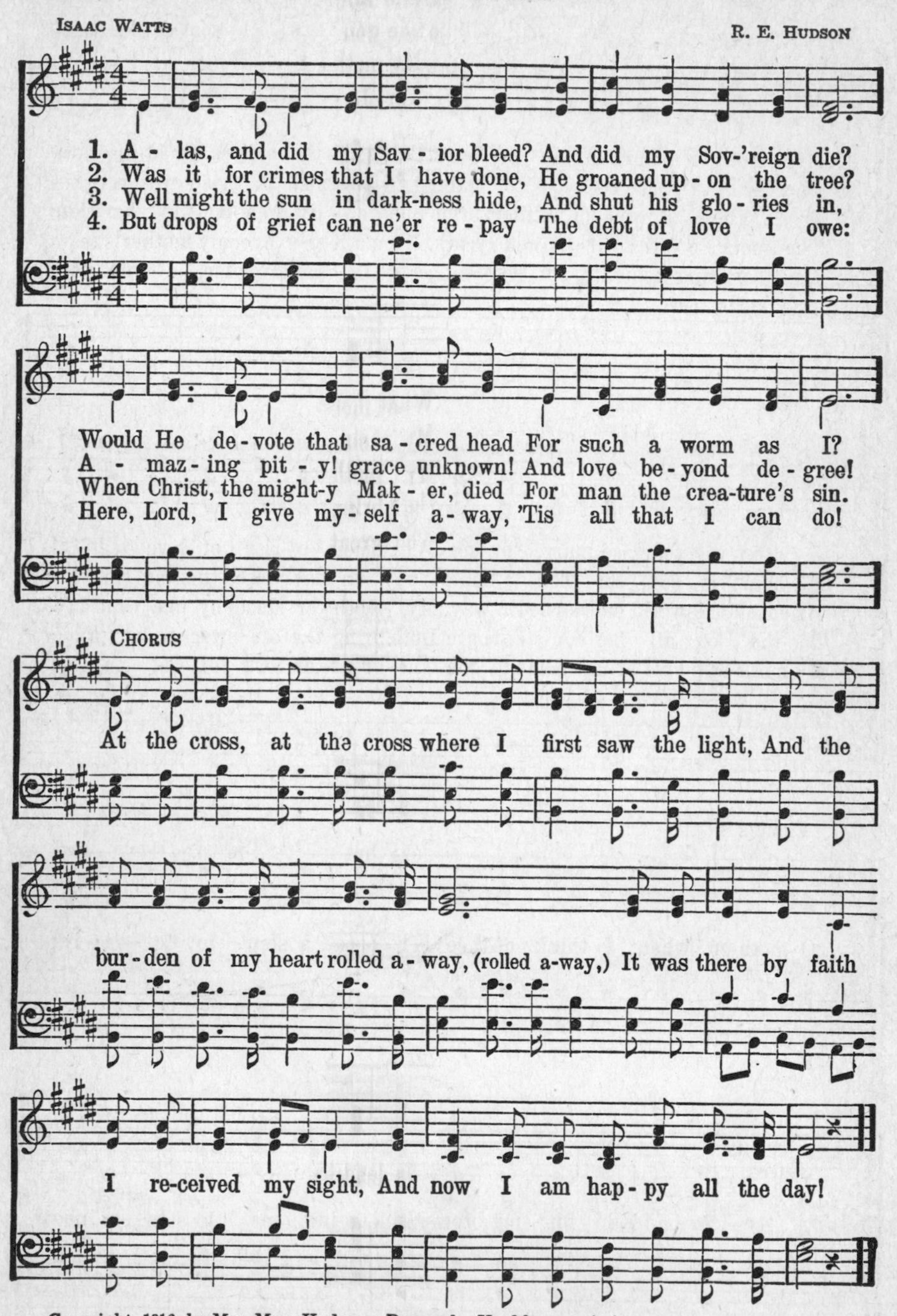
1. A - las, and did my Sav - ior bleed? And did my Sov-'reign die?
2. Was it for crimes that I have done, He groaned up - on the tree?
3. Well might the sun in dark-ness hide, And shut his glo - ries in,
4. But drops of grief can ne'er re - pay The debt of love I owe:
Would He de - vote that sa - cred head For such a worm as I?
A - maz - ing pit - y! grace unknown! And love be - yond de - gree!
When Christ, the might-y Mak - er, died For man the crea-ture's sin.
Here, Lord, I give my-self a - way, 'Tis all that I can do!
Chorus
At the cross, at the cross where I first saw the light, And the
bur - den of my heart rolled a - way, (rolled a-way,) It was there by faith
I re-ceived my sight, And now I am hap - py all the day!

296

The Solid Rock

EDWARD MOTE

WILLIAM B. BRADBURY

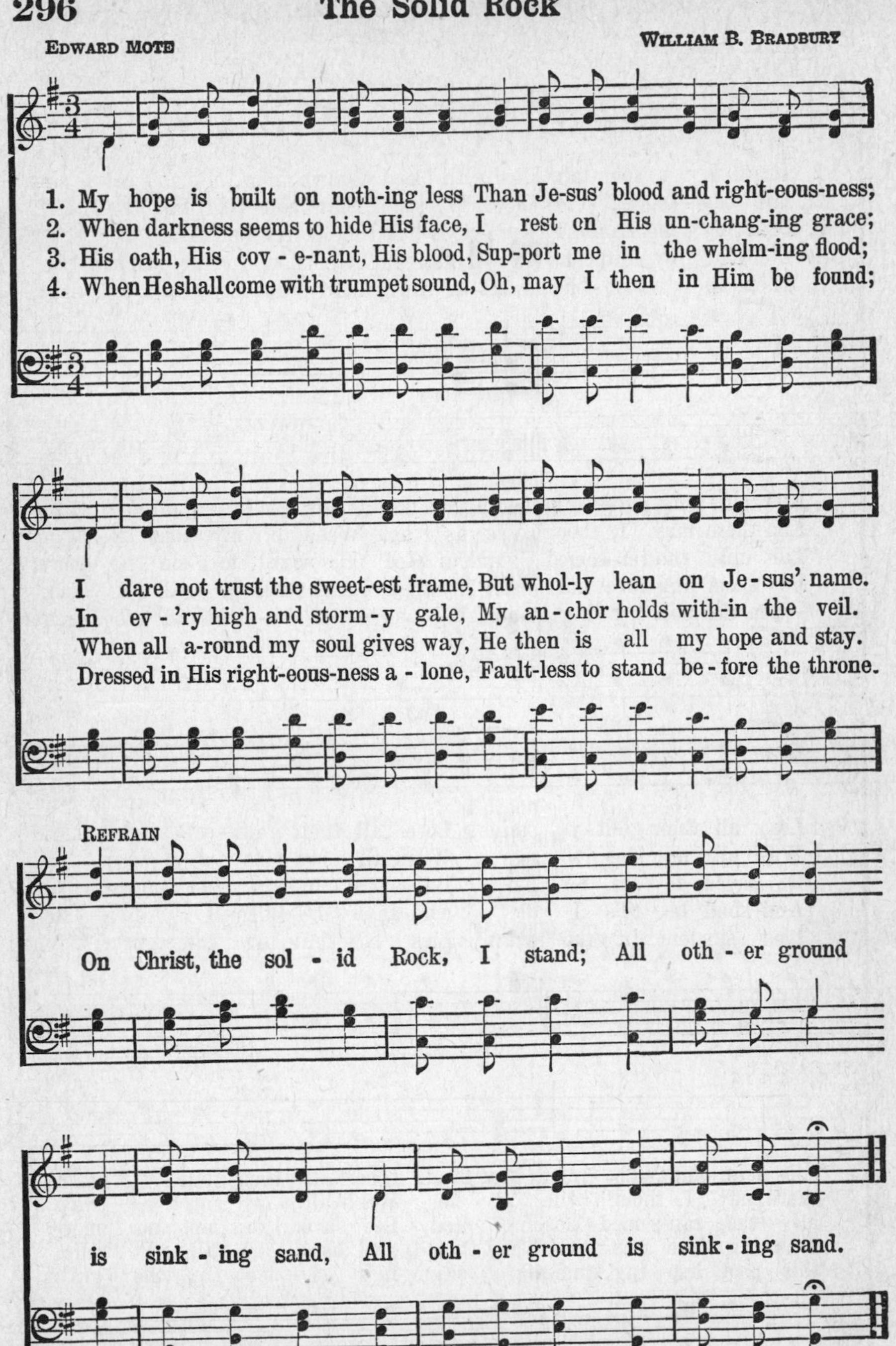
1. My hope is built on noth-ing less Than Je-sus' blood and right-eous-ness;
2. When darkness seems to hide His face, I rest on His un-chang-ing grace;
3. His oath, His cov - e-nant, His blood, Sup-port me in the whelm-ing flood;
4. When He shall come with trumpet sound, Oh, may I then in Him be found;
I dare not trust the sweet-est frame, But whol-ly lean on Je-sus' name.
In ev - 'ry high and storm-y gale, My an-chor holds with-in the veil.
When all a-round my soul gives way, He then is all my hope and stay.
Dressed in His right-eous-ness a - lone, Fault-less to stand be-fore the throne.
REFRAIN
On Christ, the sol - id Rock, I stand; All oth - er ground
is sink - ing sand, All oth - er ground is sink-ing sand.

297 There is a Fountain

William Cowper — Lowell Mason

1. There is a foun-tain filled with blood Drawn from Im-man-uel's veins;
2. The dy-ing thief re-joiced to see That foun-tain in his day;
3. Dear dy-ing Lamb, Thy pre-cious blood Shall nev-er lose its pow'r,
4. E'er since, by faith, I saw the stream Thy flow-ing wounds sup-ply,
5. Then in a no-bler, sweet-er song, I'll sing Thy pow'r to save,
And sin-ners, plunged be-neath that flood, Lose all their guilt-y stains:
And there may I, though vile as he, Wash all my sins a-way:
Till all the ran-somed Church of God Be saved, to sin no more:
Re-deem-ing love has been my theme, And shall be till I die:
When this poor lisp-ing, stamm'ring tongue Lies si-lent in the grave:
Lose all their guilt-y stains, Lose all their guilt-y stains; And
Wash all my sins a-way, Wash all my sins a-way; And
Be saved, to sin no more, Be saved, to sin no more; Till
And shall be till I die, And shall be till I die; Re-
Lies si-lent in the grave, Lies si-lent in the grave; When
sin-ners, plunged be-neath that flood, Lose all their guilt-y stains.
there may I, though vile as he, Wash all my sins a-way.
all the ran-somed Church of God Be saved, to sin no more.
deem-ing love has been my theme, And shall be till I die.
this poor lisp-ing, stam-m'ring tongue Lies si-lent in the grave.

Come, Thou Fount

ROBERT ROBINSON JOHN WYETH

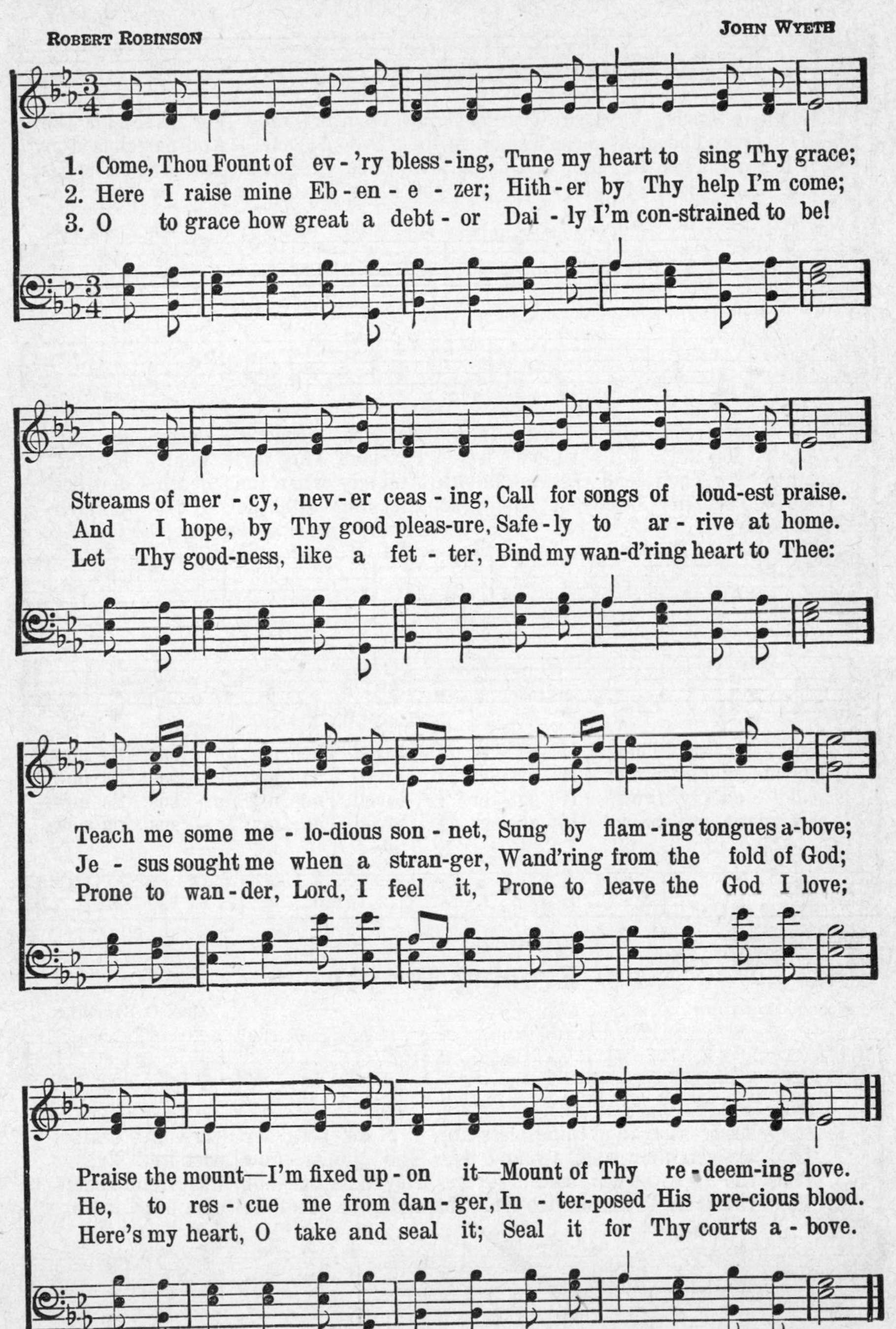
1. Come, Thou Fount of ev - 'ry bless - ing, Tune my heart to sing Thy grace;
2. Here I raise mine Eb - en - e - zer; Hith - er by Thy help I'm come;
3. O to grace how great a debt - or Dai - ly I'm con-strained to be!
Streams of mer - cy, nev - er ceas - ing, Call for songs of loud-est praise.
And I hope, by Thy good pleas-ure, Safe - ly to ar - rive at home.
Let Thy good-ness, like a fet - ter, Bind my wan-d'ring heart to Thee:
Teach me some me - lo-dious son - net, Sung by flam - ing tongues a-bove;
Je - sus sought me when a stran-ger, Wand'ring from the fold of God;
Prone to wan - der, Lord, I feel it, Prone to leave the God I love;
Praise the mount—I'm fixed up - on it—Mount of Thy re - deem-ing love.
He, to res - cue me from dan - ger, In - ter-posed His pre-cious blood.
Here's my heart, O take and seal it; Seal it for Thy courts a - bove.

299 My Jesus, I Love Thee
Author Unknown
A. J. GORDON
1. My Je - sus, I love Thee, I know Thou art mine, For Thee all the
2. I love Thee, be - cause Thou hast first lov - ed me, And pur-chased my
3. I'll love Thee in life, I will love Thee in death, And praise Thee as
4. In man - sions of glo - ry and end - less de - light, I'll ev - er a-
fol - lies of sin I re - sign; My gra - cious Re - deem - er, my
par - don on Cal - va - ry's tree; I love Thee for wear - ing the
long as Thou lend - est me breath; And say when the death - dew lies
dore Thee in heav - en so bright; I'll sing with the glit - ter - ing
Sav - ior art Thou; If ev - er I loved Thee, my Je - sus, 'tis now.
thorns on Thy brow: If ev - er I loved Thee, my Je - sus, 'tis now.
cold on my brow, If ev - er I loved Thee, my Je - sus, 'tis now.
crown on my brow, If ev - er I loved Thee, my Je - sus, 'tis now.
300 Evening Prayer
JAMES EDMESTON
GEO. C. STEBBINS
1. Sav - ior, breathe an evening bless-ing, Ere re - pose our spir - its seal:
2. Tho' de-struc-tion walk a-round us, Tho' the ar - rows past us fly;
3. Tho' the night be dark and drear-y, Darkness can-not hide from Thee;
4. Should swift death this night o'ertake us, And our couch be-come our tomb,
Copyright, 1919, by Geo. C. Stebbins. Renewal. Hope Publishing Co., owner

Evening Prayer
Sin and want we come con - fess - ing, Thou canst save, and Thou canst heal.
An - gel-guards from Thee sur-round us, We are safe if Thou art nigh.
Thou art He who, nev - er wea - ry, Watchest where Thy peo - ple be.
May the morn in heav'n a - wake us, Clad in light and death-less bloom.
301 Beneath the Cross of Jesus
ELIZABETH C. CLEPHANE
FREDERICK C. MAKER
1. Be - neath the cross of Je - sus I fain would take my stand,
2. Up - on that cross of Je - sus Mine eye at times can see
3. I take, O cross, thy shad - ow For my a - bid - ing - place;
The shad - ow of a might - y Rock With - in a wea - ry land;
The ver - y dy - ing form of One Who suf-fered there for me;
I ask no oth - er sun-shine than The sun-shine of His face;
A home with-in the wil - der - ness, A rest up - on the way,
And from my smit - ten heart with tears, Two won - ders I con - fess,—
Con - tent to let the world go by, To know no gain nor loss,
From the burn-ing of the noon-day heat, And the bur-den of the day.
The won - ders of His glo-rious love And my own worth-less-ness.
My sin - ful self my on - ly shame, My glo - ry all the cross.

The Lord is My Shepherd

JAMES MONTGOMERY

THOMAS KOSCHAT, arr. by E. O. E.

1. The Lord is my Shep-herd, no want shall I know; I feed in green
2. Thro' the val-ley and shad-ow of death tho' I stray, Since Thou art my
3. In the midst of af-flic-tion my ta-ble is spread; With blessings un-
4. Let good-ness and mer-cy, my boun-ti-ful God, Still fol-low my
pas-tures, safe-fold-ed I rest; He lead-eth my soul where the
Guard-ian, no e-vil I fear; Thy rod shall de-fend me, Thy
meas-ured my cup run-neth o'er; With per-fume and oil Thou a-
steps till I meet Thee a-bove: I seek by the path which my
still wa-ters flow, Re-stores me when wan-d'ring, redeems when op-
staff be my stay; No harm can be-fall with my Com-fort-er
noint-est my head; O what shall I ask of Thy prov-i-dence
fore-fa-thers trod, Thro' the land of their so-journ, Thy king-dom of
pressed; Re-stores me when wan-d'ring, re-deems when op-pressed.
near; No harm can be-fall with my Com-fort-er near.
more? O what shall I ask of Thy prov-i-dence more?
love; Thro' the land of their so-journ, Thy king-dom of love.

303 Jesus, Lover of My Soul
Charles Wesley
Simeon B. Marsh
Fine
1. Jesus, Lover of my soul, Let me to Thy bosom fly,
While the nearer waters roll, While the tempest still is high;
2. Other refuge have I none, Hangs my helpless soul on Thee;
Leave, ah, leave me not alone, Still support and comfort me.
3. Thou, O Christ, art all I want; More than all in Thee I find;
Raise the fallen, cheer the faint, Heal the sick, and lead the blind.
4. Plenteous grace with Thee is found, Grace to cover all my sin;
Let the healing streams abound; Make and keep me pure within.
D.C.—Safe into the haven guide, O receive my soul at last.
D.C.—Cover my defenseless head With the shadow of Thy wing.
D.C.—Vile and full of sin I am, Thou art full of truth and grace.
D.C.—Spring Thou up within my heart, Rise to all eternity.
D.C.
Hide me, O my Savior, hide, Till the storm of life is past;
All my trust on Thee is stayed, All my help from Thee I bring;
Just and holy is Thy name, I am all unrighteousness;
Thou of life the fountain art, Freely let me take of Thee;
304 Must Jesus Bear the Cross Alone?
Thos. Shepherd
Geo. N. Allen
1. Must Jesus bear the cross alone, And all the world go free?
2. The consecrated cross I'll bear, Till death shall set me free,
3. Upon the crystal pavement, down At Jesus' pierced feet,
4. O precious cross! O glorious crown! O resurrection day!
No; there's a cross for ev'ry one, And there's a cross for me.
And then go home my crown to wear, For there's a crown for me.
Joyful, I'll cast my golden crown, And His dear name repeat.
Ye angels, from the stars come down, And bear my soul away.

305 O Worship the King

ROBERT GRANT | FRANCIS JOSEPH HAYDN

1. O wor-ship the King, all - glo-rious a - bove, And grate-ful - ly
2. O tell of His might, O sing of His grace, Whose robe is the
3. Thy boun-ti - ful care what tongue can re - cite? It breathes in the
4. Frail chil-dren of dust, and fee - ble as frail, In Thee do we

sing His pow'r and His love; Our Shield and De-fend - er, the An-cient of
light, whose can-o - py space; His char - iots of wrath the deep thunder-clouds
air, it shines in the light, It streams from the hills, it de-scends to the
trust, nor find Thee to fail; Thy mer - cies how ten - der! how firm to the

days, Pa - vil - ioned in splen - dor, and gird - ed with praise.
form, And dark is His path on the wings of the storm.
plain, And sweet - ly dis - tills in the dew and the rain.
end! Our Mak - er, De - fend - er, Re - deem - er and Friend.

306 Let the Lower Lights Be Burning

P. P. B. | P. P. BLISS

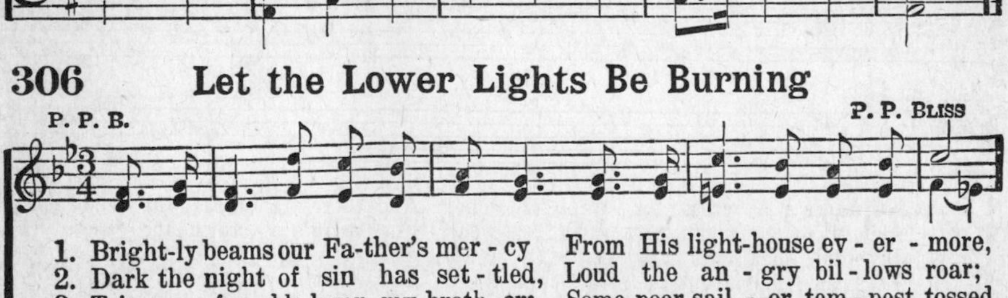

1. Bright-ly beams our Fa-ther's mer - cy From His light-house ev - er - more,
2. Dark the night of sin has set - tled, Loud the an - gry bil - lows roar;
3. Trim your fee - ble lamp, my broth- er; Some poor sail - or tem - pest tossed,

Let the Lower Lights Be Burning
FINE
But to us He gives the keep-ing Of the lights a - long the shore.
Ea - ger eyes are watching, long-ing, For the lights a - long the shore.
Try - ing now to make the har - bor, In the dark-ness may be lost.
D.S.–Some poor faint-ing, struggling sea-man You may res - cue, you may save.
CHORUS
D.S.
Let the low - er lights be burn-ing! Send a gleam a - cross the wave!
307
My Prayer
P. P. B.
P. P. BLISS
1. More ho - li - ness give me, More striv-ing with - in; More pa-tience in
2. More grat - i - tude give me, More trust in the Lord; More pride in His
3. More pu - ri - ty give me, More strength to o'ercome; More freedom from
suf - f'ring, More sor - row for sin; More faith in my Sav - ior,
glo - ry, More hope in His word; More tears for His sor - rows,
earth-stains, More long-ings for home; More fit for the king - dom,
rit.
More sense of His care; More joy in His serv-ice, More pur-pose in prayer.
More pain at His grief; More meekness in tri - al, More praise for re - lief.
More used would I be; More bless-ed and ho - ly, More, Sav-ior, like Thee.

308 Jesus, Savior, Pilot Me

EDWARD HOPPER — J. E. GOULD

1. Je - sus, Sav - ior, pi - lot me O - ver life's tem - pes-tuous sea;
2. As a moth - er stills her child, Thou canst hush the o - cean wild;
3. When at last I near the shore, And the fear - ful break-ers roar
Un-known waves be - fore me roll, Hid - ing rock and treacherous shoal;
Boisterous waves o - bey Thy will When Thou say'st to them "Be still!"
'Twixt me and the peace-ful rest, Then, while lean - ing on Thy breast,
Chart and com - pass came from Thee: Je - sus, Sav - ior, pi - lot me.
Won-drous Sov-'reign of the sea, Je - sus, Sav - ior, pi - lot me.
May I hear Thee say to me, "Fear not, I will pi - lot thee."

309 Sun of My Soul

JOHN KEBLE — PETER RITTER

1. Sun of my soul! Thou Sav - ior dear, It is not night if Thou be near;
2. When the soft dews of kind - ly sleep My wea - ry eye - lids gen - tly steep,
3. A - bide with me from morn till eve, For with-out Thee I can - not live;
4. Be near to bless us when we wake, Ere thro' the world our way we take;

Sun of My Soul

O may no earth-born cloud a - rise To hide Thee from Thy serv-ant's eyes.
Be my last tho't, how sweet to rest For-ev - er on my Sav-ior's breast.
A - bide with me when night is nigh, For with-out Thee I dare not die.
Till, in the o - cean of Thy love, We lose our-selves in heav'n a-bove.

310 Something For Jesus

S. D. Phelps
Robert Lowry

1. Sav - ior, Thy dy - ing love Thou gav - est me, Nor should I aught with-hold, Dear Lord, from Thee: In love my soul would bow, My heart ful - fill its vow, Some of-f'ring bring Thee now, Something for Thee.
2. At the blest mer - cy - seat, Plead-ing for me, My fee - ble faith looks up, Je - sus, to Thee: Help me the cross to bear, Thy wondrous love de-clare, Some song to raise, or prayer, Something for Thee.
3. Give me a faith-ful heart, Like-ness to Thee, That each de-part - ing day Hence-forth may see Some work of love be - gun, Some deed of kind-ness done, Some wand'rer sought and won, Something for Thee.
4. All that I am and have—Thy gifts so free— In joy, in grief, thro' life, Dear Lord, for Thee! And when Thy face I see, My ransomed soul shall be, Thro' all e - ter - ni - ty, Something for Thee.

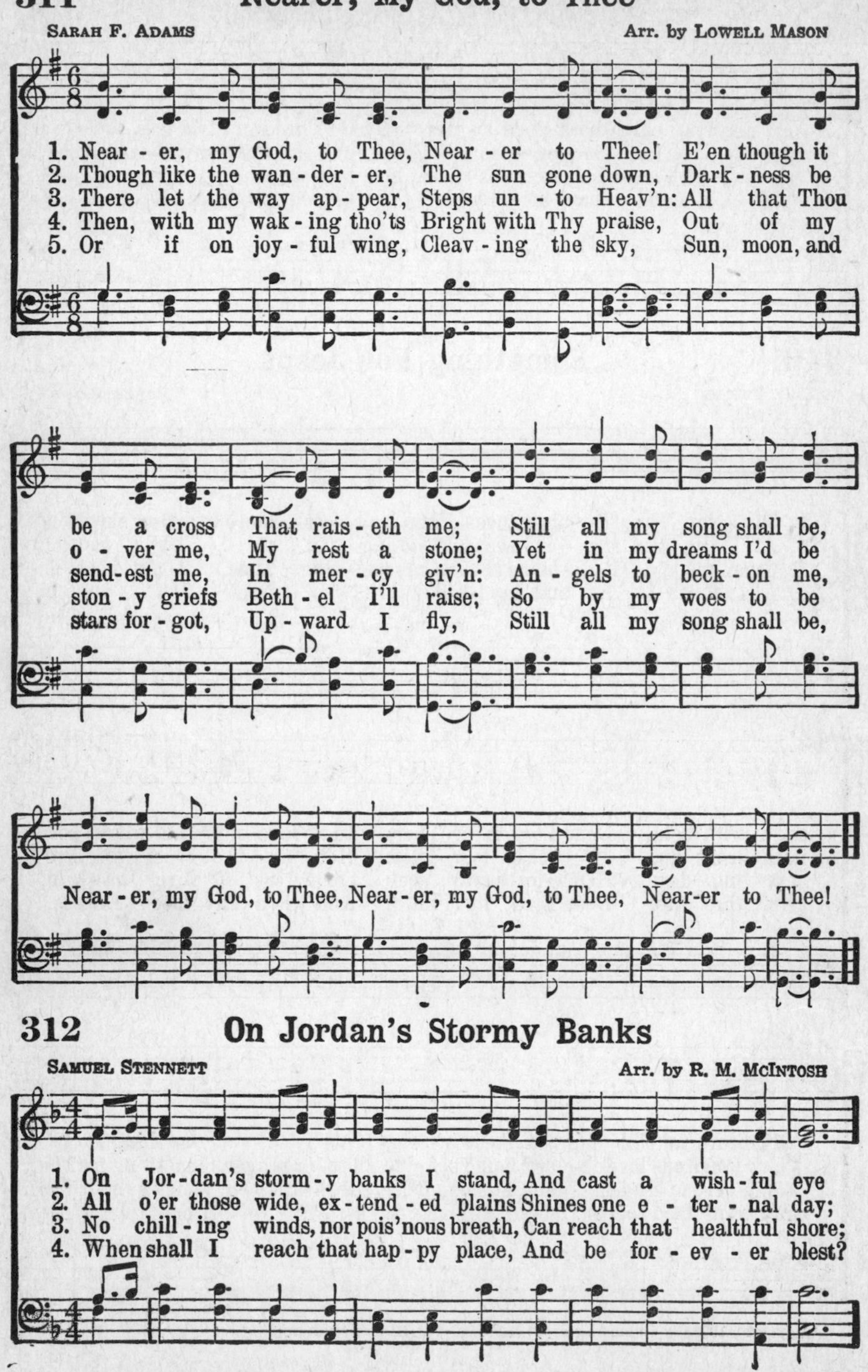
311 Nearer, My God, to Thee
Sarah F. Adams
Arr. by Lowell Mason
1. Near - er, my God, to Thee, Near - er to Thee! E'en though it be a cross That rais - eth me; Still all my song shall be,
2. Though like the wan - der - er, The sun gone down, Dark - ness be o - ver me, My rest a stone; Yet in my dreams I'd be
3. There let the way ap - pear, Steps un - to Heav'n: All that Thou send - est me, In mer - cy giv'n: An - gels to beck - on me,
4. Then, with my wak - ing tho'ts Bright with Thy praise, Out of my ston - y griefs Beth - el I'll raise; So by my woes to be
5. Or if on joy - ful wing, Cleav - ing the sky, Sun, moon, and stars for - got, Up - ward I fly, Still all my song shall be,
Near - er, my God, to Thee, Near - er, my God, to Thee, Near - er to Thee!
312 On Jordan's Stormy Banks
Samuel Stennett
Arr. by R. M. McIntosh
1. On Jor - dan's storm - y banks I stand, And cast a wish - ful eye
2. All o'er those wide, ex - tend - ed plains Shines one e - ter - nal day;
3. No chill - ing winds, nor pois'nous breath, Can reach that healthful shore;
4. When shall I reach that hap - py place, And be for - ev - er blest?

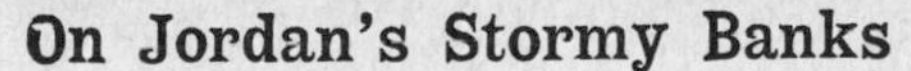

On Jordan's Stormy Banks

FINE

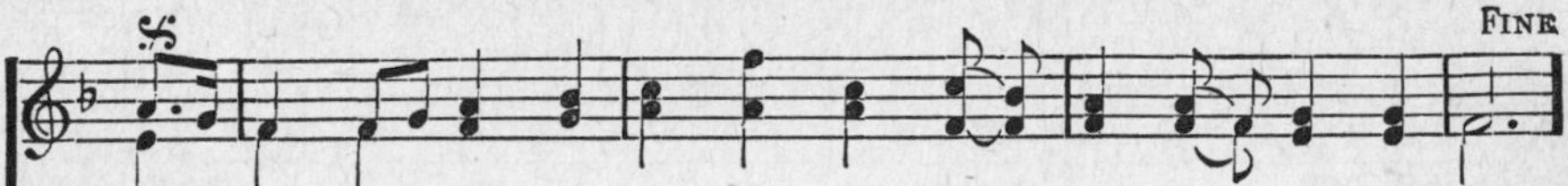

To Ca - naan's fair and hap - py land, Where my pos - ses - sions lie.
There God, the Son, for - ev - er reigns, And scat - ters night a - way.
Sick - ness and sor - row, pain and death, Are felt and feared no more.
When shall I see my Fa - ther's face, And in His bos - om rest?

D.S.—*O who will come and go with me? I am bound for the prom-ised land.*

REFRAIN — *D. S.*

I am bound for the promised land, . . . I am bound for the promised land;
prom-ised land,

313 Amazing Grace

JOHN NEWTON

1. A - maz - ing grace! how sweet the sound, That saved a wretch like me! I
2. 'Twas grace that taught my heart to fear, And grace my fears re-lieved; How
3. Thro' man - y dan-gers, toils and snares, I have al - read - y come; 'Tis
4. When we've been there ten thousand years, Bright shin-ing as the sun, We've

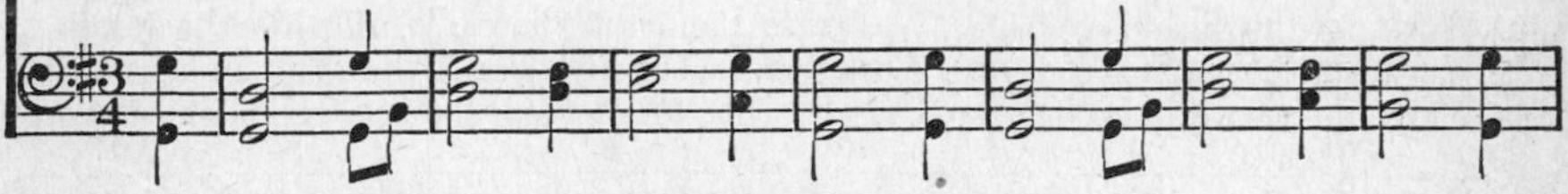

once was lost, but now am found, Was blind, but now I see.
pre - cious did that grace ap - pear The hour I first be-lieved!
grace hath bro't me safe thus far, And grace will lead me home.
no less days to sing God's praise Than when we first be - gun.

314 When I Survey the Wondrous Cross

Isaac Watts — Arr. by Lowell Mason

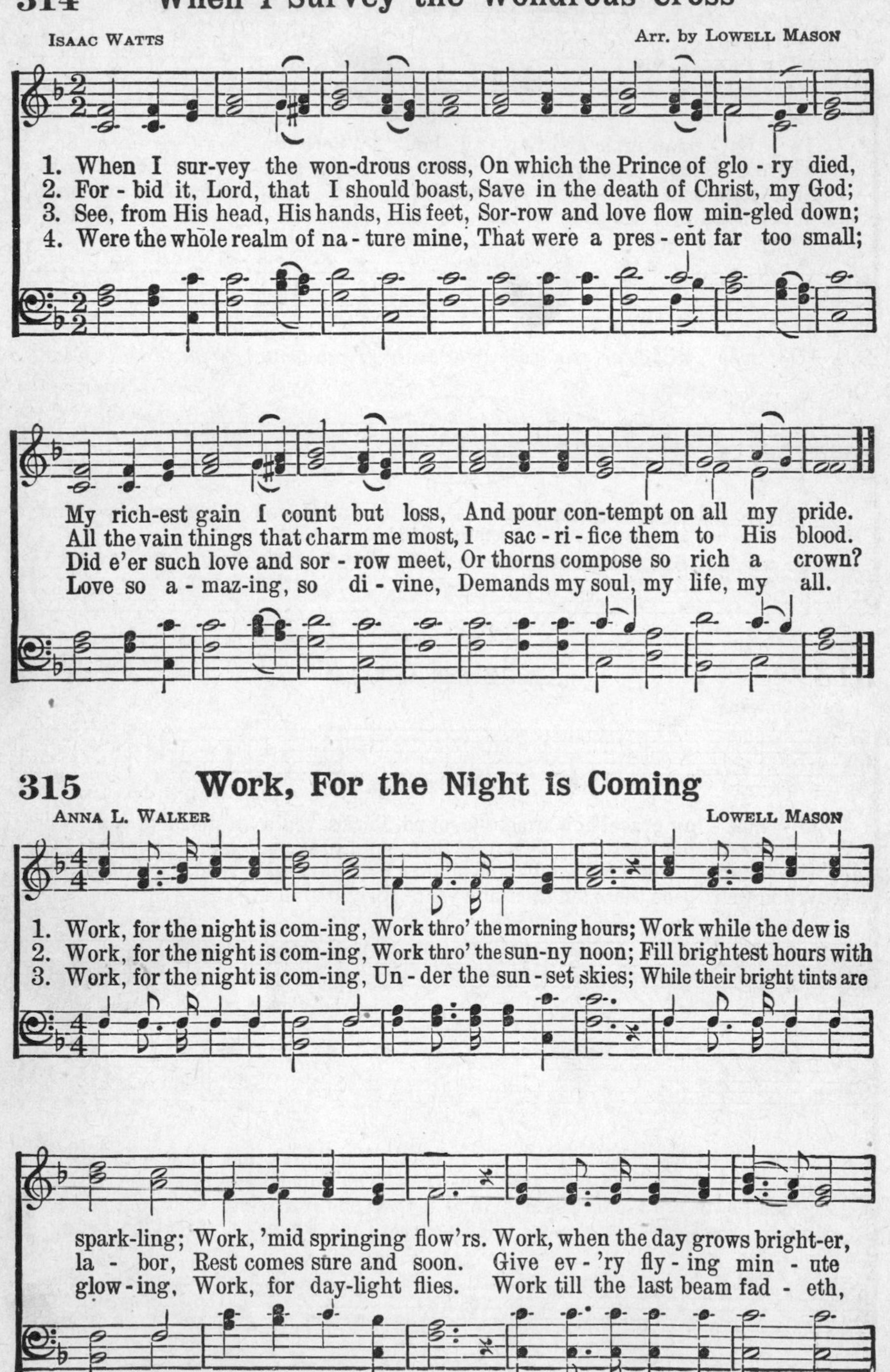

1. When I sur-vey the won-drous cross, On which the Prince of glo - ry died,
2. For - bid it, Lord, that I should boast, Save in the death of Christ, my God;
3. See, from His head, His hands, His feet, Sor-row and love flow min-gled down;
4. Were the whole realm of na - ture mine, That were a pres - ent far too small;
My rich-est gain I count but loss, And pour con-tempt on all my pride.
All the vain things that charm me most, I sac - ri - fice them to His blood.
Did e'er such love and sor - row meet, Or thorns compose so rich a crown?
Love so a - maz-ing, so di - vine, Demands my soul, my life, my all.

315 Work, For the Night is Coming

Anna L. Walker — Lowell Mason

1. Work, for the night is com-ing, Work thro' the morning hours; Work while the dew is
2. Work, for the night is com-ing, Work thro' the sun-ny noon; Fill brightest hours with
3. Work, for the night is com-ing, Un - der the sun - set skies; While their bright tints are
spark-ling; Work, 'mid springing flow'rs. Work, when the day grows bright-er,
la - bor, Rest comes sure and soon. Give ev - 'ry fly - ing min - ute
glow - ing, Work, for day-light flies. Work till the last beam fad - eth,

Work, For the Night is Coming

cres.

Work in the glowing sun; Work, for the night is com-ing, When man's work is done.
Something to keep in store; Work, for the night is com-ing, When man works no more.
Fad-eth to shine no more; Work, while the night is dark'ning, When man's work is o'er.

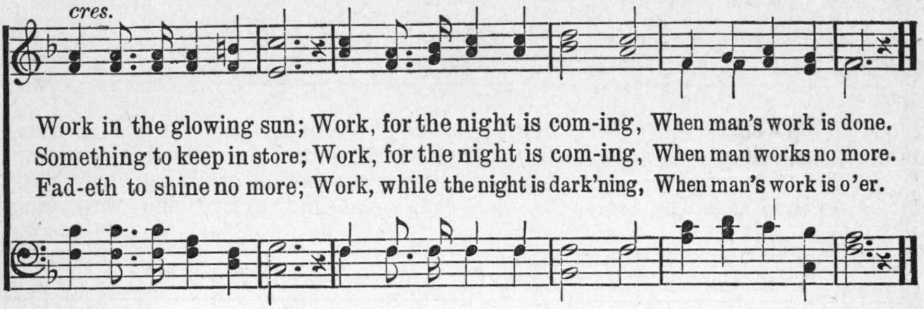

316 Rock of Ages

A. M. TOPLADY — THOS. HASTINGS

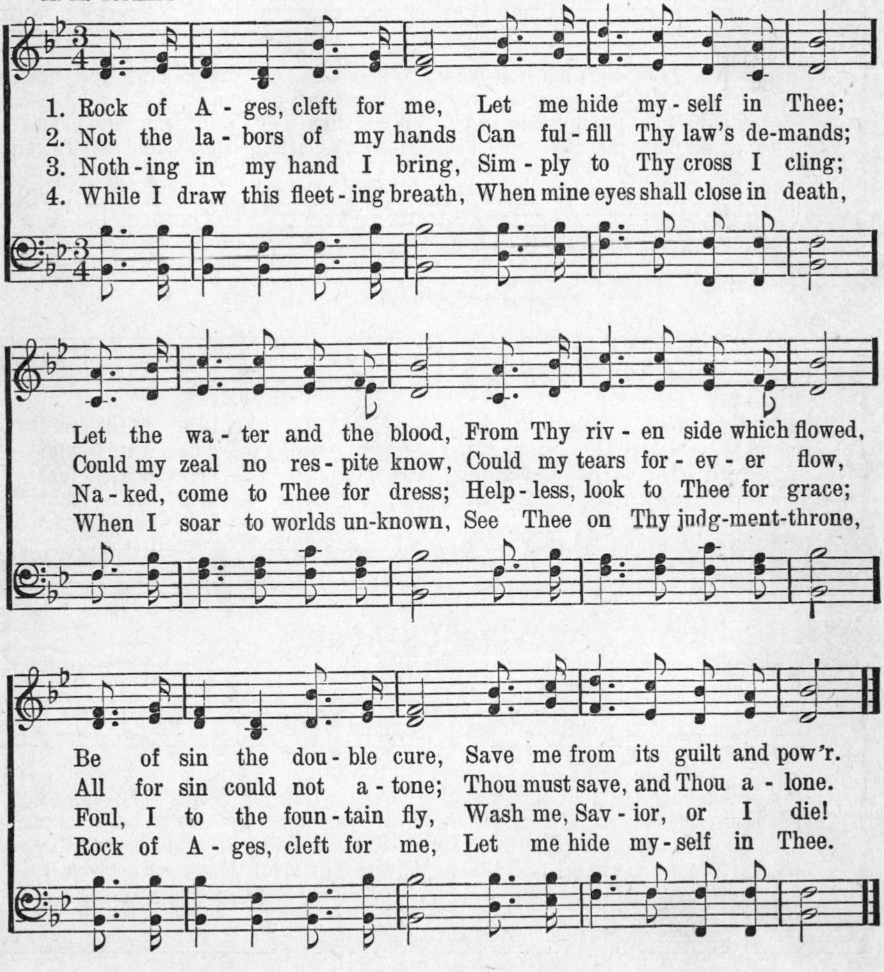

1. Rock of A - ges, cleft for me, Let me hide my - self in Thee;
2. Not the la - bors of my hands Can ful - fill Thy law's de-mands;
3. Noth - ing in my hand I bring, Sim - ply to Thy cross I cling;
4. While I draw this fleet - ing breath, When mine eyes shall close in death,

Let the wa - ter and the blood, From Thy riv - en side which flowed,
Could my zeal no res - pite know, Could my tears for - ev - er flow,
Na - ked, come to Thee for dress; Help - less, look to Thee for grace;
When I soar to worlds un-known, See Thee on Thy judg-ment-throne,

Be of sin the dou - ble cure, Save me from its guilt and pow'r.
All for sin could not a - tone; Thou must save, and Thou a - lone.
Foul, I to the foun - tain fly, Wash me, Sav - ior, or I die!
Rock of A - ges, cleft for me, Let me hide my - self in Thee.

317 Abide With Me

H. F. LYTE W. H. MONK

1. A - bide with me: fast falls the e - ven - tide; The dark-ness deep - ens; Lord, with me a - bide: When oth - er help - ers fail, and com - forts flee, Help of the help - less, O a - bide with me!
2. Swift to its close ebbs out life's lit - tle day; Earth's joys grow dim, its glo - ries pass a - way; Change and de - cay in all a - round I see; O Thou who chang-est not, a - bide with me!
3. I need Thy pres - ence ev - 'ry pass - ing hour: What but Thy grace can foil the tempter's pow'r? Who like Thy - self my guide and stay can be? Thro' cloud and sun - shine, O a - bide with me!
4. Hold Thou Thy cross be - fore my clos - ing eyes; Shine thro' the gloom, and point me to the skies: Heav'n's morning breaks, and earth's vain shad - ows flee: In life, in death, O Lord, a - bide with me!

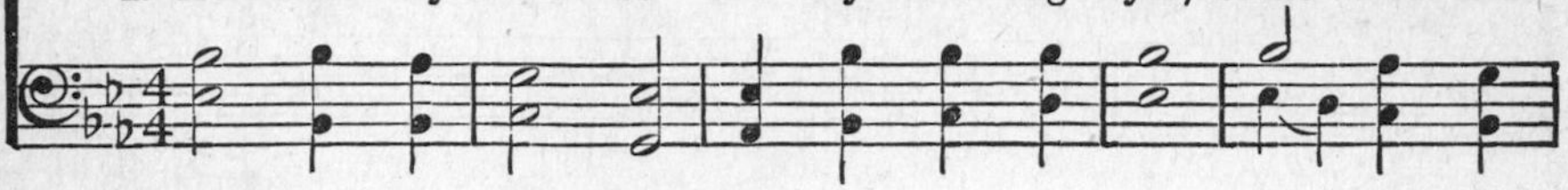

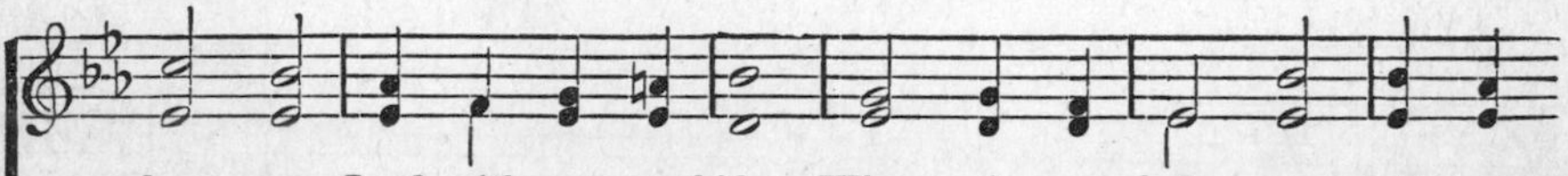

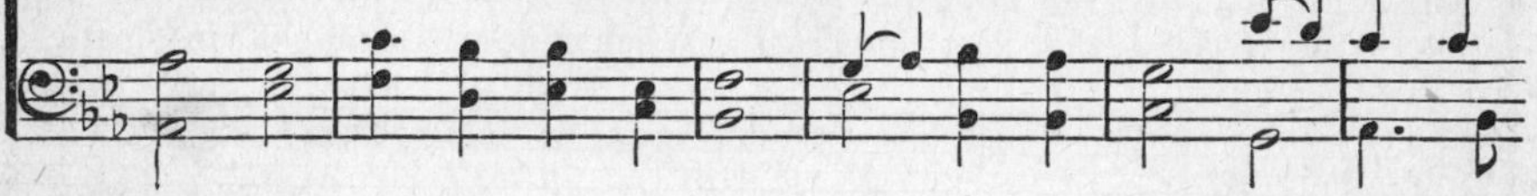

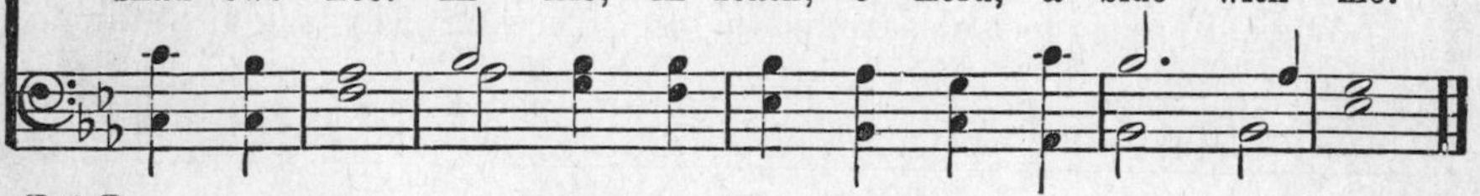

318 Revive Us Again

WM. P. MACKAY JOHN J. HUSBAND

1. We praise Thee, O God! for the Son of Thy love, For Je - sus who
2. We praise Thee, O God! for Thy Spir - it of light, Who has shown us our
3. All glo - ry and praise to the Lamb that was slain, Who has borne all our
4. Re - vive us a - gain; fill each heart with Thy love; May each soul be re-

Revive Us Again

CHORUS
died, and is now gone a - bove.
Sav - ior, and scat-tered our night. Hal - le - lu - jah! Thine the glo-ry; Hal-le-
sins, and has cleansed ev-'ry stain.
kin - dled with fire from a - bove.
lu - jah! A - men! Hal - le - lu - jah! Thine the glo - ry; Re-vive us a - gain.
319
Holy Ghost, With Light Divine
L. M. GOTTSCHALK
ANDREW REED
Arr. by H. P. MAIN
1. Ho - ly Ghost, with light di - vine, Shine up - on this heart of mine;
2. Ho - ly Ghost, with pow'r di - vine, Cleanse this guilt-y heart of mine;
3. Ho - ly Ghost, with joy di - vine, Cheer this saddened heart of mine;
4. Ho - ly Spir - it, all di - vine, Dwell with-in this heart of mine;
Chase the shades of night a - way, Turn my dark - ness in - to day.
Long hath sin, with - out con-trol, Held do - min - ion o'er my soul.
Bid my man - y woes de - part, Heal my wound-ed, bleed - ing heart.
Cast down ev - 'ry i - dol-throne, Reign su - preme, and reign a - lone.

320 Arise, My Soul, Arise

CHARLES WESLEY LEWIS EDSON

1. A - rise, my soul, a - rise, Shake off thy guilt-y fears; The bleed - ing
2. He ev - er lives a - bove, For me to in - ter - cede, His all - re-
3. Five bleeding wounds He bears, Re-ceived on Cal - va - ry; They pour ef-
4. My God is rec - on - ciled; His par-d'ning voice I hear; He owns me

Sac - ri - fice In my be - half ap-pears; Be - fore the throne my Surety stands,
deem-ing love, His pre-cious blood to plead; His blood a - toned for all our race,
fectual prayers, They strongly plead for me: "For-give him, O for-give," they cry,
for His child; I can no lon - ger fear; With con-fi - dence I now draw nigh,

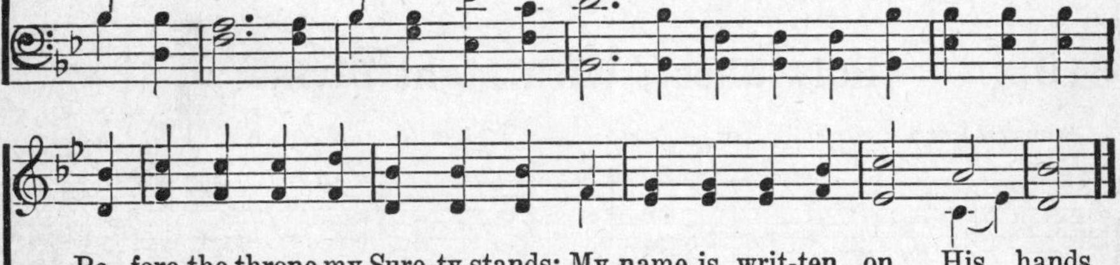

Be - fore the throne my Sure-ty stands: My name is writ-ten on His hands.
His blood a-toned for all our race, And sprinkles now the throne of grace.
"For-give him, O for-give," they cry, "Nor let that ran-somed sin - ner die!"
With con-fi-dence I now draw nigh, And, "Father, Ab - ba, Fa - ther," cry.

321 Am I a Soldier of the Cross?

ISAAC WATTS THOMAS A. ARNE

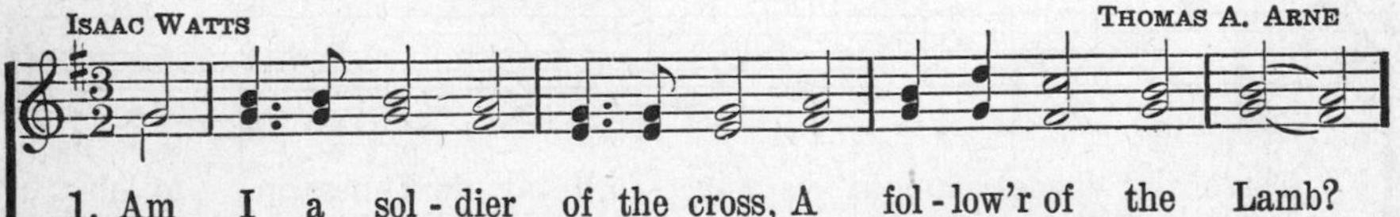

1. Am I a sol - dier of the cross, A fol - low'r of the Lamb?
2. Must I be car - ried to the skies On flow - 'ry beds of ease,
3. Are there no foes for me to face? Must I not stem the flood?
4. Sure I must fight, if I would reign; In - crease my cour - age, Lord;

Am I A Soldier of the Cross?

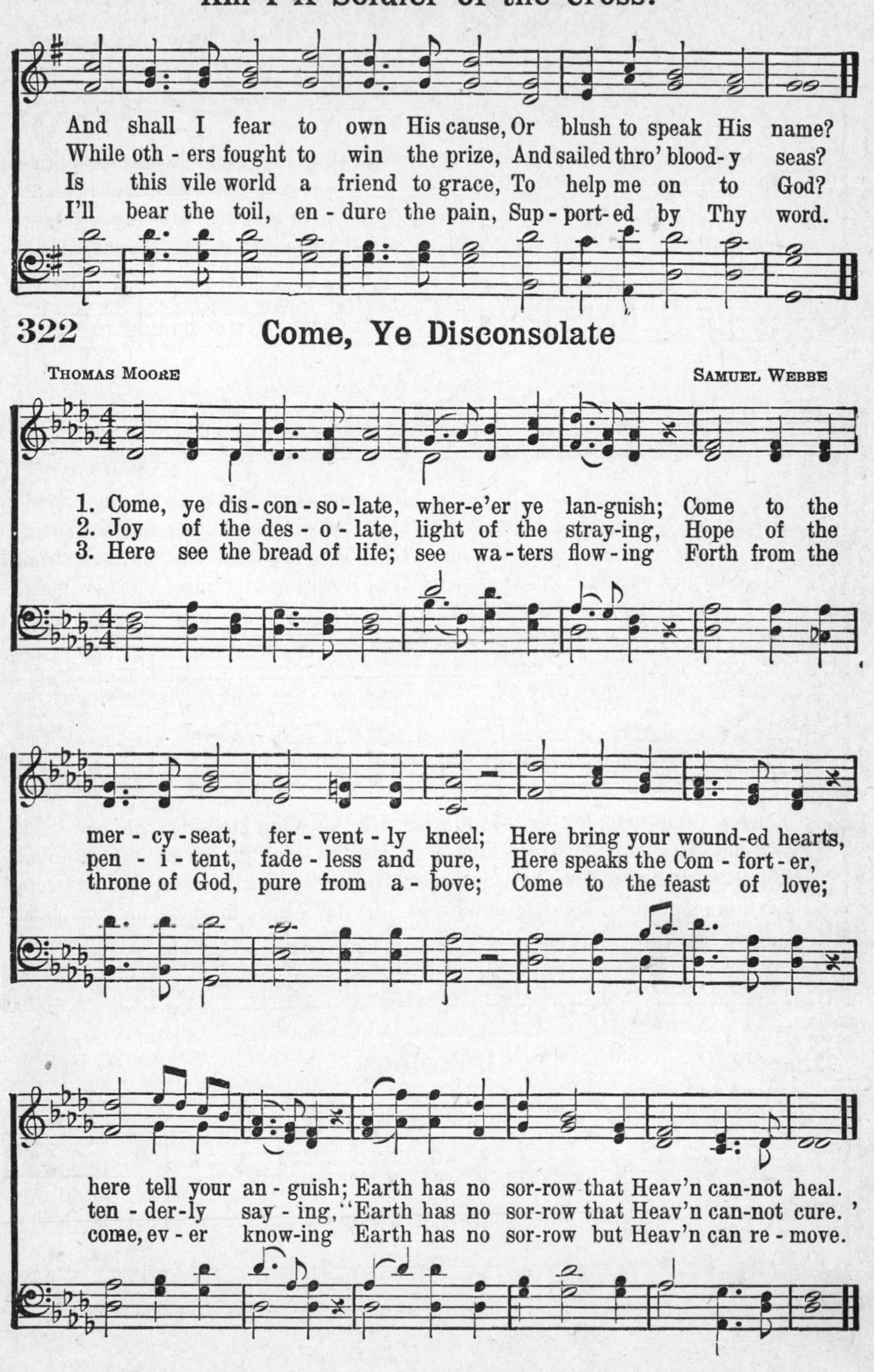

And shall I fear to own His cause, Or blush to speak His name?
While oth - ers fought to win the prize, And sailed thro' blood - y seas?
Is this vile world a friend to grace, To help me on to God?
I'll bear the toil, en - dure the pain, Sup - port - ed by Thy word.
322
Come, Ye Disconsolate
Thomas Moore
Samuel Webbe
1. Come, ye dis - con - so - late, wher-e'er ye lan-guish; Come to the mer - cy - seat, fer - vent - ly kneel; Here bring your wound-ed hearts, here tell your an - guish; Earth has no sor-row that Heav'n can-not heal.
2. Joy of the des - o - late, light of the stray-ing, Hope of the pen - i - tent, fade - less and pure, Here speaks the Com - fort - er, ten - der-ly say - ing, "Earth has no sor-row that Heav'n can-not cure."
3. Here see the bread of life; see wa - ters flow - ing Forth from the throne of God, pure from a - bove; Come to the feast of love; come, ev - er know-ing Earth has no sor-row but Heav'n can re - move.

323 His Loving-Kindness

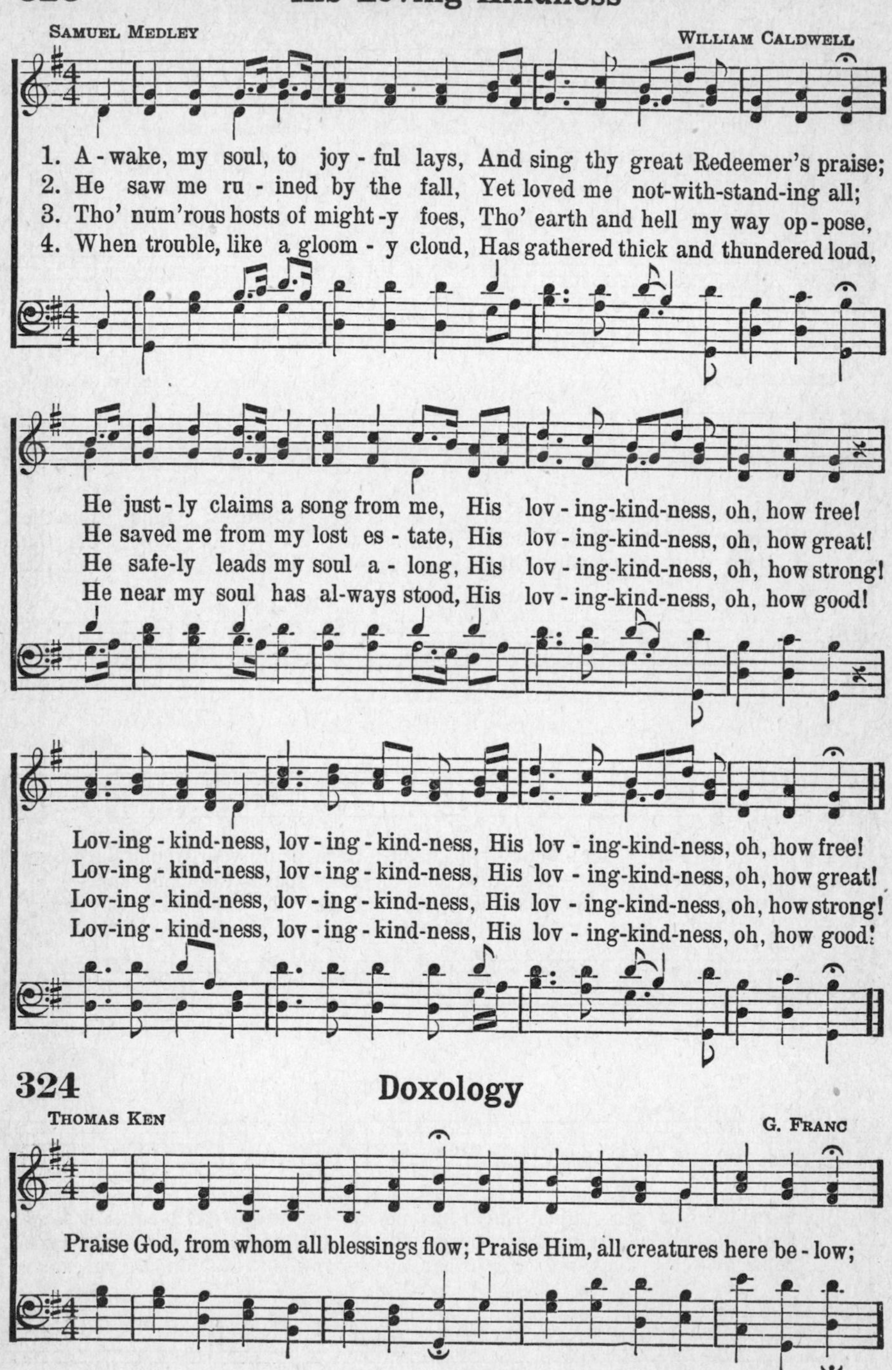
SAMUEL MEDLEY
WILLIAM CALDWELL
1. A-wake, my soul, to joy-ful lays, And sing thy great Redeemer's praise;
2. He saw me ru-ined by the fall, Yet loved me not-with-stand-ing all;
3. Tho' num'rous hosts of might-y foes, Tho' earth and hell my way op-pose,
4. When trouble, like a gloom-y cloud, Has gathered thick and thundered loud,
He just-ly claims a song from me, His lov-ing-kind-ness, oh, how free!
He saved me from my lost es-tate, His lov-ing-kind-ness, oh, how great!
He safe-ly leads my soul a-long, His lov-ing-kind-ness, oh, how strong!
He near my soul has al-ways stood, His lov-ing-kind-ness, oh, how good!
Lov-ing-kind-ness, lov-ing-kind-ness, His lov-ing-kind-ness, oh, how free!
Lov-ing-kind-ness, lov-ing-kind-ness, His lov-ing-kind-ness, oh, how great!
Lov-ing-kind-ness, lov-ing-kind-ness, His lov-ing-kind-ness, oh, how strong!
Lov-ing-kind-ness, lov-ing-kind-ness, His lov-ing-kind-ness, oh, how good!
324 Doxology
THOMAS KEN
G. FRANC
Praise God, from whom all blessings flow; Praise Him, all creatures here be-low;

Doxology
Praise Him a - bove, ye heav'n-ly host; Praise Fa-ther, Son, and Ho - ly Ghost!
325
Faith of Our Fathers
Frederick W. Faber
H. F. Hemy
1. Faith of our fa - thers! liv - ing still In spite of dun-geon, fire and sword:
2. Our fa-thers, chained in prisons dark, Were still in heart and conscience free:
3. Faith of our fa - thers! we will love Both friend and foe in all our strife:
O how our hearts beat high with joy Whene'er we hear that glo-rious word!
How sweet would be their children's fate, If they, like them, could die for thee!
And preach thee, too, as love knows how, By kind-ly words and vir-tuous life:
Faith of our fa-thers! ho - ly faith! We will be true to thee till death!
Faith of our fa-thers! ho - ly faith! We will be true to thee till death!
Faith of our fa-thers! ho - ly faith! We will be true to thee till death!

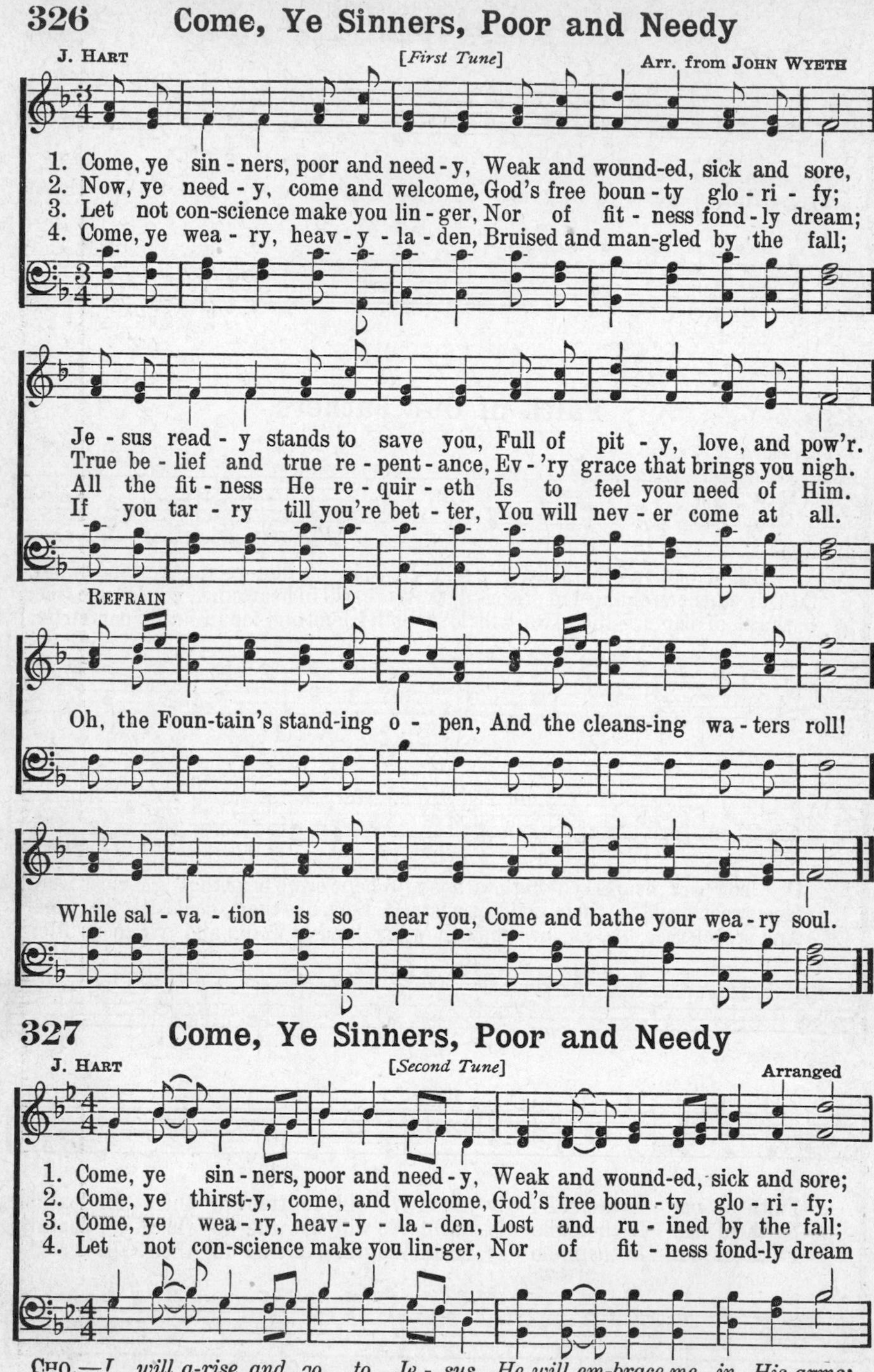
326 Come, Ye Sinners, Poor and Needy
J. Hart
[First Tune]
Arr. from John Wyeth
1. Come, ye sin - ners, poor and need - y, Weak and wound-ed, sick and sore,
2. Now, ye need - y, come and welcome, God's free boun - ty glo - ri - fy;
3. Let not con-science make you lin - ger, Nor of fit - ness fond - ly dream;
4. Come, ye wea - ry, heav - y - la - den, Bruised and man-gled by the fall;
Je - sus read - y stands to save you, Full of pit - y, love, and pow'r.
True be - lief and true re - pent - ance, Ev - 'ry grace that brings you nigh.
All the fit - ness He re - quir - eth Is to feel your need of Him.
If you tar - ry till you're bet - ter, You will nev - er come at all.
Refrain
Oh, the Foun-tain's stand-ing o - pen, And the cleans-ing wa - ters roll!
While sal - va - tion is so near you, Come and bathe your wea - ry soul.
327 Come, Ye Sinners, Poor and Needy
J. Hart
[Second Tune]
Arranged
1. Come, ye sin - ners, poor and need - y, Weak and wound-ed, sick and sore;
2. Come, ye thirst-y, come, and welcome, God's free boun - ty glo - ri - fy;
3. Come, ye wea - ry, heav - y - la - den, Lost and ru - ined by the fall;
4. Let not con-science make you lin-ger, Nor of fit - ness fond-ly dream

Cho.—*I will a-rise and go to Je - sus. He will em-brace me in His arms;*

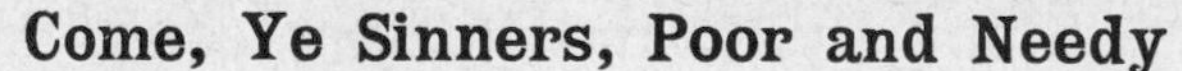

Come, Ye Sinners, Poor and Needy

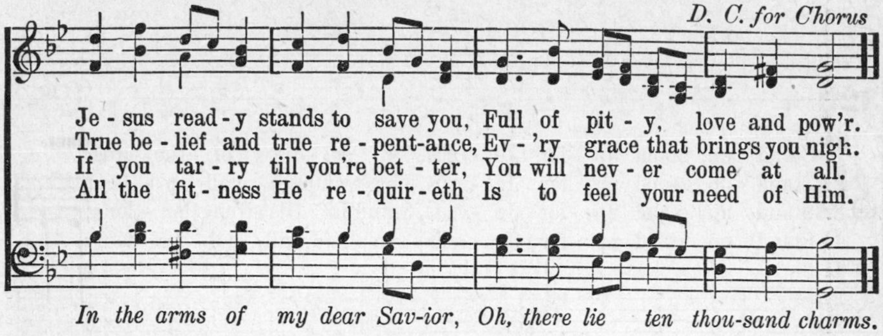

D. C. for Chorus

Je - sus read - y stands to save you, Full of pit - y, love and pow'r.
True be - lief and true re - pent-ance, Ev - 'ry grace that brings you nigh.
If you tar - ry till you're bet - ter, You will nev - er come at all.
All the fit - ness He re - quir - eth Is to feel your need of Him.

In the arms of my dear Sav-ior, Oh, there lie ten thou-sand charms.

328 All For Jesus

MARY D. JAMES — Arranged

1. All for Je - sus, all for Je - sus! All my be-ing's ransomed pow'rs:
2. Let my hands perform His bid - ding, Let my feet run in His ways;
3. Since my eyes were fixed on Je - sus, I've lost sight of all be - side;
4. Oh, what won-der! how a - maz - ing! Je - sus, glo-rious King of kings,

All my tho'ts and words and do - ings, All my days and all my hours.
Let my eyes see Je - sus on - ly, Let my lips speak forth His praise.
So en-chained my spir-it's vi - sion, Look-ing at the Cru - ci - fied.
Deigns to call me His be - lov - ed, Lets me rest be-neath His wings.

All for Je-sus! all for Je - sus! All my days and all my hours; hours.
All for Je-sus! all for Je - sus! Let my lips speak forth His praise; praise.
All for Je-sus! all for Je - sus! Look-ing at the Cru - ci - fied; fied.
All for Je-sus! all for Je - sus! Rest-ing now beneath His wings; wings.

329 Stand Up, Stand Up for Jesus

George Duffield — Adam Geibel

Unison
1. Stand up, stand up for Je - sus, Ye sol - diers of the cross;
2. Stand up, stand up for Je - sus, The trump- et call o - bey;
3. Stand up, stand up for Je - sus, Stand in His strength a - lone;
4. Stand up, stand up for Je - sus, The strife will not be long;
Lift high His roy - al ban - ner, It must not suf - fer loss:
Forth to the might - y con - flict, In this His glo - rious day:
The arm of flesh will fail you, Ye dare not trust your own:
This day the noise of bat - tle, The next, the vic - tor's song:
From vic - t'ry un - to vic - t'ry His ar - my shall He lead,
"Ye that are men now serve Him" A - gainst un - num - bered foes;
Put on the gos - pel ar - mor, Each piece put on with prayer;
To Him that o - ver - com - eth, A crown of life shall be:
rit.
Till ev - 'ry foe is van - quished, And Christ is Lord in - deed.
Let cour - age rise with dan - ger, And strength to strength op - pose.
Where du - ty calls, or dan - ger, Be nev - er want - ing there.
He with the King of glo - ry Shall reign e - ter - nal - ly.

Stand Up, Stand Up for Jesus
Chorus
Stand up for Je - sus, Ye sol - diers of the cross;...
Stand up, stand up for Je - sus,
Lift high His roy - al ban - ner, It must not, It must not suf - fer loss.
330
Stand Up for Jesus
G. Duffield
G. J. Webb
1. Stand up, stand up for Je - sus, Ye sol - diers of the cross, Lift high His
2. Stand up, stand up for Je - sus, The trump - et call o - bey; Forth to the
3. Stand up, stand up for Je - sus, Stand in His strength a - lone; The arm of
roy - al ban - ner, It must not suf - fer loss; From vic - t'ry un - to vic - t'ry, His
might - y con - flict, In this His glorious day. "Ye that are men now serve Him," A -
flesh will fail you—Ye dare not trust your own; Put on the gos - pel ar - mor, Each
ar - my shall He lead, Till ev - 'ry foe is vanquished And Christ is Lord in - deed.
gainst unnumbered foes; Let courage rise with danger, And strength to strength oppose.
piece put on with prayer, Where du - ty calls, or dan - ger, Be nev - er want - ing there.

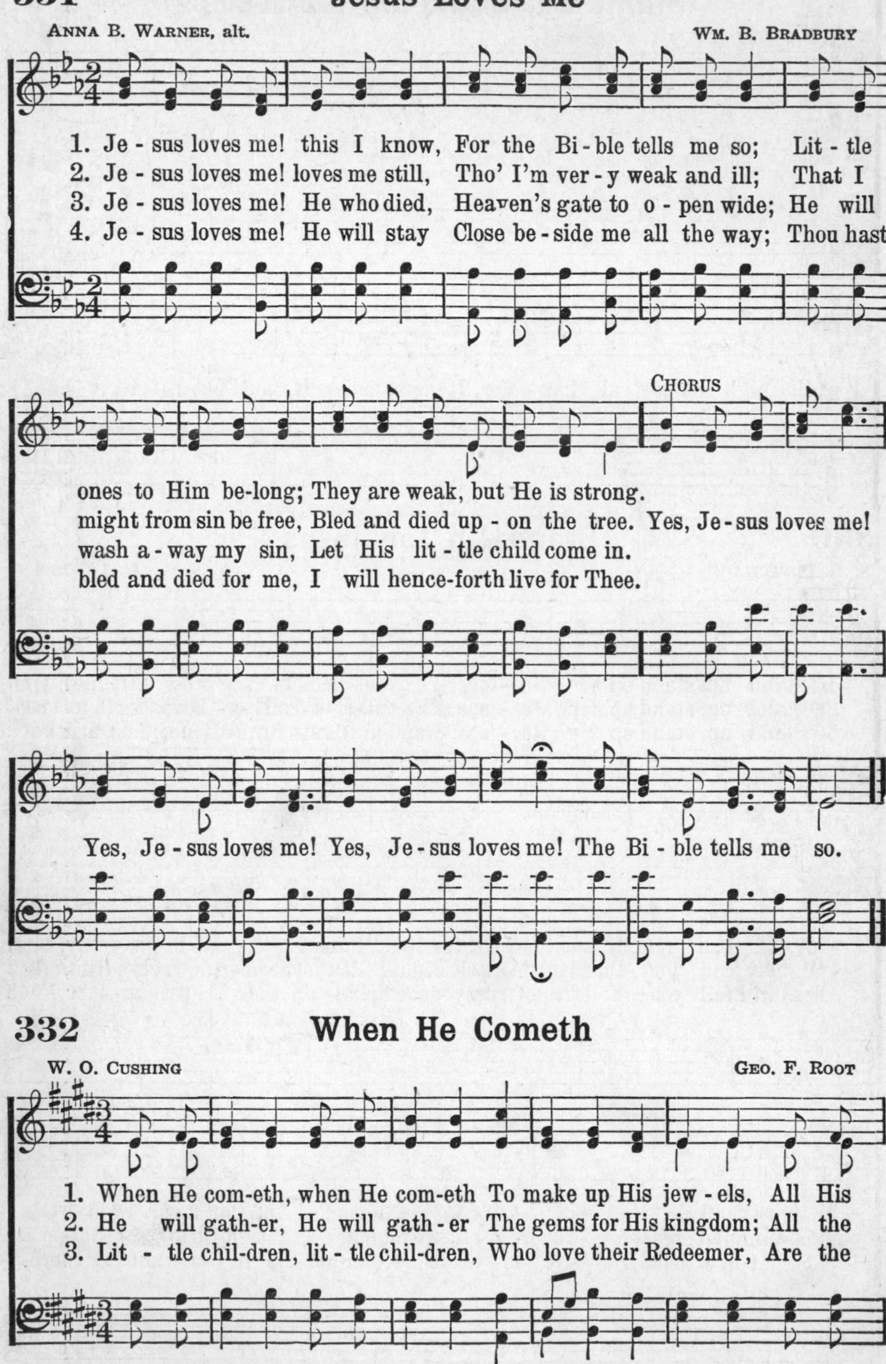
331 Jesus Loves Me
Anna B. Warner, alt.
Wm. B. Bradbury
1. Je - sus loves me! this I know, For the Bi - ble tells me so; Lit - tle
2. Je - sus loves me! loves me still, Tho' I'm ver - y weak and ill; That I
3. Je - sus loves me! He who died, Heaven's gate to o - pen wide; He will
4. Je - sus loves me! He will stay Close be - side me all the way; Thou hast
Chorus
ones to Him be-long; They are weak, but He is strong.
might from sin be free, Bled and died up - on the tree. Yes, Je - sus loves me!
wash a - way my sin, Let His lit - tle child come in.
bled and died for me, I will hence-forth live for Thee.
Yes, Je - sus loves me! Yes, Je - sus loves me! The Bi - ble tells me so.
332 When He Cometh
W. O. Cushing
Geo. F. Root
1. When He com-eth, when He com-eth To make up His jew - els, All His
2. He will gath-er, He will gath - er The gems for His kingdom; All the
3. Lit - tle chil-dren, lit - tle chil-dren, Who love their Redeemer, Are the

When He Cometh

CHORUS
jew - els, pre-cious jew - els, His loved and His own:
pureones, all the brightones, His loved and His own.
jew - els, pre-cious jew - els, His loved and His own.
Like the stars of the
They shall shine in their
1
2
morn - ing, His bright crown a - dorn - ing,
beau - ty, (Omit ....)
Bright gems for His crown.
333
Dare to Be a Daniel
P. P. B.
P. P. BLISS
1. Stand-ing by a pur-pose true, Heed-ing God's command, Hon - or them, the
2. Man - y might-y men are lost, Dar - ing not to stand, Who for God had
3. Man - y gi-ants, great and tall, Stalk - ing thro' the land, Headlong to the
4. Hold the gos - pel ban-ner high! On to vic-t'ry grand! Sa - tan and His
CHORUS
faith-ful few! All hail to Dan-iel's Band!
been a host, By join-ing Dan-iel's Band!
earth would fall, If met by Dan-iel's Band!
host de - fy, And shout for Dan-iel's Band!
Dare to be a Dan - iel,
Dare to stand a-lone! Dare to have a pur-pose firm! Dare to make it known!

334 Yesterday, To-day, Forever
A. B. Simpson
S. H. Burke
Yes-ter-day, to-day, for-ev -er, Je-sus is the same; All may change but
Je-sus nev-er! Glo-ry to His name! Glo-ry to His name! Glo-ry
to His name! All may change, but Je-sus nev-er! Glo-ry to His name!
335 Shine Just Where You Are
Ada R. Habershon
Henry Barraclough
Shine, shine, just where you are, Shine, shine, just where you are;
Send forth the light in-to the night, Shine for the Lord where you are.
Copyright, 1914. Hope Publishing Co., owner

336 Joy in My Heart

Geo. W. Cooke

1. I have the joy, joy, joy, joy, Down in my heart,
2. I have the peace that pass-eth un - der-stand-ing, Down in my heart,
3. I have the love of Je - sus, love of Je - sus, Down in my heart,

Down in my heart, Down in my heart, I have the joy, joy,
Down in my heart, Down in my heart, I have the peace that pass-eth
Down in my heart, Down in my heart, I have the love of Je - sus,

joy, joy, Down in my heart, Down in my heart to stay.
un - der-stand-ing, Down in my heart, Down in my heart to stay.
love of Je - sus, Down in my heart, Down in my heart to stay.

337 Everybody Ought to Love Jesus

Harry Dixon Loes

Ev - 'ry-bod - y ought to love Je - sus, Je - sus, Je - sus; He
Je - sus Christ, the won-der-ful Sav-ior;

died on the cross to save us from sin, Ev - 'ry-bod - y ought to love Je - sus.

338
Oh, I'm Trav'ling
C. W. J.
C. W. Jones
Oh, I'm trav-'ling, yes, I'm trav-'ling, Ev-'ry
Trav-'ling home, trav-'ling home,
foot-step is filled with song; There's a man-sion wait-ing
Ev-'ry step filled with song; There's a man-sion
for me, That's why I'm trav-'ling,— won't you come a - long?
there for me,
Copyright, 1924, by C. W. Jones. Used by permission
339
Crown the Savior King of Your Heart
M. D.
Merrill Dunlop
O why not crown the Savior King of your heart, King of your heart, and ne'er-failing Friend?
O why not crown the Sav - ior King of your heart? Why not crown Him to - day?
Copyright, 1928, by Merrill Dunlop. Used by permission

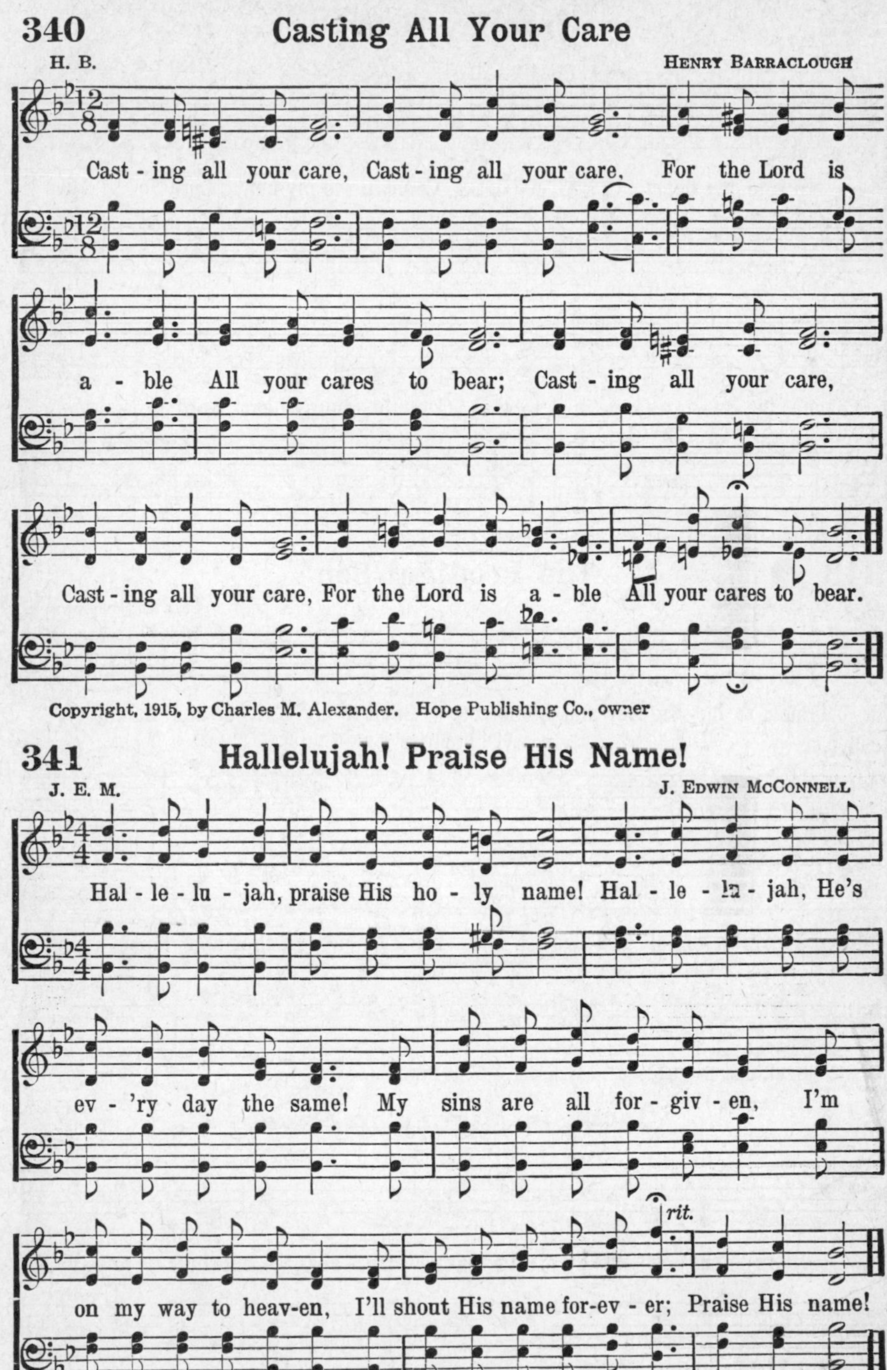
340 Casting All Your Care
H. B.
HENRY BARRACLOUGH
Cast - ing all your care, Cast - ing all your care, For the Lord is
a - ble All your cares to bear; Cast - ing all your care,
Cast - ing all your care, For the Lord is a - ble All your cares to bear.
Copyright, 1915, by Charles M. Alexander. Hope Publishing Co., owner
341 Hallelujah! Praise His Name!
J. E. M.
J. EDWIN McCONNELL
Hal - le - lu - jah, praise His ho - ly name! Hal - le - lu - jah, He's
ev - 'ry day the same! My sins are all for - giv - en, I'm
on my way to heav-en, I'll shout His name for-ev - er; Praise His name!
rit.

342
Into My Heart
H. D. C.
Harry D. Clarke
Sing prayerfully
In - to my heart, In - to my heart, Come in - to my heart, Lord Je - sus;
Come in to - day, Come in to stay, Come in - to my heart, Lord Je - sus.
Copyright, 1924, by Harry D. Clarke. Used by permission
343
The Prodigal Son
T. O. Chisholm
Geo. C. Stebbins
Back to my Fa-ther and home, . . Back to my Fa-ther and home, . .
and home,
I will a - rise and go . . . . Back to my Fa-ther and home. . .
and go
Copyright, 1914, by Charles M. Alexander. Hope Publishing Co., owner
344
Jesus is Mighty to Save
Je - sus is might-y to save, Je - sus is might-y to save,
Used by permission of the Salvation Army

Jesus is Mighty to Save

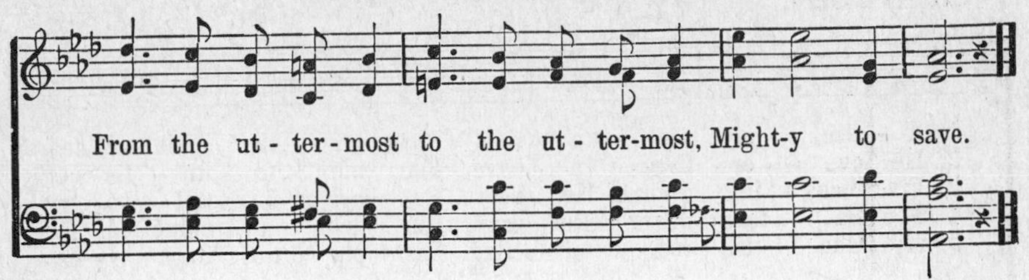
From the ut - ter - most to the ut - ter-most, Might-y to save.

345 Wounded for Me

Gladys Watkin Roberts

Music and first verse by Rev. W. G. Ovens

1. Wound-ed for me, wound-ed for me, There on the cross He was wound-ed for me; Gone my trans-gres-sions, and now I am free, All be-cause Je-sus was wound-ed for me.

2. Dy-ing for me, dy-ing for me. There on the cross He was dy-ing for me; Now in His death my re-demp-tion I see, All be-cause Je-sus was dy-ing for me.

3. Ris-en for me, ris-en for me, Up from the grave He has ris-en for me; Now ev-er-more from death's sting I am free, All be-cause Je-sus has ris-en for me.

4. Liv-ing for me, liv-ing for me, Up in the skies He is liv-ing for me; Dai-ly He's plead-ing and pray-ing for me, All be-cause Je-sus is liv-ing for me.

5. Com-ing for me, com-ing for me, One day to earth He is com-ing for me; Then with what joy His dear face I shall see, Oh, how I praise Him! He's com-ing for me.

dim.

346 Arise, My Soul, Arise

CHARLES WESLEY

Har. by D. B. TOWNER

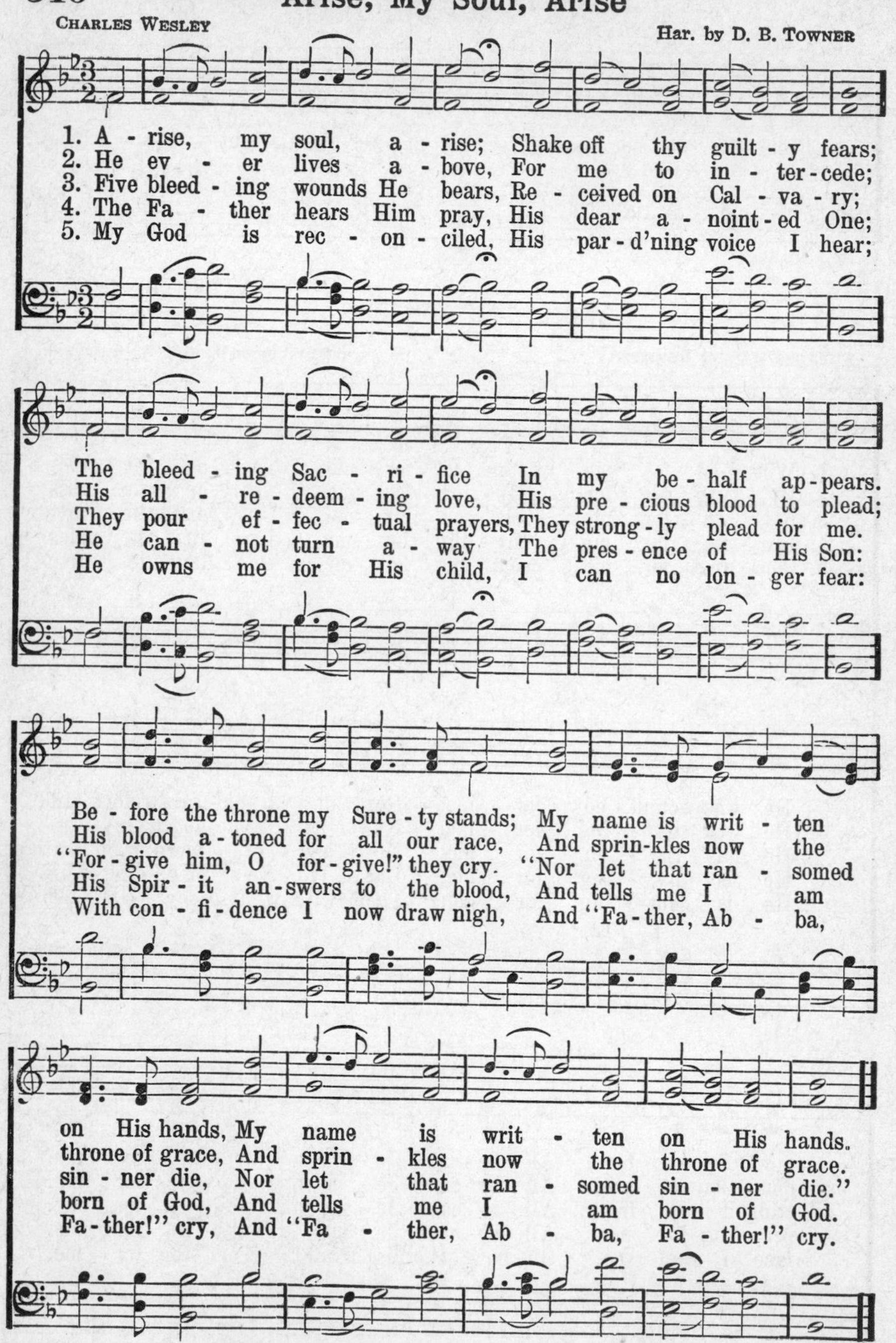

1. A - rise, my soul, a - rise; Shake off thy guilt - y fears;
2. He ev - er lives a - bove, For me to in - ter - cede;
3. Five bleed - ing wounds He bears, Re - ceived on Cal - va - ry;
4. The Fa - ther hears Him pray, His dear a - noint - ed One;
5. My God is rec - on - ciled, His par - d'ning voice I hear;
The bleed - ing Sac - ri - fice In my be - half ap - pears.
His all - re - deem - ing love, His pre - cious blood to plead;
They pour ef - fec - tual prayers, They strong - ly plead for me.
He can - not turn a - way The pres - ence of His Son:
He owns me for His child, I can no lon - ger fear:
Be - fore the throne my Sure - ty stands; My name is writ - ten
His blood a - toned for all our race, And sprin - kles now the
"For - give him, O for - give!" they cry. "Nor let that ran - somed
His Spir - it an - swers to the blood, And tells me I am
With con - fi - dence I now draw nigh, And "Fa - ther, Ab - ba,
on His hands, My name is writ - ten on His hands.
throne of grace, And sprin - kles now the throne of grace.
sin - ner die, Nor let that ran - somed sin - ner die."
born of God, And tells me I am born of God.
Fa - ther!" cry, And "Fa - ther, Ab - ba, Fa - ther!" cry.

347 Sail On!

C. H. G. CHAS. H. GABRIEL

Solo and Chorus
1. Up - on a wide and storm-y sea, Thou'rt sail-ing to e - ter - ni - ty,
2. Art far from shore, and weary-worn–The sky o'er-cast, thy can-vas torn?
3. Do com-rades trem-ble and re-fuse To fur - ther dare the taunting hues?
4. Do snarl-ing waves thy craft as-sail? Art pow'r-less, drift-ing with the gale?
ad lib.
And thy great Ad-m'ral or-ders thee:—"Sail on! sail on! sail on!"
Hark ye! a voice to thee is borne:—"Sail on! sail on! sail on!"
No oth - er course is thine to choose, Sail on! sail on! sail on!
Take heart! God's word shall nev-er fail! Sail on! sail on! sail on!
Chorus
Sail on! sail on! the storms will soon be past, The dark - ness
will not al - ways last; Sail on! sail on! sail on! sail on! God
rit e dim.
pp
lives and He commands: "Sail on! sail on!" sail on! sail on! sail on!

* May close here.

348 Wonderful Grace of Jesus

H. L. HALDOR LILLENAS

1. Won - der - ful grace of Je - sus, Great - er than all my sin; . .
2. Won - der - ful grace of Je - sus, Reach-ing to all the lost, . .
3. Won - der - ful grace of Je - sus, Reach-ing the most de - filed, . .
How shall my tongue de - scribe it, Where shall its praise be - gin? . . .
By it I have been pardoned, Saved to the ut - ter - most, . . .
By its trans-form-ing pow - er, Mak - ing him God's dear child, . .
Tak - ing a - way my bur - den, Set - ting my spir - it free; . .
Chains have been torn a - sun - der, Giv - ing me lib - er - ty; . . .
Pur - chas-ing peace and heav - en, For all e - ter - ni - ty; . . .
For the won - der - ful grace of Je - sus reach - es me.
For the won - der - ful grace of Je - sus reach - es me.
And the won - der - ful grace of Je - sus reach - es me.
CHORUS
the matchless grace of Je-sus,
Won-der-ful the matchless grace of Je - - - sus, Deep-er than the

Wonderful Grace of Jesus

3
3
the roll-ing sea; Won - - - der - ful
might-y roll - ing sea;............... Higher than the mountain,
grace, all - suf - fi - - - cient for
spar-kling like a foun - tain, All - suf - fi - cient grace for e - ven
3
me, for e - ven me, Broad - er than the scope of my trans-
me,.................
gres - sions, Great - er far than all my sin and shame,..........
gres-sions, sing it! my sin and shame,
O mag - ni - fy the pre-cious name of Je - sus, Praise His name!

349 Unfold, Ye Portals

Use original piano score for accompaniment
Molto Moderato
From GOUNOD'S "Redemption"
Arr. by PAUL BECKWITH
8va
f
Un - fold, . . . un - fold, . . un-
fold, Ye por-tals ev - er - last - ing, Un - fold, . . un - fold, . . un-
fold, Ye por-tals ev - er - last - ing, With wel - come to re - ceive
Him as - cend - ing on high; Be - hold the King of glo - ry! He
mounts up thro' the sky, Back to the heav'nly mansions hast-ing, Un-

Unfold, Ye Portals

FINE.
fold, un - fold, un - fold, . . For lo! the King comes nigh!
f Soprano
But who is He, . . the King of glo - ry?
f CHORUS
He who death o-ver-came, the Lord in bat-tle mighty.
Soprano
But who is He, the King of glo - ry?
f CHORUS
Of hosts He is the Lord; of an - gels and of pow'rs,
D. S.
The King of glo - ry is the King of the saints. Un-
ff

350 He Was Wounded for Our Transgressions

R. J. O.
Isaiah 53
Richard J. Oliver
1. Who hath be-lieved aft-er hear-ing the mes-sage, To whom is the arm of the
2. He was de-spised and by all men re-ject-ed, Weighted with sor-rows ac-
3. Like as a lamb He was bro't to the slaughter, Speechless as sheep to the
Lord re - vealed? He shall grow up as a plant new and ten-der, And as a
quaint-ed with grief; Smit-ten, af-flict-ed, by God was for-sak-en, He suffered a-
shear-ers led; He was cut off from the land of the liv-ing, For our trans-
Refrain Slowly
root out of a bar - ren field.
dry and bar-ren field.
lone; no one could bring re - lief. He was wound-ed . . . . for our trans-
bring to Him re-lief.
gres-sions on Cal - v'ry bled. He was wounded, and He was bruis'd for our trans-
on cru-el Cal-v'ry bled.
gres - sions, . . . He was bruis - ed . . . . . for our in-
gres-sions, for our trans-gres-sions, He was bruis-ed, yes, He was bruis'd, for our in-
iq - ui - ties; . . . The chas-tise-ment of our peace was up-
iq - ui - ties He suf - fered; peace was laid up-

He Was Wounded for Our Transgressions

on Him, . . . And with His stripes we are healed. . . . . . .
on the Son of God, we are healed.
351
America
S. F. Smith
Henry Carey
1. My coun - try, 'tis of thee, Sweet land of lib - er - ty,
2. My na - tive coun - try, thee, Land of the no - ble, free,
3. Let mu - sic swell the breeze, And ring from all the trees
4. Our fa - thers' God, to Thee, Au - thor of lib - er - ty,
Of thee I sing: Land where my fa - thers died, Land of the
Thy name I love: I love thy rocks and rills, Thy woods and
Sweet free-dom's song: Let mor - tal tongues a - wake; Let all that
To Thee we sing: Long may our land be bright With free-dom's
pil - grim's pride, From ev - 'ry moun - tain side Let free - dom ring!
tem - pled hills; My heart with rap - ture thrills Like that a - bove.
breathe par-take; Let rocks their si - lence break, The sound pro - long.
ho - ly light; Pro - tect us by Thy might, Great God, our King!

All Hail the Power

Edward Perronet — Oliver Holden

1. All hail the pow'r of Je - sus' name! Let an - gels pros - trate fall;
2. Ye cho - sen seed of Is - rael's race, Ye ran-somed from the fall,
3. Let ev - 'ry kin - dred, ev - 'ry tribe On this ter - res - trial ball,
4. O that with yon - der sa - cred throng We at His feet may fall!
Bring forth the roy - al di - a - dem, And crown Him Lord of all,
Hail Him who saves you by His grace, And crown Him Lord of all,
To Him all maj - es - ty as - cribe, And crown Him Lord of all,
We'll join the ev - er - last - ing song, And crown Him Lord of all,
Bring forth the roy - al di - a - dem, And crown Him Lord of all!
Hail Him who saves you by His grace, And crown Him Lord of all!
To Him all maj - es - ty as - cribe, And crown Him Lord of all!
We'll join the ev - er - last - ing song, And crown Him Lord of all!
[Second Tune]
Miles' Lane
William Shrubsole
1. All hail the pow'r of Je - sus' name! Let an-gels pros-trate fall; Bring forth the roy-al
di - a - dem, And crown Him, crown Him, crown Him, Crown Him Lord of all!

Responsive Readings

1 The Holy Scriptures

II Timothy 2:15; 3:14-17; 4:2;
Psalm 119:11, 89, 105, 129, 130, 133, 140, 49

Study to shew thyself approved unto God, a workman that needeth not to be ashamed, rightly dividing the word of truth.

But continue thou in the things which thou hast learned and hast been assured of, knowing of whom thou hast learned them;

And that from a child thou hast known the holy scriptures, which are able to make thee wise unto salvation through faith which is in Christ Jesus.

All scripture is given by inspiration of God, and is profitable for doctrine, for reproof, for correction, for instruction in righteousness:

That the man of God may be perfect, thoroughly furnished unto all good works.

Preach the word; be instant in season, out of season; reprove, rebuke, exhort with all longsuffering and doctrine.

Thy word have I hid in mine heart, that I might not sin against thee.

For ever, O Lord, thy word is settled in heaven.

Thy word is a lamp unto my feet, and a light unto my path.

Thy testimonies are wonderful: therefore doth my soul keep them.

The entrance of thy words giveth light; it giveth understanding unto the simple.

Order my steps in thy word: and let not any iniquity have dominion over me.

Thy word is very pure: therefore thy servant loveth it.

Remember the word unto thy servant, upon which thou hast caused me to hope.

2 The Glory of God

Psalm 19

The heavens declare the glory of God; and the firmament sheweth his handywork.

Day unto day uttereth speech, and night unto night sheweth knowledge.

There is no speech nor language, where their voice is not heard.

Their line is gone out through all the earth, and their words to the end of the world. In them hath he set a tabernacle for the sun,

Which is as a bridegroom coming out of his chamber, and rejoiceth as a strong man to run a race.

His going forth is from the end of the heaven, and his circuit unto the ends of it: and there is nothing hid from the heat thereof.

The law of the Lord is perfect, converting the soul: the testimony of the Lord is sure, making wise the simple.

The statutes of the Lord are right, rejoicing the heart: the commandment of the Lord is pure, enlightening the eyes.

The fear of the Lord is clean, enduring for ever: the judgments of the Lord are true and righteous altogether.

More to be desired are they than gold, yea, than much fine gold: sweeter also than honey and the honeycomb.

Moreover by them is thy servant warned: and in keeping of them there is great reward.

Who can understand his errors? cleanse thou me from secret faults.

Keep back thy servant also from presumptuous sins; let them not have dominion over me: then **shall I be upright, and I shall be** innocent from the great transgression.

Let the words of my mouth, and the meditation of my heart, be acceptable in thy sight, O Lord, my strength, and my redeemer.

3 Praise

Psalm 103

Bless the Lord, O my soul: and all that is within me, bless his holy name.

Bless the Lord, O my soul, and forget not all his benefits.

Who forgiveth all thine iniquities; who healeth all thy diseases;

Who redeemeth thy life from destruction; who crowneth thee with lovingkindness and tender mercies;

Who satisfieth thy mouth with good things; so that thy youth is renewed like the eagle's.

The Lord executeth righteousness and judgment for all that are oppressed.

He made known his ways unto Moses, his acts unto the children of Israel.

The Lord is merciful and gracious, slow to anger, and plenteous in mercy.

He will not always chide: neither will he keep his anger for ever.

He hath not dealt with us after our sins; nor rewarded us according to our iniquities.

For as the heaven is high above the earth, so great is his mercy toward them that fear him.

As far as the east is from the west, so far hath he removed our transgressions from us.

Like as a father pitieth his children, so the Lord pitieth them that fear him.

For he knoweth our frame; he remembereth that we are dust.

As for man, his days are as grass: as a flower of the field, so he flourisheth.

For the wind passeth over it, and it is gone; and the place thereof shall know it no more.

But the mercy of the Lord is from everlasting to everlasting upon them that fear him, and his righteousness unto children's children;

To such as keep his covenant, and to those that remember his commandments to do them.

The Lord hath prepared his throne in the heavens; and his kingdom ruleth over all.

Bless the Lord, ye his angels, that excel in strength, that do his commandments, hearkening unto the voice of his word.

Bless ye the Lord, all ye his hosts; ye ministers of his, that do his pleasure.

Bless the Lord, all his works in all places of his dominion: bless the Lord, O my soul.

4 Confession

Psalm 51

Have mercy upon me, O God, according to thy lovingkindness: according unto the multitude of thy tender mercies blot out my transgressions.

Wash me thoroughly from mine iniquity, and cleanse me from my sin.

For I acknowledge my transgressions: and my sin is ever before me.

Against thee, thee only, have I sinned, and done this evil in thy sight: that thou mightest be justified when thou speakest, and be clear when thou judgest.

Behold, I was shapen in iniquity; and in sin did my mother conceive me.

Behold, thou desirest truth in the inward parts: and in the hidden part thou shalt make me to know wisdom.

Purge me with hyssop, and I shall be clean: wash me, and I shall be whiter than snow.

Make me to hear joy and gladness; that the bones which thou hast broken may rejoice.

Hide thy face from my sins, and blot out all mine iniquities.

Create in me a clean heart, O God; and renew a right spirit within me.

Cast me not away from thy presence; and take not thy Holy Spirit from me.

Restore unto me the joy of thy salvation; and uphold me with thy free Spirit.

Then will I teach transgressors thy ways; and sinners shall be converted unto thee.

Deliver me from bloodguiltiness, O God, thou God of my salvation: and my tongue shall sing aloud of thy righteousness.

O Lord, open thou my lips; and my mouth shall shew forth thy praise.

For thou desirest not sacrifice; else would I give it: thou delightest not in burnt offering.

The sacrifices of God are a broken spirit:

A broken and a contrite heart, O God, thou wilt not despise.

Do good in thy good pleasure unto Zion: build thou the walls of Jerusalem.

Then shalt thou be pleased with the sacrifices of righteousness, with burnt offering and whole burnt offering: then shall they offer bullocks upon thine altar.

5 Adoration

Psalm 139 (1-12; 17, 18, 23, 24)

O Lord, thou hast searched me, and known me.

Thou knowest my downsitting and mine uprising, thou understandest my thought afar off.

Thou compassest my path and my lying down, and art acquainted with all my ways.

For there is not a word in my tongue, but, lo, O Lord, thou knowest it altogether.

Thou hast beset me behind and before, and laid thine hand upon me.

Such knowledge is too wonderful for me: it is high, I cannot attain unto it.

Whither shall I go from thy Spirit? or whither shall I flee from thy presence?

If I ascend up into heaven, thou art there: if I make my bed in hell, behold, thou art there.

If I take the wings of the morning, and dwell in the uttermost parts of the sea;

Even there shall thy hand lead me, and thy right hand shall hold me.

If I say, Surely the darkness shall cover me; even the night shall be light about me.

Yea, the darkness hideth not from thee; but the night shineth as the day: the darkness and the light are both alike to thee.

How precious also are thy thoughts unto me, O God! how great is the sum of them!

If I should count them, they are more in number than the sand: when I awake, I am still with thee.

Search me, O God, and know my heart: try me, and know my thoughts:

And see if there be any wicked way in me, and lead me in the way everlasting.

6 Joy

Philippians 4:4-13

Rejoice in the Lord alway: and again I say, Rejoice.

Let your moderation be known unto all men. The Lord is at hand.

Be careful for nothing; but in every thing by prayer and supplication with thanksgiving let your requests be made known unto God.

And the peace of God, which passeth all understanding, shall keep your hearts and minds through Christ Jesus.

Finally, brethren, whatsoever things are true, whatsoever things are honest, whatsoever things are just, whatsoever things are pure, whatsoever things are lovely, whatsoever things are of good report; if there be any virtue, and if there be any praise, think on these things.

Those things, which ye have both learned, and received, and heard, and seen in me, do: and the God of peace shall be with you.

But I rejoiced in the Lord greatly, that now at the last your care of me hath flourished again: wherein ye were also careful, but ye lacked opportunity.

Not that I speak in respect of want: for I have learned, in whatsoever state I am, therewith to be content.

I know both how to be abased, and I know how to abound: everywhere and in all things I am instructed both to be full and to be hungry, both to abound and to suffer need.

I can do all things through Christ which strengtheneth me.

7 Love

I Corinthians 13

Though I speak with the tongues of men and of angels, and have not charity, I am become as sounding brass, or a tinkling cymbal.

And though I have the gift of prophecy, and understand all mysteries, and all knowledge; and though I have all faith, so that I could remove mountains, and have not charity, I am nothing.

And though I bestow all my goods to feed the poor, and though I give my body to be burned, and have not charity, it profiteth me nothing.

Charity suffereth long, and is kind; charity envieth not; charity vaunteth not itself, is not puffed up.

Doth not behave itself unseemly, seeketh not her own, is not easily provoked, thinketh no evil;

Rejoiceth not in iniquity, but rejoiceth in the truth;

Beareth all things, believeth all things, hopeth all things, endureth all things.

Charity never faileth: but whether there be prophecies, they shall fail; whether there be tongues, they shall cease; whether there be knowledge, it shall vanish away.

For we know in part, and we prophesy in part. But when that which is perfect is come, then that which is in part shall be done away.

When I was a child, I spake as a child, I understood as a child, I thought as a child: but when I became a man, I put away childish things.

For now we see through a glass, darkly; but then face to face: now I know in part; but then shall I know even as also I am known.

And now abideth faith, hope, charity, these three; but the greatest of these is charity.

8 Patience

I Peter 1:3-9; 2:20-25

Blessed be the God and Father of our Lord Jesus Christ, which according to his abundant mercy hath begotten us again unto a lively hope by the resurrection of Jesus Christ from the dead,

To an inheritance incorruptible, and undefiled, and that fadeth not away, reserved in heaven for you,

Who are kept by the power of God through faith unto salvation ready to be revealed in the last time.

Wherein ye greatly rejoice, though now for a season, if need be, ye are in heaviness through manifold temptations:

That the trial of your faith, being much more precious than of gold that perisheth, though it be tried with fire, might be found unto praise and honour and glory at the appearing of Jesus Christ:

Whom having not seen, ye love; in whom, though now ye see him not, yet believing, ye rejoice with joy unspeakable and full of glory:

Receiving the end of your faith, even the salvation of your souls.

For what glory is it, if, when ye be buffeted for your faults, ye shall take it patiently?

But if, when ye do well, and suffer for it, ye take it patiently, this is acceptable with God.

For even hereunto were ye called: because Christ also suffered for us, leaving us an example, that ye should follow his steps:

Who did no sin, neither was guile found in his mouth:

Who, when he was reviled, reviled not again; when he suffered, he threatened not; but committed himself to him that judgeth righteously:

Who his own self bare our sins in his own body on the tree, that we, being dead to sins, should live unto righteousness: by whose stripes ye were healed.

For ye were as sheep going astray; but are now returned unto the Shepherd and Bishop of your souls.

9 Worship in Heaven

Revelation 5

And I saw in the right hand of him that sat on the throne a book written within and on the back side, sealed with seven seals.

And I saw a strong angel proclaiming with a loud voice, Who is worthy to open the book, and to loose the seals thereof?

And no man in heaven, nor in earth, neither under the earth, was able to open the book, neither to look thereon.

And I wept much, because no man was found worthy to open and to read the book, neither to look thereon.

And one of the elders saith unto me, Weep not: behold, the Lion of the tribe of Juda, the Root of David, hath prevailed to open the book, and to loose the seven seals thereof.

And I beheld, and, lo, in the midst of the throne and of the four beasts, and in the midst of the elders, stood a Lamb as it had been slain, having seven horns and seven eyes, which are the seven Spirits of God sent forth into all the earth.

And he came and took the book out of the right hand of him that sat upon the throne.

And when he had taken the book, the four beasts and four and twenty elders fell down before the Lamb, having every one of them harps, and golden vials full of odours, which are the prayers of saints.

And they sung a new song, saying, Thou art worthy to take the book, and to open the seals thereof: for thou wast slain, and hast redeemed us to God by thy blood out of every kindred, and tongue, and people, and nation;

And hast made us unto our God kings and priests: and we shall reign on the earth.

And I beheld, and I heard the voice of many angels round about the throne and the beasts and the elders: and the number of them was ten thousand times ten thousand, and thousands of thousands;

Saying with a loud voice, Worthy is the Lamb that was slain to receive power, and riches, and wisdom, and strength, and honour, and glory, and blessing.

And every creature which is in heaven, and on the earth, and under the earth, and such as are in the sea, and all that are in them, heard I saying, Blessing, and honour, and glory, and power, be unto him that sitteth upon the throne, and unto the Lamb for ever and ever.

And the four beasts said, Amen. And the four and twenty elders fell down and worshipped Him that liveth for ever and ever.

10 God's Care for His Own

Psalm 23
Matthew 6:25-34

The Lord is my shepherd; I shall not want.

He maketh me to lie down in green pastures: he leadeth me beside the still waters.

He restoreth my soul: he leadeth me in the paths of righteousness for his name's sake.

Yea, though I walk through the valley of the shadow of death, I will fear no evil: for thou art with me; thy rod and thy staff they comfort me.

Thou preparest a table before me in the presence of mine enemies: thou anointest my head with oil; my cup runneth over.

Surely goodness and mercy shall follow me all the days of my life: and I will dwell in the house of the Lord for ever.

Therefore I say unto you, Take no thought for your life, what ye shall eat, or what ye shall drink; nor yet for your body, what ye shall put on. Is not the life more than meat, and the body than raiment?

Behold the fowls of the air: for they sow not, neither do they reap, nor gather into barns; yet your heavenly Father feedeth them. Are ye not much better than they?

Which of you by taking thought can add one cubit unto his stature?

And why take ye thought for raiment? Consider the lilies of the field, how they grow; they toil not, neither do they spin:

And yet I say unto you, That even Solomon in all his glory was not arrayed like one of these.

Wherefore, if God so clothe the grass of the field, which to day is, and to morrow is cast into the oven, shall he not much more clothe you, O ye of little faith?

Therefore take no thought, saying, What shall we eat? or, What shall we drink? or, Wherewithal shall we be clothed?

(For after all these things do the Gentiles seek:) for your heavenly Father knoweth that ye have need of all these things.

But seek ye first the kingdom of God, and his righteousness; and all these things shall be added unto you.

Take therefore no thought for the morrow: for the morrow shall take thought for the things of itself. Sufficient unto the day is the evil thereof.

11 Our Refuge

Psalm 46; Psalm 91

God is our refuge and strength, a very present help in trouble.

Therefore will not we fear, though the earth be removed, and though the mountains be carried into the midst of the sea;

Though the waters thereof roar and be troubled, though the mountains shake with the swelling thereof.

There is a river, the streams whereof shall make glad the city of God, the holy place of the tabernacles of the Most High.

God is in the midst of her; she shall not be moved: God shall help her, and that right early.

The heathen raged, the kingdoms were moved: he uttered his voice, the earth melted.

The Lord of hosts is with us; the God of Jacob is our refuge.

Come, behold the works of the Lord, what desolations he hath made in the earth.

He maketh wars to cease unto the end of the earth;

He breaketh the bow, and cutteth the spear in sunder; he burneth the chariot in the fire.

Be still, and know that I am God: I will be exalted among the heathen, I will be exalted in the earth.

The Lord of hosts is with us; the God of Jacob is our refuge.

He that dwelleth in the secret place of the Most High shall abide under the shadow of the Almighty.

I will say of the Lord, He is my refuge and my fortress: my God; in him will I trust.

Surely he shall deliver thee from the snare of the fowler, and from the noisome pestilence.

He shall cover thee with his feathers, and under his wings shalt thou trust: his truth shall be thy shield and buckler.

Thou shalt not be afraid for the terror by night; nor for the arrow that flieth by day;

Nor for the pestilence that walketh in darkness; nor for the destruction that wasteth at noonday.

A thousand shall fall at thy side, and ten thousand at thy right hand; but it shall not come nigh thee.

Only with thine eyes shalt thou behold and see the reward of the wicked.

Because thou hast made the Lord, which is my refuge, even the Most High, thy habitation;

There shall no evil befall thee, neither shall any plague come nigh thy dwelling.

For he shall give his angels charge over thee, to keep thee in all thy ways.

They shall bear thee up in their hands, lest thou dash thy foot against a stone.

Thou shalt tread upon the lion and adder: the young lion and the dragon shalt thou trample under feet.

Because he hath set his love upon me, therefore will I deliver him: I will set him on high, because he hath known my name.

He shall call upon me, and I will answer him: I will be with him in trouble; I will deliver him, and honour him.

With long life will I satisfy him, and shew him my salvation.

12 Comfort

John 14:1-4; 16-18; 25-27

Let not your heart be troubled: ye believe in God, believe also in me.

In my Father's house are many mansions: if it were not so, I would have told you. I go to prepare a place for you.

And if I go and prepare a place for you, I will come again, and receive you unto myself; that where I am, there ye may be also.

And whither I go ye know, and the way ye know.

And I will pray the Father, and he shall give you another Comforter, that he may abide with you for ever;

Even the Spirit of truth; whom the world cannot receive, because it seeth him not, neither knoweth him: but ye know him; for he dwelleth with you, and shall be in you.

I will not leave you comfortless; I will come to you.

These things have I spoken unto you, being yet present with you.

But the Comforter, which is the Holy Ghost, whom the Father will send in my name, he shall teach you all things, and bring all things to your remembrance, whatsoever I have said unto you.

Peace I leave with you, my peace I give unto you: not as the world giveth, give I unto you. Let not your heart be troubled, neither let it be afraid.

13 Our Great Savior

John 1:1-10: 6:35, 47-51; 10:9-11

In the beginning was the Word, and the Word was with God, and the Word was God.

The same was in the beginning with God.

All things were made by him; and without him was not any thing made that was made.

In him was life; and the life was the light of men.

And the light shineth in darkness; and the darkness comprehended it not.

There was a man sent from God, whose name was John.

The same came for a witness, to bear witness of the Light, that all men through him might believe.

He was not that Light, but was sent to bear witness of that Light.

That was the true Light, which lighteth every man that cometh into the world.

He was in the world, and the world was made by him, and the world knew him not.

And Jesus said unto them, I am the bread of life: he that cometh to me shall never hunger; and he that believeth on me shall never thirst.

Verily, verily, I say unto you, He that believeth on me hath everlasting life.

I am that bread of life.

Your fathers did eat manna in the wilderness, and are dead.

This is the bread which cometh down from heaven, that a man may eat thereof, and not die.

I am the living bread which came down from heaven: if any man eat of this bread, he shall live for ever: and the bread that I will give is my flesh, which I will give for the life of the world.

I am the door: by me if any man enter in, he shall be saved, and shall go in and out, and find pasture.

The thief cometh not, but for to steal, and to kill, and to destroy:

I am come that they might have life, and that they might have it more abundantly.

I am the good shepherd: the good shepherd giveth his life for the sheep.

14 Christ's Humiliation and Exaltation

Isaiah 53:1-9
Philippians 2:5-11

Who hath believed our report? and to whom is the arm of the Lord revealed?

For he shall grow up before him as a tender plant, and as a root out of a dry ground: he hath no form nor comeliness; and when we shall see him, there is no beauty that we should desire him.

He is despised and rejected of men; a man of sorrows, and acquainted with grief: and we hid as it were our faces from him; he was despised, and we esteemed him not.

Surely he hath borne our griefs, and carried our sorrows: yet we did esteem him stricken, smitten of God, and afflicted.

But he was wounded for our transgressions, he was bruised for our iniquities: the chastisement of our peace was upon him; and with his stripes we are healed.

All we like sheep have gone astray; we have turned every one to his own way; and the Lord hath laid on him the iniquity of us all.

He was oppressed, and he was afflicted, yet he opened not his mouth: he is brought as a lamb to the slaughter, and as a sheep before her shearers is dumb, so he openeth not his mouth.

He was taken from prison and from judgment: and who shall declare his generation? for he was cut off out of the land of the living: for the transgression of my people was he stricken.

And he made his grave with the wicked, and with the rich in his death; because he had done no violence, neither was any deceit in his mouth.

Let this mind be in you, which was also in Christ Jesus:

Who, being in the form of God, thought it not robbery to be equal with God:

But made himself of no reputation, and took upon him the form of a servant, and was made in the likeness of men:

And being found in fashion as a man, he humbled himself, and became obedient unto death, even the death of the cross.

Wherefore God also hath highly exalted him, and given him a name which is above every name:

That at the name of Jesus every knee should bow, of things in heaven, and things in earth, and things under the earth;

And that every tongue should confess that Jesus Christ is Lord, to the glory of God the Father.

15 Sin and God's Plan of Salvation

Romans 3:19-28; 4:5-8; Ephesians 2:8-9

Now we know that what things soever the law saith, it saith to them who are under the law: that every mouth may be stopped, and all the world may become guilty before God.

Therefore by the deeds of the law there shall no flesh be justified in his sight: for by the law is the knowledge of sin.

But now the righteousness of God without the law is manifested, being witnessed by the law and the prophets;

Even the righteousness of God which is by faith of Jesus Christ unto all and upon all them that believe: for there is no difference:

For all have sinned, and come short of the glory of God;

Being justified freely by his grace through the redemption that is in Christ Jesus:

Whom God hath set forth to be a propitiation through faith in his blood, to declare his righteousness for the remission of sins that are past, through the forbearance of God;

To declare, I say, at this time his righteousness: that he might be just, and the justifier of him which believeth in Jesus.

Where is boasting then? It is excluded. By what law? of works? Nay: but by the law of faith.

Therefore we conclude that a man is justified by faith without the deeds of the law.

But to him that worketh not, but believeth on him that justifieth the ungodly, his faith is counted for righteousness.

Even as David also describeth the blessedness of the man, unto whom God imputeth righteousness without works.

Saying, Blessed are they whose iniquities are forgiven, and whose sins are covered.

Blessed is the man to whom the Lord will not impute sin.

For by grace are ye saved through faith; and that not of yourselves: it is the gift of God:

Not of works, lest any man should boast.

16 Justification by Faith

Romans 5:1-11

Therefore being justified by faith, we have peace with God through our Lord Jesus Christ:

By whom also we have access by faith into this grace wherein we stand, and rejoice in hope of the glory of God.

And not only so, but we glory in tribulations also; knowing that tribulation worketh patience;

And patience, experience; and experience, hope:

And hope maketh not ashamed; because the love of God is shed abroad in our hearts by the Holy Ghost which is given unto us.

For when we were yet without strength, in due time Christ died for the ungodly.

For scarcely for a righteous man will one die: yet peradventure for a good man some would even dare to die.

But God commendeth his love toward us, in that, while we were yet sinners, Christ died for us.

Much more then, being now justified by his blood, we shall be saved from wrath through him.

For if, when we were enemies, we were reconciled to God by the death of his Son,

Much more, being reconciled, we shall be saved by his life.

And not only so, but we also joy in God through our Lord Jesus Christ, by whom we have now received the atonement.

17 Victory Over Sin

Romans 6:1-14

What shall we say then? Shall we continue in sin, that grace may abound?

God forbid. How shall we, that are dead to sin, live any longer therein?

Know ye not, that so many of us as were baptized into Jesus Christ were baptized into his death?

Therefore we are buried with him by baptism into death: that like as Christ was raised up from the dead by the glory of the

Father, even so we also should walk in newness of life.

For if we have been planted together in the likeness of his death, we shall be also in the likeness of his resurrection:

Knowing this, that our old man is crucified with him, that the body of sin might be destroyed, that henceforth we should not serve sin.

For he that is dead is freed from sin.

Now if we be dead with Christ, we believe that we shall also live with him:

Knowing that Christ being raised from the dead dieth no more; death hath no more dominion over him.

For in that he died, he died unto sin once: but in that he liveth, he liveth unto God.

Likewise reckon ye also yourselves to be dead indeed unto sin, but alive unto God through Jesus Christ our Lord.

Let not sin therefore reign in your mortal body, that ye should obey it in the lusts thereof.

Neither yield ye your members as instruments of unrighteousness unto sin: but yield yourselves unto God, as those that are alive from the dead, and your members as instruments of righteousness unto God.

For sin shall not have dominion over you: for ye are not under the law, but under grace.

18 Christian Sacrifices

Romans 12:1-2
I Peter 4:1-2; 12-14; II Timothy 1:7-12,
Hebrews 13:15, 16

I beseech you therefore, brethren, by the mercies of God, that ye present your bodies a living sacrifice, holy, acceptable unto God, which is your reasonable service.

And be not conformed to this world: but be ye transformed by the renewing of your mind, that ye may prove what is that good, and acceptable, and perfect will of God.

Forasmuch then as Christ hath suffered for us in the flesh, arm yourselves likewise with the same mind; for he that hath suffered in the flesh hath ceased from sin;

That he no longer should live the rest of his time in the flesh to the lusts of men, but to the will of God.

Beloved, think it not strange concerning the fiery trial which is to try you, as though some strange thing happened unto you;

But rejoice, inasmuch as ye are partakers of Christ's sufferings; that, when his glory shall be revealed, ye may be glad also with exceeding joy.

If ye be reproached for the name of Christ, happy are ye; for the Spirit of glory and of God resteth upon you: on their part he is evil spoken of, but on your part he is glorified.

For God hath not given us the spirit of fear; but of power, and of love, and of a sound mind.

Be not thou therefore ashamed of the testimony of our Lord, nor of me his prisoner: but be thou partaker of the afflictions of the gospel according to the power of God.

Who hath saved us, and called us with an holy calling, not according to our works, but according to his own purpose and grace, which was given us in Christ Jesus before the world began;

But is now made manifest by the appearing of our Saviour

Jesus Christ, who hath abolished death, and hath brought life and immortality to light through the gospel:

Whereunto I am appointed a preacher, and an apostle, and a teacher of the Gentiles.

For the which cause I also suffer these things: nevertheless I am not ashamed;

For I know whom I have believed, and am persuaded that he is able to keep that which I have committed unto him against that day.

By him therefore let us offer the sacrifice of praise to God continually, that is, the fruit of our lips giving thanks to his name.

But to do good and to communicate forget not: for with such sacrifices God is well pleased.

19 Christian Conduct

Colossians 3:1-17

If ye then be risen with Christ, seek those things which are above, where Christ sitteth on the right hand of God.

Set your affection on things above, not on things on the earth.

For ye are dead, and your life is hid with Christ in God.

When Christ, who is our life, shall appear, then shall ye also appear with him in glory.

Mortify therefore your members which are upon the earth; fornication, uncleanness, inordinate affection, evil concupiscence, and covetousness, which is idolatry:

For which things' sake the wrath of God cometh on the children of disobedience:

In the which ye also walked some time, when ye lived in them.

But now ye also put off all these; anger, wrath, malice, blasphemy, filthy communication out of your mouth.

Lie not one to another, seeing that ye have put off the old man with his deeds;

And have put on the new man, which is renewed in knowledge after the image of him that created him:

Where there is neither Greek nor Jew, circumcision nor uncircumcision, Barbarian, Scythian, bond nor free: but Christ is all, and in all.

Put on therefore, as the elect of God, holy and beloved, bowels of mercies, kindness, humbleness of mind, meekness, longsuffering;

Forbearing one another, and forgiving one another, if any man have a quarrel against any: even as Christ forgave you, so also do ye.

And above all these things put on charity, which is the bond of perfectness.

And let the peace of God rule in your hearts, to the which also ye are called in one body; and be ye thankful.

Let the word of Christ dwell in you richly in all wisdom;

Teaching and admonishing one another in psalms and hymns and spiritual songs, singing with grace in your hearts to the Lord.

And whatsoever ye do in word or deed, do all in the name of the Lord Jesus, giving thanks to God and the Father by him.

20 Christian Triumph

Romans 8:18, 28-39

For I reckon that the sufferings of this present time are not worthy to be compared with the glory which shall be revealed in us.

And we know that all things work together for good to them that love God, to them who are the called according to his purpose.

For whom he did foreknow, he also did predestinate to be conformed to the image of his Son, that he might be the firstborn among many brethren.

Moreover whom he did predestinate, them he also called: and whom he called, them he also justified: and whom he justified, them he also glorified.

What shall we then say to these things? If God be for us, who can be against us?

He that spared not his own Son, but delivered him up for us all, how shall he not with him also freely give us all things?

Who shall lay any thing to the charge of God's elect? It is God that justifieth.

Who is he that condemneth? It is Christ that died, yea rather, that is risen again, who is even at the right hand of God, who also maketh intercession for us.

Who shall separate us from the love of Christ? shall tribulation, or distress, or persecution, or famine, or nakedness, or peril, or sword?

As it is written, For thy sake we are killed all the day long; we are accounted as sheep for the slaughter.

Nay, in all these things we are more than conquerors through him that loved us.

For I am persuaded, that neither death, nor life, nor angels, nor principalities, nor powers, nor things present, nor things to come. Nor height, nor depth, nor any other creature, shall be able to separate us from the love of God, which is in Christ Jesus our Lord.

21 Chastening

I Corinthians 3:11-15; Hebrews 12:5-11; I Corinthians 11:31, 32; I John 1:9

For other foundation can no man lay than that is laid, which is Jesus Christ.

Now if any man build upon this foundation gold, silver, precious stones, wood, hay, stubble;

Every man's work shall be made manifest: for the day shall declare it, because it shall be revealed by fire; and the fire shall try every man's work of what sort it is.

If any man's work abide which he hath built thereupon, he shall receive a reward.

If any man's work shall be burned, he shall suffer loss: but he himself shall be saved; yet so as by fire.

My son, despise not thou the chastening of the Lord, nor faint when thou art rebuked of him:

For whom the Lord loveth he chasteneth, and scourgeth every son whom he receiveth.

If ye endure chastening, God dealeth with you as with sons; for what son is he whom the father chasteneth not?

But if ye be without chastisement, whereof all are partakers, then are ye bastards, and not sons.

Furthermore we have had fathers of our flesh which corrected us, and we gave them reverence: shall we not much rather be in subjection unto the Father of spirits, and live?

For they verily for a few days chastened us after their own pleasure; but he for our profit, that we might be partakers of his holiness.

Now no chastening for the pres-

ent seemeth to be joyous, but grievous:

Nevertheless afterward it yieldeth the peaceable fruit of righteousness unto them which are exercised thereby.

For if we would judge ourselves, we should not be judged.

But when we are judged, we are chastened of the Lord, that we should not be condemned with the world.

If we confess our sins, he is faithful and just to forgive us our sins, and to cleanse us from all unrighteousness.

22 Heaven

Revelation 21:1-4; 10-12, 14; 22-27; 22:1-5

And I saw a new heaven and a new earth: for the first heaven and the first earth were passed away; and there was no more sea.

And I John saw the holy city, new Jerusalem, coming down from God out of heaven, prepared as a bride adorned for her husband.

And I heard a great voice out of heaven saying, Behold, the tabernacle of God is with men, and he will dwell with them, and they shall be his people, and God himself shall be with them, and be their God.

And God shall wipe away all tears from their eyes; and there shall be no more death, neither sorrow, nor crying, neither shall there be any more pain: for the former things are passed away.

And he carried me away in the spirit to a great and high mountain, and shewed me that great city, the holy Jerusalem, descending out of heaven from God,

Having the glory of God: and her light was like unto a stone most precious, even like a jasper stone, clear as crystal:

And had a wall great and high, and had twelve gates, and at the gates twelve angels, and names written thereon, which are the names of the twelve tribes of the children of Israel:

And the wall of the city had twelve foundations, and in them the names of the twelve apostles of the Lamb.

And I saw no temple therein: for the Lord God Almighty and the Lamb are the temple of it.

And the city had no need of the sun, neither of the moon, to shine in it: for the glory of God did lighten it, and the Lamb is the light thereof.

And the nations of them which are saved shall walk in the light of it: and the kings of the earth do bring their glory and honour into it.

And the gates of it shall not be shut at all by day: for there shall be no night there.

And they shall bring the glory and honour of the nations into it.

And there shall in no wise enter into it any thing that defileth, neither whatsoever worketh abomination, or maketh a lie: but they which are written in the Lamb's book of life.

And he shewed me a pure river of water of life, clear as crystal, proceeding out of the throne of God and of the Lamb.

In the midst of the street of it, and on either side of the river, was there the tree of life, which bare twelve manner of fruits, and yielded her fruit every month: and the leaves of the tree were for the healing of the nations.

And there shall be no more curse: but the throne of God and

of the Lamb shall be in it; and his servants shall serve him:

And they shall see his face; and his name shall be in their foreheads.

And there shall be no night there;

And they need no candle, neither light of the sun; for the Lord God giveth them light: and they shall reign for ever and ever.

23 Second Coming

Acts 1:1-11; I Thessalonians 4:13-18

The former treatise have I made, O Theophilus, of all that Jesus began both to do and teach,

Until the day in which he was taken up, after that he through the Holy Ghost had given commandments unto the apostles whom he had chosen:

To whom also he shewed himself alive after his passion by many infallible proofs, being seen of them forty days, and speaking of the things pertaining to the kingdom of God:

And, being assembled together with them, commanded them that they should not depart from Jerusalem, but wait for the promise of the Father, which, saith he, ye have heard of me.

For John truly baptized with water; but ye shall be baptized with the Holy Ghost not many days hence.

When they therefore were come together, they asked of him, saying, Lord, wilt thou at this time restore again the kingdom to Israel?

And he said unto them, It is not for you to know the times or the seasons, which the Father hath put in his own power.

But ye shall receive power, after that the Holy Ghost is come upon you: and ye shall be witnesses unto me both in Jerusalem, and in all Judea, and in Samaria, and unto the uttermost part of the earth.

And when he had spoken these things, while they beheld, he was taken up; and a cloud received him out of their sight.

And while they looked steadfastly toward heaven as he went up, behold, two men stood by them in white apparel;

Which also said, Ye men of Galilee, why stand ye gazing up into heaven? this same Jesus, which is taken up from you into heaven, shall so come in like manner as ye have seen him go into heaven.

But I would not have you to be ignorant, brethren, concerning them which are asleep, that ye sorrow not, even as others which have no hope.

For if we believe that Jesus died and rose again, even so them also which sleep in Jesus will God bring with him.

For this we say unto you by the word of the Lord, that we which are alive and remain unto the coming of the Lord shall not prevent them which are asleep.

For the Lord himself shall descend from heaven with a shout, with the voice of the archangel, and with the trump of God; and the dead in Christ shall rise first:

Then we which are alive and remain shall be caught up together with them in the clouds, to meet the Lord in the air: and so shall we ever be with the Lord. Wherefore comfort one another with these words.

1 Ephesians 1:15-23

Wherefore I also, after I heard of your faith in the Lord Jesus, and love unto all the saints,

Cease not to give thanks for you, making mention of you in my prayers;

That the God of our Lord Jesus Christ, the Father of glory, may give unto you the spirit of wisdom and revelation in the knowledge of him:

The eyes of your understanding being enlightened; that ye may know what is the hope of his calling, and what the riches of the glory of his inheritance in the saints,

And what is the exceeding greatness of his power to us-ward who believe, according to the working of his mighty power,

Which he wrought in Christ, when he raised him from the dead, and set him at his own right hand in the heavenly places,

Far above all principality, and power, and might, and dominion, and every name that is named, not only in this world, but also in that which is to come:

And hath put all things under his feet, and gave him to be the head over all things to the church, which is his body, the fulness of him that filleth all in all.

2 Ephesians 3:14-21

For this cause I bow my knees unto the Father of our Lord Jesus Christ,

Of whom the whole family in heaven and earth is named,

That he would grant you, according to the riches of his glory, to be strengthened with might by his Spirit in the inner man;

That Christ may dwell in your hearts by faith; that ye, being rooted and grounded in love,

May be able to comprehend with all saints what is the breadth, and length, and depth, and height;

And to know the love of Christ, which passeth knowledge, that ye might be filled with all the fulness of God.

Now unto him that is able to do exceeding abundantly above all that we ask or think, according to the power that worketh in us.

Unto him be glory in the church by Christ Jesus throughout all ages, world without end. Amen.

3 Psalm 119:49, 50, 57, 67, 81, 89, 90, 105, 129-132

Remember the word unto thy servant, upon which thou hast caused me to hope.

This is my comfort in my affliction: for thy word hath quickened me.

Thou art my portion, O Lord: I have said that I would keep thy words.

Before I was afflicted I went astray: but now have I kept thy word.

My soul fainteth for thy salvation: but I hope in thy word.

For ever, O Lord, thy word is settled in heaven.

Thy faithfulness is unto all generations: thou hast established the earth, and it abideth.

Thy word is a lamp unto my feet, and a light unto my path.

Thy testimonies are wonderful: therefore doth my soul keep them.

The entrance of thy words giveth light; it giveth understanding unto the simple.

I opened my mouth, and panted: for I longed for thy commandments.

Look thou upon me, and be merciful unto me, as thou usest to do unto those that love thy name.

Topical Index

COMMUNION

CONFLICT

CONSECRATION

CROSS

DEVOTIONAL

(for other listings see Praise)

FAITH

(for other listings see Trust)

FELLOWSHIP

(for other listings see Communion)

GRACE

GUIDANCE

HEAVEN

HOLY SPIRIT

HOPE

INVITATION

(for other listings see Repentance)

JOY

LOVE

MISSIONARY

NAME OF JESUS

PEACE

PRAISE

PRAYER

PROMISE

REDEMPTION

(for other listings see Atonement)

REPENTANCE

SALVATION

SECOND COMING

SERVICE

SOLOS AND SPECIALS

SPECIAL OCCASIONS

TESTIMONY

(for other listings see Praise)

TRUST

(for other listings see Faith)

VICTORY

(for other listings see Praise)

WORSHIP

(for other listings see Praise)

Index of Responsive Readings

General Index

Titles are in SMALL CAPS; first lines in lower case type.

GENERAL INDEX